For my cousin
Best Wish[illegible]
you and yours.

Love,
Cousin Richie

THE

COST

OF

COURAGE

RICHARD R. SCHNEIDER, MD

Published by Richard R. Schneider, MD
Pittsburgh, Pennsylvania

THE COST OF COURAGE

ISBN-13: 978-0-615-14769-7
Trade Paperback

Library of Congress #2007904088

Cover Design: Brandon M. Bittner
Interior Design: Kathleen M. Gall

Please contact the author at:
http://richardrschneidermd.com
richardrschneidermd@comcast.net

Printed in Canada

DEDICATION

This book is dedicated to the hundreds of doctors and nurses I have known who always place the welfare of their patients above their own, and without whom my life's work would not have been possible.

TABLE OF CONTENTS

INTRODUCTION

"Congress shall make no law…abridging the freedom of speech…" In America, it is against the law to yell "Fire" in a crowded theater, except if there is actually a fire. If you are the first to see the fire and warn others then you are a hero. The American healthcare system is on fire. This book describes my first person experiences as a cardiologist with the healthcare industry as both a patient and as a physician.

I have personally benefited greatly from being privileged to practice cardiology in this country. Doctors in the United States are granted enormous power and are amongst the most financially well off. But with this privilege comes enormous responsibility. In the words of President George H. W. Bush prior to the first Gulf War: "The only legitimate use of power is to help others." Unfortunately, in today's medical industry this power is being misused by too many for their own personal greed and lust for power. This has corrupted the system in such a way that those doctors and nurses who do truly care about the patients they serve have become subservient to the greedy and power hungry. The system must be changed.

Our current healthcare system rewards quantity, not quality. Quality is given lip service, but those who care more for their patients than for the dollar are frequently discriminated against and suffer retribution. Intrinsic to this dysfunctional system is an utter lack of doctor accountability. Figuratively speaking, in today's healthcare industry, unless a doctor is sued for malpractice, as long as he brings in the bucks, he can pretty much get away with anything short of shooting a patient.

I was forced to retire from medicine because I fought for my patients against powerful doctors who abused their power for their own personal benefit. While my life turned out for the better, many other doctors in similar circumstances may have had their lives and careers ruined because they stood up for their patients. For this reason I am compelled to publish my story. Any profits from the sale of this book will be donated to charities committed to improving the quality of patient care.

I will propose an economically sound, free market solution, based on Medicare, to this unfortunate mess. I believe that literally tens, if not hundreds, of thousands of Americans die needlessly every year because our healthcare system values money and power over quality patient care. Millions of others, who don't die, suffer pain and disability from improper medical care. This is true whether or not a patient has health insurance. Almost every lay person I talk to has a horror story about his own or a family member's experience with healthcare. This occurs simultaneously with the fact that we spend more than twice as much per person on healthcare, including the uninsured and non citizens, than any other country in the world. In addition, the current system, without question, wastes *hundreds of billions of dollars annually.*

Because this book is also a memoir, I have included the story of my personal life. Many falsehoods have been perpetrated against me. I, therefore, must use this opportunity to defend my honor and tell the truth. By telling my personal history, I define my character, both professionally and personally, to explain why I made the choices I present. Ultimately, my personal life, and the lies told about me, intersected with my professional life when I became a patient subject to the abuses of the healthcare system.

I believe that justice can only be attained through truth. Because I seek a measure of justice, unattainable to me in the system, I cannot offer anything that is not true. To tell a lie would simply defeat my purpose of gaining justice. Everything in this book is true to the best of my recollection and knowledge. I qualify statements that represent any degree of conjecture on my part. And, of course, any person's memory can be mistaken, especially about events that occurred decades ago.

This book defames no person or institution and violates no contractual agreement of which I am aware. I do not intend to harm anyone. If any of the persons I discuss find what they did embarrassing, I say this to them: If one does not want people to know what you did, then don't do it in the first place.

I have tried to live my life by this principle. A person's character is defined by the choices he makes in difficult situations. The reader will decide for himself whether or not I have lived up to my own standards. Some people say courage is doing the right thing even when it can adversely affect you personally. I think this is true. But any courage I may have displayed in my life or in my writing pales into utter insignificance when compared to the Marines on Bloody Ridge in Guadalcanal in September, 1942, or the soldiers on Omaha Beach in June, 1944. They died so that I have the right to speak the truth. For me not to do so, when so many are dying and suffering needlessly, would be cowardice.

PART I

THE EARLY YEARS

CHAPTER 1

THE BEGINNING

What is the purpose of this book? Most importantly, I want to explain the fundamental reasons for the mess the American healthcare system has become in the present day (2007). I will discuss my experiences that indicate the poor quality of medical care today and the reasons why I believe this has happened. I will offer solutions that have all been stated by others, but from the point of view of a private practitioner with years of experience in the business side of medicine. Most cardiologists who write articles or books about medicine are people who have spent their entire careers in the academic world. These cardiologists take care of patients as well as teach and do research, but they usually work for large institutions and do not sign their own paychecks. They are not in a position to make their own business deals. They have the security of working in a large institution that is unlikely to go out of business, and they count on house staff to take care of their hospitalized patients. For most academics, the mandate is "publish or perish." Also, most academics are limited to responsibility for only their own area of expertise. As the nationally prominent expert in congestive heart failure, Dr. Milton Packer, once told me, "I only have to know one disease." Of course, this is not literally true, but you get the idea.

The second purpose of this book is to defend myself against the false allegations and attempts at character assassination that have been made against me over the years, when I stood up for patients. I will try to explain how the politics of medicine causes disruption of the doctor/patient relationship. My overall thesis is predicated on the principal that quality patient care requires continuity of care. This continuity requires that the welfare of patients be the first consideration in society's decisions on how to structure the practice of medicine. The doctor/patient relationship must be sacrosanct.

The difficulties in medicine today are not due to the bad practices of a few "bad apples," or patients' and lawyers' greed in malpractice claims. The problems are not due to the lack of digitized medical records either, not that this is a bad idea, but this in and of itself will not solve the problem. The problems are structural and based on the fundamental economic structure of medical care in this country. In the chapters that follow, I will tell anecdotes about what I have seen and heard. I will mention some names, not out of hostility but out of a desire to make the situations real and verifiable. My life is good and I have no serious regrets. Medicine has been extremely good to me despite the personal pain I have experienced. Most importantly, everything I will write about is absolutely true to the best of my knowledge and recollection. I will not, however, mention any patients' names. I will also describe in considerable detail my own illness and how it interfaced with my career. I want my family and friends to be able to know me even after I am no longer able to tell my story.

On some level, my story is a morality tale. I relate my desire to always do the morally and ethically correct thing. A person's underlying character is best revealed by his choices in difficult situations. Does a doctor stand up for a patient when external forces are exerted on him to violate his standards of patient care? The nature of my character evolved over time. For this reason, I believe it necessary to portray my personal life. I want to describe how similar character traits affected my professional and personal relationships. The stories are told chronologically. For the most part, my personal life is told in separate chapters from my professional life.

My active medical career essentially came to an end on July 17, 2001. I was sitting in the office of the Director of the Pennsylvania Physician's Health Program in Harrisburg, Pa., Dr. Thomas Hobbs. On the speakerphone, the President of the Medical Staff, Dr. Stanley Wetschler, at Jefferson Hospital, located in a southern suburb of Pittsburgh, said to me: "You are a perfectionist who expects other doctors to live up to your standards."

I had begun my medical career in 1969 as a medical student at the University of Michigan. I hadn't ever expected to be a doctor. When I was five, in 1952, my extended family inquired about what I wanted to be when I grew up, and I replied, "A nucular (sic) physicist." I was fascinated by science and seemed to have an aptitude for math. Most smart Jewish boys in Brooklyn, NY in 1952 were probably encouraged to become doctors. My fraternal grandfather had come from Russia in 1911. I was the first grandson on my father's side of the family. There had never been a doctor in my family. The 1950's were a time when science was highly regarded. Our scientific know-how had recently won the greatest war in human history and saved freedom on our planet. Many of the great scientists had been Jewish, and I wanted to be like them. I had heard tales of the concentration camps in Europe. To encourage me to eat, my mother would always say I looked like a concentration camp victim. I knew I was fortunate to be alive. I loved America for what it had done for me personally.

I learned in school that anyone could succeed in America, but that you had to work very hard and play by the rules. In elementary school in Brooklyn, I was not a very good student. I wanted to do things my own way on occasion. My temperament was a little rambunctious. I was independent minded. From the age of six I was allowed out in the neighborhood by myself to play. The Carroll Movie Theater was on the corner. No streets had to be crossed to get there, so I went alone every Saturday. At age five I took a nickel (enough for a candy bar) from my mother's purse and hid it in my shoe. My father suspected something and questioned me. I was naturally worried and didn't want to tell him. Then he said something I never forgot. "I promise I will never punish you and will always reason with you. But you must never lie to me." I produced the coin and gave it to him. He kept his word and I never lied to him. From this I reasoned that if I always told the truth in life I would always be reasoned with. Little did I know....

My family lived in a one-bedroom apartment until January, 1956 when we moved to Bethpage, Long Island, a working class and lower middle class community; I was nine, my sister Lauren five. My father had to borrow five thousand dollars from my mother's mother for the down payment on a small three bedroom house. The condition was she would have a small apartment to herself in the den area with its own entrance. I had the smallest bedroom. My sister got a larger one because it was explained to me that girls needed a bigger room than boys. I was nonetheless quite happy with my circumstances but longed for my old neighborhood in Brooklyn. My father chose Bethpage because it was reported to have good schools. Children's education was the most important thing in my father's value system.

I entered fourth grade in Bethpage in the middle of the school year. They tested me and I was considered gifted. I was given a reading workbook to complete on my own. I knew I was behind. I completed the book without difficulty, but I felt I never really caught up. Math and science were a different matter and I quickly went to the top of the class. I became valedictorian in junior high school. However, in high school, because of my grades in English and German, I fell to fifth in my class at graduation. I was, however, one of only three National Merit Finalists in my year, based partially on the fact that I scored 793 in the math SAT.

Because the New York Regents Scholarships could only be used for colleges in New York State, my choice of colleges was limited. My father could not afford a private university. I applied to Columbia and Cornell, but I was reluctant to go to an Ivy League school because of what I perceived to be too much social competition from wealthy students. The University of Rochester was almost on the same level, especially in physics, in which it ranked thirteenth nationally. When I went for my interview at Columbia, the interviewer indicated that I was likely to be accepted. Then he said that he assumed Columbia was my first choice. I responded instantly that, no, Rochester was my first choice. I had told the truth and expected to be judged on my qualifications. I didn't know then what I know now, that colleges pride themselves on the rate at which their offers of admission are accepted by applicants. When I got my rejection from Columbia I was a little surprised but not disappointed because Rochester really was my first choice. At Cornell, the interviewer indicated that I would probably be accepted but was not one of "the chosen" and he could not assure my father that I would get scholarship money. They got into a little argument. Not surprisingly, I wasn't accepted. Fortunately, Rochester offered me a sizeable grant that wouldn't require me to take out any loans or to work during college. My father was able to afford the difference.

I liked the U. of R. from the first day. I made friends easily and loved the freedom of being away from my psychologically abusive and dysfunctional family. College life was wonderful. I did, however, fall into what in retrospect was my first depression. My depression was centered on leaving behind the first girl I fell in love with. Her name was Terry Feder. I never had a real girlfriend in high school. We had only gotten together for a couple of months prior to my leaving for college. The relationship had never progressed beyond kissing, which was normal for 1964, but we had expressed love for each other. I had taken an all-night bus to Rochester, an eight-hour ride. I looked at her photograph and cried intermittently all night. This set the tone for much of my adult life.

I settled into college life sans girls. I was only 17 and the drinking age in New York at the time was 18. The school acted *in loco parentis*, a term which meant we could drink beer on campus. Most Friday and Saturday nights there were all-campus parties with music, dancing, and all the beer you could drink for 25 cents (the price went up a little over the years). I learned contract bridge and became somewhat addicted to it. I became president of the chess club. Mostly, though, I studied and studied and studied. One of the reasons I chose to major in physics was because I viewed it as the most difficult field of study, and I wanted to prove my abilities to myself and to the world.

I was certainly correct about the difficulty. Rochester attracted physics majors from many parts of the state and country. Out of approximately 750 freshmen, I was told that 75 were aspiring physics majors. My recollection is that a student could not be formally accepted into the physics department until junior year. There were two levels of physics and calculus courses offered to freshmen. The lower level was for non-physics majors, such as pre-med students. My freshman calculus course exemplified what I was up against. I had taken AP calculus as a senior in high school and scored a four out of five on the AP exam, enough to apply for college credit. I didn't apply for credit because I figured the college level course would be a little more vigorous. I was wrong. It was a *lot* more vigorous. There were 75 students in the class. It was taught by a full professor of mathematics. I don't remember his name but he was very intimidating. On the first day he told us he would not be giving any A's in the course. He then proceeded directly into the first lecture. It made me feel as if I had never taken calculus before.

I worked my ass off in that course. I always felt that I had not really mastered the material. I recall that we usually worked on our own, although we would occasionally work the homework problems together; this was allowed as it did not count for much in our grades. One's grade was determined mostly by the mid-term and final exams, which consisted of problems and blue books in which to write the answers, period. If there were some multiple choice questions I don't remember them. I was pretty scared going into the final. I knew I had to do well enough to maintain my chances to be accepted into the physics department my junior year. I really did not feel very confident about my performance, since the problems were very difficult, so I concentrated as hard as I could and did my best. I finished, just hoping that I had not embarrassed myself.

I remember being in the classroom when we got the graded blue books back. With resignation I quickly opened it. B+. I was incredulous. A few students shared grades with each other but not many. It was sometime later that the final course grades were posted. At Rochester grades were posted publicly by student number so we could see how we compared to our classmates. However, no one knew anyone else's number. My final grade was B+. I looked through the other grades. There were no A's. I looked through again. There were no other B+'s. I double checked. I couldn't believe it. I felt my future was bright.

The physics program at Rochester was very vigorous. Our minds were trained to understand the scientific method in thorough mathematical terms. Lab reports became twenty-page treatises, long sections of which were devoted to error analysis designed to help us really understand why experimental findings could be in error. We were trained to scrutinize for random and systematic errors. I became acutely aware of looking for fallacies in experimental design, measurement errors, and statistical analysis that could lead to false conclusions. This is frequently referred to in lay terms as "how to lie with statistics." I didn't realize it at the time, but this skill and knowledge were integral to my future practice of medicine, not just in medical research, but even more importantly in understanding the results of scientific studies as they applied to day-to-day patient care. I never considered a career in medicine, but I gradually became more and more interested in biological systems because of their immense complexity. I wanted to understand the basic laws governing the development and functioning of life, especially the human brain. Senior year I took a freshman level biology course in order to begin to learn the basics of biological systems.

My academic goal in college was to be accepted to graduate school in physics at Harvard, which, at the time, was ranked fourth in the country in physics. My grades were good, but I didn't know how I stacked up against the students at other universities.

The GRE, Graduate Record Examination, is the test all undergraduates are required to take for admission to Ph.D. programs. It is similar to the SATs for college. Studying for the GRE in physics was really not possible, since it tested everything you were supposed to know from an undergraduate physics education. I knew I had to do well to be accepted at Harvard from a small school like Rochester. I took the exam without incident, and I felt pretty good about my efforts when I walked out of the examination room. Several weeks later our scores were posted by student number. My score was 740 out of a possible 800, or 98th percentile: the highest score in my graduating class. A few weeks later I received my letter of acceptance from Harvard. I also received acceptances from Yale and the University of Michigan, among others.

Again, financial considerations led to my decision to go to Michigan, which had offered me a very generous stipend. It turned out to be an extremely fortunate choice, as without it, I might never have been able to pursue my career in medicine. Michigan was ranked 13th in physics, tied with Rochester. I wanted to try a large university after the small community at Rochester, and I had always been a fan of Michigan football.

At graduation, my parents were present for one of the great pleasant surprises of my life. Only 14 of the original 75 physics students had made it through to graduate in physics. Of the fourteen, four were honored with a Bachelor of Science in Physics with Highest Distinction (summa cum laude). I was one of the four, although my grades were not quite high enough for this honor. I guess the physics department decided to look beyond my grades to my entire performance. I left college with a sense of accomplishment and self-esteem well beyond my expectations. Unfortunately, I really didn't know what I wanted to do with my life.

CHAPTER 2

THE WAR YEARS

I spent the summer of 1968, the year I graduated from Rochester, at Brookhaven National Laboratory as a research assistant in solid state physics. During my senior year in college, I had a part-time job helping one of the physics graduate students, Bruce Brandt, with his work on thin films and superconductivity at very low temperatures. I had applied for a summer job at Brookhaven and was hired to help a physicist there who was preparing to conduct research on thin films. The trouble was that his machine didn't arrive until near the end of August, so my summer was extremely boring.

But it wasn't unproductive. I spent most of my time at Brookhaven reading *Atlas Shrugged* and *The Fountainhead* by Ayn Rand. These novels espoused the virtues of individual commitment to hard work and doing the best job possible in any endeavor, regardless of social status. My father had always taught me that it didn't matter what I did in life just as long as I did a good job. He didn't care if I was "a ditch digger or a brain surgeon," as long as I did it well. He said, "If you do a good job, they can never get you." It turned out that many people did try to "get me" throughout my life, but because I followed his advice, they were never able to. That summer I had time to contemplate my career. Solid state physics did not seem very exciting.

This was the summer after the Tet offensive in Vietnam. In 1965, as the build-up of American forces in Vietnam began, I supported the war as a legitimate war against communism. Gradually my support dwindled, and by 1968 I was firmly aware of the futility of the endeavor and massive loss of life, including Vietnamese civilians. Lyndon Johnson announced his refusal to run again that spring, and Bobby Kennedy was assassinated in June. I became alienated from the political process.

My student deferment for being in college had ended. No deferments were given for graduate school, even in a potentially defense-related field like physics. My lottery number was 96 out of 365. I was classified 1A for the draft, able to be called for my draft physical at any time. My draft board was the North Shore of Long Island, which had one of the highest proportions of college graduates in the country and had a quota to fill. Draft resistance was everywhere. I did not want to die in Vietnam for no reason. Besides, I was not good soldier material, being a very skinny 5-foot-9. Everyone I knew and met was looking for a way out. Some people went to Canada, some claimed they were homosexual, and one person I knew had a small patch of psoriasis that caused him to fail his draft physical. Some of my friends were going to medical school, which would postpone service for another four years. I contemplated a career in medicine. The thought of four more years of school had always seemed daunting. However, since college had gone by so quickly, four more years didn't seem very long. I started to look into med schools.

That fall I moved to Ann Arbor, a hotbed of student unrest and war protesting. People referred to the town as the Berkeley of the Midwest. I was very clean-cut and very straight. My first semester at the University of Michigan I took graduate level courses in quantum mechanics and thermodynamics. With an eye to med school, I also took undergraduate organic chemistry, a med school prerequisite I did not take in college. I got an A+ in thermodynamics but only a B+ in quantum mechanics. In comparison, organic chemistry was very easy because it was an undergraduate level course, and I easily got an A.

By now I was becoming more and more interested in biology. I signed up for a course in biophysics for the spring semester. As I met some of the faculty and other graduate students in physics, I began to realize that I was simply not smart enough to make any significant contribution in that field. My thoughts turned more and more to medicine. I felt that, as a doctor, I could make my contribution to society one patient at a time. Besides, I wanted to work with people, not with machines, and I cherished the idea of having life-long relationships with my patients. In November, 1968, *Time Magazine* ran a long article about medicine. I remember reading it and starting to ache with a powerful desire to be a doctor. I collected my med school applications and set to work.

1969 was not a good year to apply to medical school. Because of the draft, med school applications soared, and anyone changing into medicine was suspected of draft dodging. By now I had definitely decided on a career in medicine and had resolved that, even if I were drafted, I would go to med school after I got out of the service.

During college we had to take a personality test that assessed our interest in different careers, but we did not get the results until late in senior year. The results had confirmed my lack of interest in fields such as literature and languages, and my interest in science and math was confirmed. To my surprise, the field for which I was most suited was medicine. I didn't make too much of it at the time, but as my interest in medicine soared, I looked at the test results in a new light and realized I was meant to be a doctor.

I was rejected outright by six medical schools. Michigan, which was the highest ranked med school to which I had applied, put me on their waiting list in early April, 1969. A week later, I flunked my draft physical for being underweight (not even large enough to be cannon fodder). I was 1YP, later changed to 4F. Notifying the admissions committee about my change in draft status, I thought, was not appropriate. A few weeks prior, Congress had appropriated money to train more doctors because of the national doctor shortage, and Michigan had increased the size of its incoming med school class from 200 to 225. Because of my 4F status, I knew I would be able to complete my master's degree in physics and reapply to med school the following year without suspicion of being a draft dodger. Fortunately, this was not necessary because I received my acceptance to Michigan in mid April.

I was able to tell Dr. Robert Green, the Dean of Students, that he could now be *sure* I was there because I wanted to be, not because I had to be. Interestingly, two years later, Dr. Sloan, the chief of cardiac surgery and chairman of the med school admissions committee, was interviewed by the *Michigan Daily*, the student newspaper. When asked which undergraduate majors were most likely to lead to admittance to med school, he said it really didn't make any difference because they were all treated the same—except for physics majors, because they tended to be smarter than anybody else. Phew, did I luck out or what? That summer I worked as a junior engineer at Grumman Aircraft in Bethpage, doing wind tunnel testing on models of the F-14 wing assembly. I was relieved when the plane did not go into active service until after we got out of Vietnam in 1973.

CHAPTER 3

MEDICAL SCHOOL

Medical school was a lot more expensive than college. Although Michigan was a public university, I was considered an out-of-state student. Tuition and living expenses would be the same as Rochester but without the scholarship. My father was kind enough to pay for half; the rest had to be in loans. I rented a room for $60 a month and sold the 1967 Olds 442 convertible my father had gotten me for college graduation. He wanted me to keep it, but I couldn't afford the upkeep. Instead I bought a 1965 Plymouth Valiant convertible for $450 and managed to hold it together for the next four years.

I was very excited to be in the magical world that would unveil the secrets that few people were privileged to learn. Something the dean of the Medical School said during orientation week has stayed with me until the present. He said: "We will teach you a lot during the next four years. Fifty percent will be true. The other fifty percent is not. Your job for the next twenty years is to find out which is which." He was absolutely correct, but first I had to learn the whole 100%.

I dove into the material, putting in as much time as I had in college. First year classes consisted mostly of physiology, biochemistry and anatomy. The first two were very interesting and required many of the skills I had learned in physics. Anatomy, on the other hand, was rote memorization. All courses were pass-fail, meaning no grades were given. We did, however, have our final exam grades posted by student number. Out of more than 200 students, I had scored third in physiology and fourth in biochemistry. I think this was the reason I was given a partial scholarship for my sophomore year. I mention this now because my understanding of cardiovascular physiology was to ultimately lead to my forced retirement from medicine more than thirty years later.

I hoped to continue my outstanding academic performance for the next three years, but it wasn't easy, since so much of the remainder of med school was just memorization. I certainly did well enough, but the analytical skills I had learned in physics were not nearly as important as sheer memory power. The intellectual excitement was not as intense. I fell into the top twenty percent of my class rather than the top ten percent, and my scholarship was not renewed. In college I had been admitted to Phi Beta Kappa, but I was not admitted to Alpha Omega Alpha (AOA), the medical school equivalent. A lot of this had to do with the fact that all grades during the last two years of med school were subjective evaluations of clinical performance. I performed well, as patient care responsibilities came naturally to me, but I just couldn't seem to get honors in any course.

I began to spend more energy on my personal life. I really enjoyed clinical medicine, especially the contact with the patients. I knew I wanted to be a clinician and not a researcher. I did many of my clinical rotations at Wayne County Hospital because students there had more hands-on responsibilities. I delivered babies and was responsible for sewing up all the episiotomies on my deliveries. An episiotomy is a two-inch incision extending inferiorly and to the side from the vaginal opening. This procedure is done to prevent vaginal tearing during delivery. I became quite proud of the precise subcuticular (beneath the skin) stitching I was taught to use. I felt a personal responsibility to have a perfect plastic surgical type result for each of the young poor women who had to come to a county hospital for their medical care.

It was during this rotation that I experienced the first indication of problems I would encounter with too much frequency throughout my medical career. As a third year med student, I worked directly with one of the ob-gyn residents. At that time, ob-gyn attracted students with lower med school rankings than most other specialties. One day, a resident ordered intravenous cephalothin for a patient who had a history of penicillin allergy. Cephalothin is the generic name for Keflin, a synthetic antibiotic with similar effectiveness to penicillin. I had completed the pharmacology course the previous year and knew it was fresher in my mind than in the resident's, who had taken pharmacology at least three years prior. I had learned that approximately 10% of patients with a penicillin allergy could be allergic to Keflin. Most drug allergies are not fatal, but a penicillin allergy could cause a fatal reaction called anaphylaxis. While Keflin was less likely to cause this, we had learned to be very cautious administering Keflin to patients with a penicillin allergy. I told the resident about this and he told me I was completely wrong. We went back and forth. He told me he had a master's degree in physical chemistry. I told him I had a degree in physics, trumping his degree. I knew I was right and refused to give in. Not long after I was called into Dr. Green's office and told he got a letter from the ob-gyn department complaining about me, saying I would not be welcome as a resident in their department. I was already in psychotherapy for periodic depression by that time, and he felt that was a good enough response on my part. I had never had any complaints about my behavior since kindergarten. I had no complaints on any of my other clinical rotations either. I felt the problem was caused by a lack of understanding of clinical medicine within the ob-gyn department. In retrospect, I was right.

Intellectual disagreements in college and in the other departments of the medical school were accepted and encouraged. In math and physics courses, students were urged to point out mathematical mistakes to the professors. This was routine academic discourse. I had been rigorously trained to ferret out any scientific or mathematical inconsistencies. The other departments accepted and valued my intellectual vigor, and most of my evaluations referred positively to these traits. In fact, during my senior year, some of the attending physicians at University Hospital (the main med school hospital) told me I belonged at Harvard because of my rigor. I had no further problems until years later, when I began to encounter what I considered to be the less-than-admirable aspects of medical culture. These encounters are what led me to write this book.

Life in Ann Arbor was good. I dated a lot and had a few friends, but I never developed the close personal friendships with men that I had had in college. During my year in graduate school I was friends with Bob Kass, a fellow physics grad student. Bob was from New Jersey, so we were from similar cultural backgrounds. He was brilliant and went on to get his Ph.D. in only 3½ years, a school record. He was one reason I knew I was not smart enough to be a really productive physicist. We lost touch when I transferred into the medical school.

Most of the guys in med school were from various parts of Michigan, and most of the Jewish guys were from the suburbs of Detroit. An exception was Bob Burack, a Jewish medical student from Chicago; we became pretty good friends.

Slowly I began to realize that you could take the boy out of the city, but you couldn't take the city out of the boy. By senior year I realized how boring Ann Arbor seemed compared to New York, and I began to crave the intensity of the big city. I resolved to go to New York or Boston for internship and residency, and I set my heart on Mount Sinai in New York. No one had gone to Mount Sinai from Michigan for many years. In the Jewish culture of New York at that time, there was no higher place. Mount Sinai was famous for its clinical expertise. Many famous researchers had worked there, but it did not have its own medical school until the late 1960's.

Fulfilling my dream was not going to be easy, but I knew I had a chance because Michigan was one of the top ten med schools in the country, and my college transcript still might count for something. Although I was not in the top ten percent of my med school class, I did have excellent recommendations from my professors and I had scored in the 93rd percentile on parts I and II of the National Board of Medical Examiners examinations. I applied to seven programs total in New York and Boston, shying away this time from Columbia and Cornell. One of the hospitals I applied to was Beth Israel in Boston, the most clinically-oriented of the Harvard teaching hospitals, but I knew I had no chance there.

Mel Kahn interviewed me for Sinai. A cardiologist in private practice in Manhattan, he was also an assistant editor of the *American Journal of Cardiology* (AJC), then the official journal of the American College of Cardiology (ACC). Simon Dack was one of the founders of the ACC after WWII. Dr. Dack was world famous and one of the professors at Mount Sinai in private practice in Manhattan. He was the editor in chief of the AJC from its inception until his death many years later. The AJC was one of only two major cardiology journals at that time, the other being *Circulation*, the official journal of the American Heart Association. *Circulation* was more of a research journal, and AJC was mostly devoted to clinical research.

Dr. Kahn asked me what I wanted in an internship. I gave him a one word answer: "Excellence." Just prior to the end of the interview, he said "You're not AOA, and I guess your beard is just the style, but we'll rank you high and you rank us high." He was referring to the national matching program in which no offers could be made or officially accepted. All applicants listed the hospitals in their order of preference, and the programs listed their applicants in their order of preference. The computer matched each graduate with the highest ranked program that had accepted that graduate. I couldn't believe my ears. It was a dream come true.

The results of the match came out in April, several months after my interview. I knew that I did not have a legal or definite commitment, but my chances were good. The months leading up to the match results were anxious for most fourth year medical students, myself included. When I got my envelope, I opened it immediately. I was going to Mount Sinai! As happy as I was at the time, I had no idea how important that fact was going to be for me.

People I hardly new at Michigan came up to me in the hallways to congratulate me. A couple of professors told me that they didn't know why, but the best clinicians they had known had trained or worked at Mount Sinai.

Throughout May and June of 1973, I was preoccupied with graduation tasks. I had trepidations about moving to Manhattan, since I was a Brooklyn kid who had grown up on Long Island. Manhattan was a foreign place inhabited by rich people, and I didn't know how I was going to afford to live there on an intern's salary of $12,900. I pleaded with the lady in charge of real estate at the hospital to get me an apartment in the Sinai house staff building. I cajoled her, I flattered her, and I pleaded with her. The result was a 13' x 13' studio apartment on the 3rd floor for $160 a month. The apartment was on 97th and Park, while the part of the hospital I worked in was on 99th and Madison. At the time, I thought that this was not the safest of neighborhoods, and I worried about being mugged. I also worried about what would be expected of me. I reassured myself that I was well prepared, having gone to such a good medical school. I was wrong.

CHAPTER 4

INTERNSHIP

The main teaching floors at Mt. Sinai were the third and fourth floors of the Klingenstein Clinical Center (KCC). Each floor was divided into a north and south section. We called them the wards, but they actually consisted of mostly semi-private rooms containing two beds each. There were also a few four-bed and single-bed rooms. The largest section had forty-two beds, the smallest thirty-four. In order to encourage independent thinking by the residents, attending physicians were not allowed to write orders on their patients. If they wanted something for their patients, they could write a note on the chart or speak directly with the resident or intern taking care of their patients on the wards.

Each of the four sections had its own team of house staff and medical students. It consisted of the chief resident (a senior resident three years out of med school), two assistant residents (two years out of med school), three interns, and a few third and fourth year medical students. The chief was in total control of all the patients on his or her floor.

My first rotation, in July, 1973, was on the private side of the hospital, the side that faced Fifth Avenue. I spent August at a New York City municipal hospital that was affiliated with Mount Sinai (City Hospital Center at Elmhurst) across the East River in Queens. My first assignment at Sinai was in September on 3North, one of two floors with 42 beds. Sinai had had four interns per floor up until my year, when budgetary constraints forced the hospital to decrease the number to three. Each intern was responsible for an average of 14 patients. We slept in the conference room on the ward every third night, but for the first three months on the wards we usually did not get any sleep as we worked through the night. The interns were responsible for doing everything for their patients. This included the histories and physicals, doing and mounting EKGs, drawing all the blood, physically doing the urinalysis, starting and maintaining all the IVs, filling out blood and test request forms, entering all the lab results onto the patient charts by hand, spinning hematocrits in a centrifuge, testing stools for occult blood, and even physically wheeling the patients to the radiology department when necessary (which was more often than not). We also had to do all the lumbar punctures (spinal taps), thoracenteses (the removal of fluid from the chest cavity using a needle), and blood cultures. Any patient with a blood problem required the intern to examine the blood smear under a microscope. I'm sure I'm leaving something out, but you get the idea.

We were expected to report to work at 6:30 a.m. On the days we were on call we worked all night and through the next day until about 6 p.m., sometimes later. I would always go directly home, eat a TV dinner, and be asleep by 7 p.m. so I would be able to function in top form in the morning. The next day I would have a few hours in the evening for myself, which I spent reading about our patients' diseases in the medical journals and individual articles given to us by the residents. Every third weekend we would get off Friday evening and not have to report to work until Sunday. This was our only full day off. I never stayed up late on Saturday night, and I don't remember having a single date my first three months on the wards.

To complicate matters, Mount Sinai did not have a medical intensive care unit. This would be inconceivable for any hospital today. There was a six-bed coronary care unit—for a 1,000-bed hospital! There was always a tremendous demand for beds on the wards. Patients were almost always admitted from the emergency room, and then only if they were very sick. Rarely, a private attending physician (we just called them "attendings") would call the chief resident on the floor to take a very interesting case directly from home to the ward. This meant that the patients we took care of would very commonly be cared for in the intensive care unit in today's hospitals.

Extremely sick patients from hospitals and doctor's offices from the entire New York City metropolitan area would come to our emergency room for evaluation and admission. Anyone without an acute heart attack would go to the intern on call. Sinai had very active hematology, oncology, and gastroenterology services. We cared for patients with acute GI bleeding, liver failure with secondary coma, leukemia patients in crises with bacterial blood infections and shock, acute renal failure requiring dialysis, respiratory failure requiring a mechanical ventilator, bacterial meningitis, and all manner of other serious acute illnesses. Patients with cardiac problems other than large heart attacks were managed with a portable cardiac monitor that could be placed in the hall outside a patient's room so the alarm from the machine might be heard by a nurse or doctor outside the patient's room. My medical school experience at Michigan had provided me with nothing remotely resembling this situation. It was overwhelming. I constantly faced problems I had never dealt with before. I was in almost constant motion and under constant stress. I had gained 13 pounds by lifting weights during medical school, boosting myself up to a whopping 142. After a couple of months of internship, I was back down to 129.

Mistakes were not allowed at Mount Sinai. Period. Every patient was seen by an intern and separately by the resident. The residents slept in the hospital as well, usually in an on-call room in another part of the hospital. This was a different system than at, say, New York Hospital, the main teaching hospital for Cornell medical school, where interns functioned on their own at night. This could—and did—present problems. Libby Zion was an 18-year-old woman who died at New York Hospital unnecessarily because of a blatant error made by an intern working alone at night. The first New York State law controlling house staff hours was named after her. The case was a scandal and created outrage in the general populous.

I never saw anything like it at Mount Sinai. As a physics student I had studied the mathematical bases of error formation and the methods for reducing errors to a minimum. Redundant layers of controls and fail safe systems were analyzed. These are the basis of systems used to prevent errors in high-risk environments, such as aircraft, and are used in modern manufacturing techniques to maintain quality control. After a resident saw the patient, he would discuss the case with the intern. Every "i" had to be dotted; every "t" had to be crossed; every lab result and x-ray personally reviewed. The case had to be presented in its entirety to the chief resident on morning rounds. The chief would then make sure everything was done completely and properly. New orders were given to the intern to execute. The chief was responsible for everything on all 42 patients. Excuses and passing the buck were not tolerated.

Every case was presented to the attending physicians that afternoon when the entire team would meet together to discuss each case. In addition, house staff would discuss each patient with the patient's private attending and with all the consulted sub-specialists. Almost all the attendings were brilliant men with years of experience in clinical private practice. Some were world famous, like Dr. Janowitz in gastroenterology, Dr. Schaffner in liver disease, and Dr. Dack in cardiology. Some had studied under the greats and were talented enough to make it in the highly-competitive world of Manhattan.

Because the Mount Sinai School of Medicine was only a few years old, full-time academic physicians were few, unlike at Michigan, where almost all the attendings were full-time academics with much less clinical experience. The best attendings could get to the essence of the most complicated cases in just a few minutes. Errors or misunderstandings by the chief resident would be picked up and discussed on afternoon attending rounds. The great physicians who had come before were known as the "giants." Their eras were referred to as the "Days of the Giants." I was to spend ten years in this environment.

As a new intern, I knew that the only way I could avoid mistakes was to make sure my superiors knew what I was up to. I don't remember making any fatal mistakes during my internship, but I do remember one I almost made. The patient was a middle-aged man who came in short of breath. We did not have any of the sophisticated tests we have today to determine heart function, and the patient was getting more short of breath. I thought the patient was going into heart failure, or "pulmonary edema," as it was called. This is a condition in which blood backs up from the heart and fluid fills the lungs. In those days, intravenous morphine was one of the standard therapies for this condition. I went into the nursing station and filled a syringe with 15 milligrams of morphine. I clearly remember holding the syringe in my right hand and walking toward the patient's room. About half way there I stopped and said to myself, "What are you doing?!" I had suddenly realized that the problem could be primarily a lung problem and not heart failure. I hurried back into the nursing station and disposed of the morphine. It turned out it was a lung problem; the morphine could have stopped the patient's breathing and possibly, if not probably, killed him.

Of course, I made many errors as a new intern, most of them errors of omission, not commission, which were picked up by the residents and corrected. To limit my errors, I wrote down every instruction I was given by the residents on rounds in a small notebook I carried with me at all times. I put a small box next to each entry and put an "X" in it as each task was completed. No error was considered to be too small for the residents to point out. For example, I remember that one resident had suggested that I check the serum potassium on a certain patient. The potassium had been okay, but the patient was on medication that might occasionally cause a low level of potassium. I drew the blood and sent it to the lab. It was a day after a night on call, and I was anxious to go home and get some sleep. At sign-out rounds, I mentioned to the on-call team that the potassium was pending. The resident said that if the potassium was low I needed to know about it now, not later, and I was responsible for getting the result before I went home. In retrospect, I know he was being a little too compulsive, but that was life in the big city.

Since I put everything I had into being successful at Mount Sinai, I would periodically ask the residents how I was doing. The response was usually that I was doing fine. This was not the case for one of my co-interns. He had graduated very high in his class from Wayne State Medical School, which was near Ann Arbor. As I was too busy to pay much attention to what was going on between the other interns and the residents, I was only vaguely aware that he was making some mistakes, so it came somewhat as a shock to me when he was fired. I knew these people were serious about quality medical care, and the intern's dismissal really drove that notion home.

The other intern on the floor was Bill Untereker. Bill was a brilliant guy who had graduated from Williams College and Columbia Med School. I remember Bill getting very mad at himself for missing the diagnosis of hypothyroidism on an elderly woman. She had the classical finding for this disorder: loss of the outside of both eyebrows and hoarseness of voice. The patient was subsequently diagnosed correctly and did well. Many experienced doctors would have missed this diagnosis on clinical exam, but Bill felt that, even as a new intern, he was expected to have picked it up.

Standards were high. I found this out personally one night on call. John Ambrose was the assistant resident (AR) on call with me. John had graduated first in his class at New York Medical College. He was one of the smartest people I have ever known and totally dedicated to quality patient care. I thought I had been doing a pretty good job at that time. At about 11 p.m. we were walking together down the hall on the floor, which was quiet and almost empty. He put his right arm around my shoulder in a friendly way and softly said, "Rich, I know you're an easy-going guy, but you simply have to be more compulsive." No one before or since has ever called me "easy-going." He meant it in good faith and that's the way I took it, since I had enormous respect and admiration for John. I resolved to be even more thorough and meticulous, and throughout my career I never stopped trying. I realized that the only way to achieve excellence in the eyes of the institution was to constantly strive for perfection.

We had always been told by our residents that we would become a lot more efficient the second half of the year. The learning curve was steep. The enormous amount of time and energy we devoted to our jobs paid off as our ability increased dramatically. By the second half of the year, I was able to do a lot more on my own. The residents had also been learning, and they developed more confidence in us and in themselves. I started to get some sleep on my on-call nights by then, but never more than three hours. By the end of the year I was ready to take on the responsibility of supervising the new interns.

CHAPTER 5

RESIDENCY

The responsibilities of a first year resident (AR) were more than those of an intern. We were now the second line of defense against clinical errors. We were no longer expected to do the "scut" work on the patients, which was the responsibility of the interns and whatever medical students were assigned to our service. We still helped out on busy nights when there was too much work for them. We saw every patient admitted to our service and made decisions in consultation with the interns. We called the shots and we took the blame for any mistakes. We had the chief residents, the attendings, and the subspecialty fellows to back us up if we needed advice. The first year residents had two other responsibilities: searching the medical literature for articles relevant to our patients, and working in the emergency room and deciding which patients were so sick that they needed to be admitted to the hospital.

At Sinai we had a saying: "The literature is king." AR's were expected to go to the medical library every day after morning rounds to find and make copies of journal articles about questions that arose about the patients and for general review of their diseases. We had constant discussions and occasional arguments about medical issues, and everyone was expected to quote the relevant articles to back up their position. Needless to say, in such a competitive environment the discussions would occasionally be quite lively. *The New England Journal of Medicine* usually came in the mail to our homes every Tuesday. If you hadn't reviewed it by Wednesday morning, you would be relegated to observer status in the back-and-forth that took place on morning rounds. Years later, the term "evidenced based medicine" entered the parlance of medicine. I was at first perplexed by this phrase because I didn't realize there was any other kind. I was wrong.

Admitting patients from the ER was a critical function for the residents. The interns in the ER saw most of the patients. The residents reviewed each case with them and made a decision to admit patients to the floors, send them home, or find a bed on the private side of the hospital for patients who weren't very sick. You never wanted to send patients home if you thought they would get worse with outpatient treatment. On the other hand, you would not want to admit a patient who didn't need to be admitted.

Admission to the floors was done in rotation to the four clinical services (3N, 3S, 4N, and 4S). Empty beds would frequently be in short supply and needed to be given to patients who needed them the most. Another important factor was the amount of work each admission represented to your colleagues upstairs. Each admission could require hours of work for the doctors on the floors, who were totally dependent on the resident in the ER to admit only patients that needed to be admitted. Therefore, the ER resident had to have excellent clinical judgment. Residents who didn't have enough confidence in their own ability to recognize when a patient could be safely sent home would admit patients unnecessarily, making life miserable for the house staff upstairs. Every night the on-call staff would get the word as to who was in the ER. Residents working in the ER would be classified as "rocks" or "sieves." I was proud to be called a "rock." To the best of my knowledge, I never inappropriately sent a patient home. This required getting the correct diagnosis, prescribing the correct medications, and making sure the patient was instructed to get the proper follow-up care as an outpatient.

In those days no pressure was applied by the hospital to keep the beds full for financial reasons, so the house staff had no financial incentive to admit patients. The atmosphere demanded only one thing: making the correct medical decision for each patient. Attendings, on the other hand, would get paid by the patients' insurance for each day a patient was in the hospital. But because the resident had the final say, the attendings would have to convince the resident in the ER that their patient had to be admitted. This fact fostered in the residents an ability to stand up to authority and exert their own clinical judgment. For me, this meant the attendings had no choice but to reason with me. I had no trouble exerting myself in this regard, for this was exactly what my very strong-willed father and I had become accustomed to. It meant that I always stood up for what I thought was right, both ethically and medically. This attitude and behavior on my part was going to cause me a lot of trouble with authority figures throughout my career. I have to admit, though, that I occasionally did things in later years that I felt forced to do by my superiors, things that I later regretted. Of course, I always kept an open mind and frequently could be convinced to change it.

During the first year of residency, as during internship, we spent a month at Elmhurst, the municipal hospital across the East River in Queens. At Elmhurst, the ARs had more responsibility because there were no chief residents and the patients had no private attendings. The attendings were full-time academic faculty of the Mount Sinai Medical School. The ARs ran the show. Each medical floor had approximately 40 beds divided up into three separate services. Elmhurst had three separate residency programs. The Elmhurst program consisted of mostly foreign-born graduates of foreign medical schools. The joint program between Elmhurst and Sinai consisted mostly of American medical school graduates who would spend some of their time at Mount Sinai, but not on the floors at Sinai. Sinai residents and interns spent one month per year at Elmhurst. At that time, each team consisted of house staff only from the same program.

The patients at Elmhurst were sick, very sick. The hospital had the oldest patients of any hospital in New York City. The surrounding neighborhood consisted of people born in 43 different countries. We saw patients from Russia, Vietnam, Greece and other countries, many of whom did not speak a word of English. Many elderly patients were too sick to give any useful medical history. Some of the house staff said it could be similar to practicing veterinary medicine. Each of the three teams cared for about fifteen patients at any give time, but the numbers could rise to as many as twenty-two. The average number of deaths per month for all three teams on any give floor was seventeen.

It was here at Elmhurst that I learned that not all doctors are the same, and that there can be a real difference in outcomes among different doctors. During the month I was at Elmhurst, I and my intern, Stuart Green, had only one death: a patient with incurable metastatic cancer of the pancreas. When we went off service at the end of the month, we signed out our patients to a non-Sinai team. One of the medical students with us stayed on with the new team. When I spoke with him weeks later, he told me that our patients were neglected by the new team and many died unnecessarily.

During my AR year, I was able to do a lot of reading on all manner of diseases. One in particular was congestive heart failure. I knew I was going to be a cardiologist, so I spent most of my time learning about the other organ systems, knowing this would be the last training I would get in non-cardiology areas. We had many patients with "heart failure." It seemed to me at the time that no one really knew what heart failure was. Every attending had his own definition. The diagnosis had to be made by history, physical examination, and chest x-ray. Cardiac catheterization was relatively dangerous, and echocardiography was one-dimensional and in its infancy.

Determined to understand what I considered to be a scientific mess, I read everything I could find in the literature and textbooks. I came to realize that "congestive heart failure" was not a real diagnosis but rather an amalgam of many disorders. Sometimes these were congestive, sometimes related to the heart, and sometimes not really a failure of anything. The term could be applied to any one of a large number of diseases of the blood vessels, heart muscle, heart valves, and sometimes non-cardiovascular diseases such as anemia or septicemia (blood infection). Any combination of these was also possible in any given patient. I realized then that I had to learn about each one of these diseases individually. I had to understand how these diseases could manifest individually and in any number of combinations and permutations.

The skills I had learned in physics and mathematics gave me a deep understanding about analyzing systems with multiple variables, and I could analyze complex interrelationships among dependent and independent variables. I could tease out cause and effect relationships within and among organ systems. In the ensuing decades, as I learned more and more cardiology and did thousands of cardiac catheterizations, echocardiograms, and stress tests, I continually refined my understanding. I believe my patients benefited greatly from my approach. Years later, my understanding of heart failure was to lead to character assassination and my early retirement from medicine for health reasons.

CHAPTER 6

CHIEF RESIDENCY

The second year residents were referred to as chief residents, unlike the current meaning of "chief resident," which usually is used to designate a third-year resident with administrative responsibilities. Our year was mostly filled with electives in other specialties or subspecialties. I took two months of infectious diseases, one month of anesthesiology to learn how to intubate the trachea, and others which I don't recall. Our most important assignment, however, was as the chief resident on one of the floors for two or three months. I was assigned to 3S—Three South—for three months in the middle of the academic year. This was the final preparation for going out into the world to practice internal medicine on our own…or it was the final preparation for two or more years of fellowship training in one of the subspecialties, such as cardiology. Three South, with 42 beds, was the largest floor. I had total responsibility for everything that happened to each and every patient on that floor for three full months. My backup consisted of our assigned ward attendings, the private attendings of the patients who had one, and the consulting services. I and my two ARs rotated on call every third night and would sleep in the hospital to supervise the intern on call. I knew difficult problems would routinely crop up on nights I was not on call, but I considered myself responsible for the patients even when I was not on call. I instructed the ARs on-call to contact me any time for any problem they were unsure about. This meant I made myself available 24/7 for three solid months with no days off. I didn't do this to seem macho or advance my career. I was just adhering to my father's advice to do the best job I could. I knew I had a year's more knowledge and experience than the

ARs because I knew how much clinical judgment I had developed during my past year of training. It was the same policy I set for myself as a full-time faculty member and later in private practice.

I was always nice on the phone when an AR or intern called me at home. I wanted them to call me because I did not want mistakes to occur on our patients. This was the Sinai culture. I never knew whether other chiefs had the same policy; I just did it because it was the right thing to do. On the other hand, if I went to work the next day and found that a significant and avoidable mistake had been made because I wasn't called, I wasn't always nice. Very few mistakes were made during my three months, and I think the people who worked under my supervision were proud of their own performance. That's not to say I didn't ruffle their feathers a few times, but I only remember one occasion in which I reduced someone to tears.

I was toughest on the ARs because they had more responsibilities and experience than the interns and medical students. One anecdote stands out in my mind and would prove to be a portent of a recurring theme in my career. One month I was fortunate to have two very bright and capable ARs. Mike Lederman had graduated from a top-notch medical school—Case Western, I think, but I'm not sure. For three weeks Mike suffered my criticisms. Most of these occurred during house staff rounds in the morning without attendings present. I wanted the whole team to learn from each other's mistakes because we all learned from everyone's mistakes. I did not play favorites, and I did not shy away from acknowledging my own mistakes. I don't think the others felt any differently than Mike did. Then one day Mike verbalized his feelings to me. I don't remember his exact words but in paraphrase he said something like this: "At first I thought you were overbearing. Now I realize that you are a 'wise man.'" I know this was how I was generally regarded—very tough but fair, highly capable, and truly dedicated. At the completion of the three months, I was proud of my performance mainly because of how well our patients had done and because I had helped in the development of other physicians in the Sinai tradition.

CHAPTER 7

CARDIOLOGY

I knew I wanted to be a cardiologist from my first day of medical school. Not only did cardiology seem the most interesting field in medicine, it would also allow me to put my physics education to practical use. The heart is a mechanical pump that would require understanding of fluid dynamics, i.e., an understanding of the concepts of flow, pressure, and volume. The electrical system of the heart required an understanding of electromagnetism. The heart and blood vessels were elastic and required an understanding of potential and kinetic energy and the difference between the two. The entire human body was a machine that took in energy in the form of food, performed work and put out heat, as do all machines.

I had gotten an A+ in thermodynamics in graduate school and had a deep understanding of the relationships between energy, work, temperature, and heat. As a cardiologist, I knew I would get to work closely with patients, which was my main reason for switching from physics to medicine. I would need skills in psychiatry and psychology, in which I had a strong interest because of my own problems. I had toyed with the idea of being a psychiatrist but dismissed it because it was too difficult: The brain was too complex, the most complex of all the organs. By comparison, cardiology—as difficult as it was—seemed relatively simple. My idea at the time was to do a cardiology fellowship for two years after three years of internal medicine training. I saw myself as a general internist with a special expertise in cardiology. I planned on practicing in a solo private practice in one of the upscale suburbs of New York City. I wanted a quiet life in which I would do good one patient at a time. Of course, I knew that I would have to get up in the middle of the night for emergencies, but this was the price I had to pay to do what I wanted.

Most residents begin exploring fellowship programs more than one year prior to completion of their internal medicine residency. I started looking in early 1975 for a fellowship starting July, 1976. Fortune smiled on me in 1974, at which time Mount Sinai was recruiting for a new chairman for the Department of Medicine. The board of trustees thought cardiovascular disease was the most promising field in which the hospital could grow. Richard Gorlin was selected for the position. Dr. Gorlin was a world famous cardiologist who had devised the formula for calculating the area of a diseased and narrowed mitral valve.

The mitral valve is the valve between the left atrium and the left ventricle. The left atrium is the chamber of the heart that receives blood from the lungs. The blood then flows across the mitral valve into the main pumping chamber of the heart, the left ventricle. At that time, this narrowing of the mitral valve, called mitral stenosis, was very common. It was caused by rheumatic fever, a complication of strep throat. The narrowing of the valve occurs years after the throat infection. Effective treatment for strep throat did not exist until penicillin became available after World War II. People who had had rheumatic fever prior to WWII would present with symptoms of heart failure. Among the first heart operations was a procedure to reopen the mitral valve. Today, because of effective antibiotic therapy for strep throat, mitral stenosis is very rare in the developed world but is still a common problem in countries such as India and Egypt. Dr. Gorlin's formula was invaluable for the treatment of this life-threatening disease. At the time he was recruited to Mount Sinai, he was Associate Professor of Medicine at Harvard and on the staff of the Peter Bent Brigham Hospital in Boston, one of the world's most renowned research and teaching hospitals.

Dr. Gorlin brought a team of cardiologists with him. Dr. Michael Herman was the new chief of cardiology and Dr. Louis Teicholtz was named associate chief of cardiology at Mount Sinai. Alan Bahler came as a senior cardiology fellow. The addition of these men to the Sinai staff created a faculty that I felt was second to none, and Mount Sinai became the premier cardiology program in New York City. I set my heart on being accepted for fellowship, but, even as a Mount Sinai resident, my admission to the program was not assured. Two of the residents in my year, Bill Untereker and Mark Swartz, cut their medical residencies short by six months in order to start their fellowships early. I was fortunate they did this because it left all six spots for the following year open. I worked very hard getting to know the cardiology faculty and giving them the opportunity to evaluate my abilities. I published my first paper as an assistant resident; it was a case report about a patient I helped care for during my rotation in the coronary care unit. For my year, Sinai accepted one resident from each of the major medical programs in the city: NYU, Columbia, Cornell, Einstein, Beth Israel, and Mt. Sinai. I was the lucky resident from Sinai, and I felt that my acceptance was a real accomplishment. I had applied to programs in Boston and Northern California, but New York was my home and I wanted to stay there.

CHAPTER 8
FELLOWSHIP

Of the six cardiology fellows in my year, four ultimately entered private practice and two stayed in academics. Milton Packer started intense research into the treatment of congestive heart failure in his first year of fellowship. He went on to become a world-famous expert in the field of congestive heart failure, with professorships at Columbia and Southwestern Medical Center in Texas. Steve Horowitz was being groomed for chief of cardiology at Beth Israel Hospital in New York. Isaac Weiner went to a Beverly Hills private practice in electrophysiology (a subspecialty in the electrical systems of the heart). Jay Midwall started what ultimately became a huge invasive cardiology group in Florida. Steve Kunkes practiced clinical cardiology in southwestern Connecticut.

Dr. Gorlin, however, seemed to want most of us to go into research and pursue careers in academics. He and some of the other faculty apparently thought that I was planning to go into research because of my background in physics. I did some research with Dr. Teicholtz on Doppler echocardiography, which was eventually published, but the equipment at that time was very primitive and of little use clinically. I looked into possible research on the thermodynamics of the heart, but this turned out to be a dead end. I really had little or no interest in fame. I just wanted a nice, quiet life in the suburbs. I focused on being the best clinical cardiologist I could be, reading as much as I had time for and applying the knowledge to actual patients.

As first year fellows, we had to sleep in the hospital every fifth night. We responded to every cardiac arrest in the hospital, a fairly routine occurrence in a 1,000-bed hospital. Our job was to be in charge of the team of nurses, doctors, and ancillary personnel that came to each arrest. I decided to keep track of my success rate in reviving patients.

Cardiac arrest is almost always characterized by an abnormal heart rhythm. A normal heart rhythm is a necessary but not sufficient condition for saving the patient. Whether or not the patient survived depended on the severity of the patient's underlying disease process. My job was to restore normal rhythm as the first crucial step. Of course, this is not always accomplished. Doctors are not graded on this and do not publish research about it, but I felt it was a good indicator to test if I knew what I was doing. I kept track of eighteen consecutive arrests I directed. I was able to restore normal rhythm in seventeen, which I knew was pretty good results. I continued to grade my clinical abilities in various ways throughout my career, but not every doctor did. The absence of evaluation of clinical performance, I believe, is one of the major problems in medicine today.

Cardiac catheterization is a procedure in which a long narrow tube is advanced from an artery or vein in one of the extremities into the heart. This was first accomplished in 1927 by a German doctor, who passed a urinary catheter from his own vein into his heart and took an x-ray picture to prove his accomplishment. The procedure did not come into general clinical use until the 1950's. By 1976, when I started to learn it, it was still considered to be a relatively difficult and potentially dangerous procedure. At that time, catheterization was usually performed in large teaching hospitals by full-time academic cardiologists. None of the private cardiologists at Mt. Sinai performed it. Not all the fellows wanted to learn to do it, and, because I was interested in private practice, I initially did not express interest. But during the first year of fellowship, it seemed to me that outside New York City more cardiologists were performing caths in private practice. I always had good hand and eye coordination, so I decided to learn. During the first year of fellowship, we were only allowed to pass catheters through veins into the right side of the heart because this was far less dangerous than passing a catheter into the left side of the heart via an artery. During the second year we learned left heart catheterization and gradually were given more and more responsibility, but we were always supervised by an attending. As we fed the catheters into the heart under x-ray guidance, we measured pressures in the various chambers. We injected a radio opaque liquid into the coronary arteries and heart chambers so we could take x-ray motion pictures. The liquid was the same contrast agent, or dye, used to take x-rays of the kidneys.

The main risks of the procedure included the patient having a heart attack or stoke that could be fatal, and the list of other possible complications was quite long. Catheterization is a diagnostic test, not a treatment. Because of the potential complications, we were taught that the test should only be performed when the information gained was crucial in deciding the diagnosis and treatment for the patient. In other words, if the results of the catheterization would not alter what was to be done for the patient, then the catheterization was not to be done.

Today the American Heart Association and the American College of Cardiology publish extensive guidelines for cardiologists as to when and in whom the procedure should be performed. The basic premise of these guidelines is that the benefits to be gained for the patient from the procedure have to outweigh the risks. This requires a thorough knowledge of the natural history of all heart diseases and the various therapeutic options. Learning this is a life-long process for every cardiologist in that it changes with each discovery of new information about heart disease.

Sometimes the most important thing that you can do for your patients is to determine that they *do not* need a catheterization. Before each catheterization the cardiologist has to ask himself the same question: "Is this catheterization really necessary for this patient at this time?" The answer is not always "yes" or "no;" it is sometimes "maybe." In any event, the risks and the benefits of the procedure *must* be discussed with the patient and his *informed* consent must be obtained. Alternative procedures and/or therapies *must* be discussed with the patient. If this is not done and the patient has a serious complication from an unnecessary procedure, it can be grounds for a malpractice suit. These concepts were drummed into our heads as medical residents at

Mount Sinai for *all* procedures and surgeries, and this theme will reoccur in later chapters.

One unfortunate incident during my fellowship stands out in my memory. Patients admitted to the hospital for catheterization in those days would come in the afternoon before the procedure, which was scheduled for the next day. The fellow assigned to the case would see the patient on the evening of the admission. We would talk to and examine them, explain the procedure, and obtain informed consent. This was usually a straight-forward process.

One evening I met with a middle-aged woman with a disease of her mitral valve. She needed the procedure in order to be evaluated for open heart surgery to replace the valve. On my examination, I felt that she had excess fluid in her lungs, probably due to heart failure caused by the valve. Although I agreed she needed the catheterization, I thought this was not the right time to do it. She needed more medical treatment to get the fluid out of her lungs first. We were all taught and knew that the risk of catheterization was much higher in patients with uncontrolled heart failure. Sometimes it was necessary to do the procedure in patients with heart failure, but this was not one of those times. This was an elective procedure, not an emergency, and I felt that the patient should be treated for a day or two to clear the excess fluid from her lungs. This was not an unusual course of action.

Given my predilection for avoiding mistakes, I called the attending who was to do the case to express my concern. He was a junior attending but extremely bright and accomplished and well trained. I was quite surprised when he dismissed my concerns and said we should do the procedure anyway. It would have been considered improper to go over his head to one of his superiors to plead my case. Besides, he was an attending and I was just a fellow; maybe I was wrong.

The next morning the patient was brought to the cath lab. My job was to do the less risky right heart cath. The attending was to do the left heart. I had just started to look for the vein in her right arm—I had not even put in the catheter—when she suddenly stopped breathing and her heart stopped. Immediately the nurses in the room called a code and the attending came and ran the code. No one said I had done anything that caused the problem, but I was questioned by the senior faculty about what had occurred. The attending assigned to do the case was held responsible for not addressing my concerns and for causing the patient's death. I knew I had done my job, but I questioned whether I should have done more. It was not the last time I faced similar circumstances.

By the end of my fellowship in 1978 I felt as competent as one could expect, although I didn't feel comfortable doing caths without backup from someone more experienced. I was good enough to take a job that included doing caths in addition to mostly doing clinical cardiology. Lou Teicholtz, then the associate chief of cardiology at Sinai, had offered me a position as director of the cath lab at Elmhurst. It was not a plum job. I turned it down in favor of finding a job in private practice in the suburbs. In New York City, all the catheterization laboratories were controlled by the seven medical schools in the city. Only full-time salaried cardiologists were able to work in these labs. The medical schools needed the income from the procedures to fund other aspects of the institutions. I found a job that seemed ideal: I was to be the third man in a long-established practice in Plainfield, New Jersey, only thirty miles southwest of Manhattan. I would be able to do cath in a hospital in Paterson, NJ about fifteen miles north. The call schedule would be every third night, which would allow me to have a life outside of medicine. My experiences in Plainfield would reshape my life. But first I must digress to explain who I was at that point in my life.

CHAPTER 9

RELATIONSHIPS

My mother, Evelyn Schneider, was born in 1922 in a suburb of Pittsburgh, Pennsylvania. Her father, Ralph Lipton, was a pharmacist. I was told that I had inherited my mental abilities from him. I never met the man. He was divorced from my grandmother, Jane, when my mother was two years old. Age two is probably the worst age for a child to experience the divorce of her parents. I was told that my grandfather subsequently went to jail for selling pure grain alcohol from his pharmacy during prohibition. In 2003, I learned from one of my cousins that my grandmother had turned him in to the police. I don't know if this is true, but it is totally consistent with my grandmother's personality. Subsequent to the divorce, my mother and her sister, Cele Hope, two years older, were left by their mother to live with an aunt in the poor coal mining country of central Pennsylvania. My mother never really recovered from the events of her early childhood. Her mother kept her away from her father. She last saw him when she was five years old. He died in his late fifties. I think this left a hole in her heart.

In the 1930's my mother and her sister were reunited with their mother and moved to Coney Island in Brooklyn after my grandmother remarried. My mother was very bright. She was an A student in high school. In those days girls didn't go to college. She became a legal secretary after graduating from high school. She married my father, Morris Schneider, in 1945. I was born one year later. I don't think they had enough time together before I was born. With me to look after, I think my mother focused less attention on my father, not an uncommon occurrence after the birth of the first born. There was still enough emotional support to go around for everyone, and my mother was very attached to me. After my sister, Lauren, was born in 1950, however, this was no longer the case, and my mother became extremely stressed. The fact that all four of us slept in the same bedroom didn't help matters any. My father was a struggling young accountant and couldn't afford a larger place. My parents fought a lot, and my mother began to yell and scream, even in my father's absence. My father exacerbated the situation, as he just fought with her. My sister and I became pretty close as we tried to support each other emotionally amidst the chaos. While we were never abused directly, each parent would try to enlist us as any ally against the other.

Although I remember being fairly happy in Brooklyn, things definitely took a turn for the worse when we moved to the suburbs in January, 1956. As I mentioned before, my mother's mother moved in with us in return for lending us the money for the down payment on our house. She and my mother fought constantly. Eventually she moved out, but my mother just seemed to yell more and more. She would fly into uncontrollable rages at all times of the day and night. I was frequently awakened at 3 a.m. by the sound of my mother screaming at the top of her lungs, fighting with my father. They insulted each other with the foulest of obscenities. Overtly sexual verbal combat was unrestrained. It was not language to which children should be exposed. My mother would frequently open the windows so they entire street could hear her. My friends were afraid to come to my house because she would yell at them for no reason.

I was the older child and chief peacemaker in the family. My parents always turned to me to help them solve their problems, an impossible task for a child. I knew my mother needed professional help, but my father always said he couldn't afford it. Every time my mother started yelling, he yelled back at her, only making things worse. It was like throwing gasoline on a fire. For years and years I did everything I could to help them. I never received any acknowledgement for my efforts, but I did receive a lot of criticism for being "selfish." I cared a lot about my parents' happiness, but obviously I had little effect on improving the situation. I liked my father but never forgave him for not effectively handling my mother's problems properly. In retrospect, I'm not sure anyone could have helped her. Years later I came to realize she probably had a condition known as "borderline personality disorder," a virtually incurable form of mental illness that may have been caused by the emotional trauma she endured as a small child. In the 1950s and 1960s, when I lived with her, the medications we have today were not available. She did go for talk therapy on one occasion, to no benefit.

In addition to this mess, both my parents seemed to have a sexual attraction to the child of the opposite sex. I'm sure my father was jealous of me. I know he loved me deeply, but these feelings sometimes played out in less than subtle ways. Years later, my sister told me of my father's attraction to her. There is no question in my mind that this situation was damaging to both my sister and me, but I think my sister suffered more because she was alone with them after I went to college and she developed into a very attractive young lady. My college friends went crazy for my sister and couldn't understand why I didn't feel the same. I really didn't. I think it was biological, but I just never had any sexual feelings about anyone in my family. I did, however, develop an extremely strong attraction to girls. In high school, I couldn't get anywhere near girls who looked like my sister. I think her presence did increase my sense of longing for a girlfriend, however.

My sexual feelings about girls began when I was five years old, though I didn't know the facts of life at that age. I remember having fantasies about a girl in my kindergarten class, and I played doctor on occasion with girls my own age. On my last day of school in fourth grade at P.S. 189 in Brooklyn, a girl in my class named Elaine came up to me in the playground. To my great surprise, she started kissing me on the lips and told me she loved me.

I learned the facts of life from my friends at age nine. During puberty, sexual thoughts preoccupied me, but I was not much different than a lot of boys my age. The first time I "made out" with a girl was at age twelve. This was kissing only. I was a very visual person and just looking at the beautiful girls in my school drove me a little crazy. I would describe it as "Water, water everywhere and not a drop to drink." This was before the pill and legalization of abortion. I knew only one friend who claimed to have had sex during high school. I felt strongly that sex should only accompany love. I was completely unsuccessful finding either. I was extremely skinny (I was 5'9" and 118 pounds when I graduated from high school) and had very curly hair at a time when it was out of style. Even my friends would call me "kink."

I was also pretty hyper, so nervous and high-strung that I could barely sit still in many of my classes. Years later at a high school reunion, one of my high school acquaintances told me I had been difficult to be around because I was so energetic. I'm sure he was correct. In retrospect, I did have sexual opportunities with two very attractive girls in high school but, despite my desire, I was too afraid to follow up. Mostly I suffered repeated rejection in my attempts to form romantic relationships. I attributed this to a lack of sexual desirability. My anxiety and neediness were probably more likely reasons.

I remember riding my bicycle at age eleven when I noticed an unpleasant feeling of uneasiness come over me. I recognized it as anxiety and did not like it at all. My anxiety was sometimes triggered by circumstances but it also seemed to occur for no reason at all. I didn't think much of it at the time, but anxiety has accompanied me throughout my life. I used to have recurring nightmares in which I would be left behind by my parents. My excessive neediness toward women probably resulted from the lack of emotional support that all children need from their mothers. I always had positive feelings about girls because of my positive, very early childhood relationship with my mother before my sister was born. My need for the love of a woman to replace the love I felt I didn't get from my mother was simply counterproductive to forming a grownup relationship with a woman.

One anecdote is illustrative. As a junior in college, I developed a friendship with a senior woman named Karen. Karen was quite attractive, but I didn't think she was romantically interested in me because I thought she had a boyfriend and because I was younger than she was. We would dance together at campus dances, which we both enjoyed very much. One evening she came back to my suite in the dorm. At that point I had only had sex with two girls, both of whom I was in love with and with whom I had had a monogamous relationship. I had never even had a real date with Karen. We were sitting on the couch when she lay down with her head on the side bolster and her feet between my legs. She spread her knees and put her left foot in my crotch. We continued to talk, and I wanted to start talking a little intimately about whom I was as a person. I brought up the problems I had had with my mother and that I thought that, because of them, I had a tendency to need mothering from a woman. I didn't mean it to say I wanted her to mother me; I would have been quite happy to have slept with her, especially since she was on the pill. She excused herself and abruptly left. I thought about her for days but she would never see me again. It taught me a lesson I didn't forget.

In some of the chapters that follow I will describe some of my other relationships, or aspects thereof, that I feel were significant to my attitudes toward love and sex. Although the relationships I describe are numerous, they represent a small fraction of my interactions with the opposite sex, both sexual and nonsexual. Because so much of my life has been consumed by my need for sex and love, this memoir would not be an accurate representation of who I am as a person if I did not devote a large portion of it to my intimate personal life.

Ultimately, my personal life and my professional life intersected in dramatic fashion. Nefarious, unscrupulous people used my sexual and emotional needs against me in dishonest ways to attack me in order to accomplish their own selfish agenda. In doing so, they seriously damaged my career and my health.

One episode in particular formed my early relationships with girls. The summer after my freshman year in college my friend Mark, who was a year younger than me, introduced me to a friend of his girlfriend, Barbara. Barbara was sixteen. She and Mark had been having sex. Her friend Phyllis was fifteen. We dated for most of the summer and engaged in some sexual activities short of intercourse. I was still a virgin and so was she, and I thought she was too young to have intercourse. I didn't realize that was what she wanted because she didn't say so. I was crazy about her, and I still had the notion that one should be in love to have sex. Her sixteenth birthday was in August. At her sweet sixteen party, I told her privately that I loved her. She broke up with me almost immediately. Apparently, she was a lot more interested in losing her virginity than in committing to a relationship. Eventually I learned that sometimes women just wanted sex, not love. I learned that if it was okay for girls to want to have sex with me without an emotional commitment, then it was okay for me to do the same.

The first woman I slept with was Kay. She was eighteen and a freshman in college; I was nineteen and a sophomore. She had dated my friend Jon. One day we were sitting around playing cards when she started to play with my ankle with her foot under the table. I had a very strict code of ethics. Before I would ask Kay out on a date, I asked Jon for his permission. He said he wasn't interested in her anymore and consented. Kay and I fell in love. She was a virgin as well and everything seemed the way it was supposed to be for our first time. We spent most of the spring of 1966 together, but we went home that summer to separate states. That autumn we saw each other briefly before she broke up with me. At that point I had had my heart broken by five different girls in little more than two years. This happened once more before I met Sandy.

CHAPTER 10

SANDY

I met Sandy during my junior year in college. She was a freshman and also from Long Island, from an upper middle class community on the south shore. I thought she was beautiful. I courted her as best as I could until she finally seemed interested, and I was very careful to avoid seeming needy. There was no question that I adored her. Despite this, I don't recall ever telling her I loved her or vice versa. From my perspective, this was to avoid rejection. I was the first man she ever slept with.

I wanted to marry Sandy but knew she was only seventeen and wanted to experience more of life before settling down. She was sexually adventurous and wanted to have sex with other people. We never "went steady" and I never asked her to limit herself. I just felt that when she was ready she would let me know. This went on for four years, during which we broke up and got back together more times than I can remember. Every time I saw her with another boy or she told me she had sex with someone else, it tore me up inside. Her mother never seemed to approve of me. Her daughter marrying a physicist did not fit into her visions for her daughter's future. Being a nice guy and caring about her daughter were not enough. I think she was afflicted with a Jewish mother's desire for her daughter to marry a professional, and I always felt that she encouraged Sandy to find someone else. Except for these problems, Sandy and I did get along well both in and out of bed.

After I graduated and moved to Ann Arbor, I continued to visit Sandy in Rochester and she visited me in Ann Arbor once. Interestingly, after I was accepted to medical school in April, 1969, her attitude toward me changed. Suddenly she seemed more willing to commit, and even her mother now seemed to accept me. After Sandy graduated from Rochester, in May, 1970, she moved to Manhattan and invited me to stay with her for the month of June. During that month, my feelings for her changed. I resented not being accepted for who I was, but only because I was now a "good catch." I wanted to be loved for being me, not my money or prestige. Besides, she had let herself gain more than twenty pounds, and my physical attraction to her had waned.

After I went back to Ann Arbor that summer, I didn't call her again. I don't remember how I found out, but she married a social worker a few years later and moved to the Boston area. Years later, in 1997, at a time of great upheaval in my life, I got her phone number from the new Rochester alumni directory and called her. My intention was not to see her again; I just needed to make a connection as part of the full review of my life to that point. We chatted for a few minutes, and she told me that I hadn't been very nice to her. I apologized but did not explain why I behaved as I did. Maybe someday she'll read this and find out. She went on to say that what she remembered most about our relationship was the "great sex." Sandy added that she had gained a lot of weight and now weighed 185 pounds. (When I met her, she was 5'4" tall and was a svelte and sexy 102 pounds.) When I asked how her two younger sisters were doing, she said that, unlike her, "They are still very beautiful." Sandy was still married and seemed content.

After we got off the phone, I thought how sad it was that she let herself get into that condition. I was convinced she was eating as a substitute for sexual gratification. At that time I was in the process of being forced to examine my own sexuality. What she said reinforced much of my thinking about my sexuality and about human sexuality in general. The fact that she seemed to have experienced deep sexual frustration in her life was similar to what I had experienced in mine. One of my major goals in life had always been to achieve a satisfying and meaningful lifelong relationship with one woman; for me it was about love and sex, not one or the other.

CHAPTER 11

MED SCHOOL AND SEX

At the beginning of my year in graduate school I met Lynn, a freshman at Michigan. We had sex on our first date, something I had never experienced before, and I asked her why she had done it. She said it was because I was from New York and she thought that was what I expected. We dated for a few months, but I was not in love with her. Eventually she got tired with the situation and we rarely slept together, although we did become best friends. She was always there for me emotionally and clearly filled the void left by my mother. I always tried to be there for her as well. I had had a similar relationship with a girl in college, Marty, which was very loving but completely asexual. I even wore Marty's high school ring on my pinky as a sign of our attachment.

I didn't have much success dating during graduate school, but that all changed after I was accepted to med school. I remember in particular one beautiful blonde undergraduate who worked the cash register in our campus dining hall and repeatedly refused to go out with me. We chatted for months when I saw her in the checkout line. One day I said, "Guess what, Marilyn? You now know another medical student." She then accepted my invitation to go out. Suddenly, I was no longer the dorky nerd physics student; I was the hot, sexy medical student. I was the high school quarterback, the rock musician, the lottery winner. My life had changed, but not really. I still longed for love. I was just willing to accept sex and "like" until I could find both sex and love.

I fell in love three times in Ann Arbor and the first time was with Liz. I was a freshman in med school and she was a beautiful, intelligent senior undergraduate from the suburbs of Detroit. While she befriended me, she would never go out with me on a date, and I think I was just too nervous for her. My freshman year I would go back to my small rented room in the evening and hope for a message from her. I eventually got over her and moved on, but we maintained a friendship until I graduated. It was funny that, right before I left for New York, she called me, asking me to "come over to my place for a good-bye fuck." She wanted to complete the relationship, not continue it, but I had desired her for so long I wasn't about to say no. Although sex is almost never bad, sleeping with Liz was less than passionate on both our parts. In a way, it was just an affirmation of the meaning our friendship had had for the previous four years.

The second time I fell in love was during my sophomore year. After playing tennis one morning near the undergraduate dorms, I saw a beautiful girl with long dark brown hair, sitting on the grass nearby. I did not hesitate to strike up a conversation. Terry, a graduate student in audiology from Evansville, Indiana, was charming and intelligent. While not a virgin, she had limited prior sexual experience. When we were in bed together, I misinterpreted something she said about her panties being "her last protection" as an attempt to tease me unfairly, and I raised my voice to her. We never had sex. I was totally unequipped to deal with her concerns about sex at that point in my life and felt rejected and vulnerable emotionally. She asked me out on a date subsequently, but I acted cold and aloof in order to protect myself. That was the end of it. I was terribly upset with myself for my behavior. Looking back on it, we were both too immature to form a lasting relationship. I think she ended up being engaged to a senior medical student aspiring to become a dermatologist.

The last time I fell in love in Ann Arbor was near the end of my senior year. I had noticed Susan around campus for several years. She was just my type: thin, pretty, and not too tall. After she graduated from the U of M, she took a job as a research assistant at the medical school in hopes of getting into medical school. One day I saw her at the entrance to the hospital cafeteria and said hi to her. She said, "I think you're part of my karma."

On our first date we went back to my apartment. She asked me, "How do I know you're not a pig?" I knew I was seriously interested in her and reassured her that I was a decent guy. The sexual experience we had that night was truly extraordinary and unique in my life. We were both multiply orgasmic. In my mid-twenties I would routinely have intercourse continuously for ninety minutes without losing my erection and achieve three orgasms during that time period. I have read that only approximately 30% of women have purely vaginal orgasms. During that memorable night and next morning, Susan had twenty purely vaginal orgasms, and I came ten times. I was just so turned on by her beauty and sexuality that I couldn't get enough of her that night. I definitely wanted her forever, but this was not to be the case.

At the time I was dating a few women. I knew Susan was somewhat promiscuous because my friend Harriet had lived near her in a dorm room as an undergraduate and told me that Susan had had a steady stream of men spending the night in her room. I told Harriet that I didn't mind that because I would take it as a compliment to be chosen by a woman who had so many choices. I certainly didn't think Susan would want to commit to a monogamous relationship with me after only one date. I was wrong. We just seemed to be on different wavelengths. I never found out exactly what she was thinking. I certainly would have been monogamous with her if she had indicated she wanted me to be, but she never did. This didn't stop me from asking her to come with me to New York, an offer she declined. I couldn't stop thinking about her for months after I moved to New York. I kept asking her to come but she had been accepted to medical school at Wayne State University in Detroit. I thought that I would never see her again.

Two years later, in 1975, she came to New York and wanted to see me. I was living in a small studio apartment in the Sinai house staff building on 97th and Park. I was ecstatic. Unfortunately, I was dating someone, but I was not in a monogamous relationship and did not see any reason to decline to see her. She didn't want to go out; she just wanted to have sex. The woman I was dating called me before Susan came over because she wanted to see me that evening. I was on the phone trying to get off when Susan knocked on my door. She had to cool her heels in the hallway until I could get off the phone, and by the time I could let her in she was pretty upset. However, Susan still wanted to have sex with me, including anal sex. I was so happy to be with her that I again asked her to move to New York and live with me, but again she refused. Timing is so important in finding a mate. One needs to meet the right person, but it has to be at the right time. This was the second time Susan came into my life during a time of busy social activity on my part. Remarkably, it was not the last.

In 1978, during my cardiology fellowship, Susan came to Mount Sinai to do an elective in cardiology. One day a group of cardiologists and medical students were reviewing a coronary angiogram in the cramped dark viewing room. Susan was sitting in a chair and I was standing behind her. I started to rub her buttocks and she moved backwards toward me to give me better access. We ended up back in her room in the nurses' quarters, and we jumped right in, but this time Susan started to talk to me about her masochistic fantasies. I left, wanting to see her again as soon as possible. I wanted to play out some of her fantasies with her, but she refused to even see me again.

Although I was living with Barbara at this point, I was willing to turn my life upside down for Susan, but only if she could make a commitment to me. I was 31 years old and tired of playing games. I still felt strongly about her, but I wasn't going to let my feelings for her ruin my life.

Two days later, on a Friday afternoon, Susan paged me at the hospital. She wanted me to come to her room after work and tie her up, as I had previously suggested. Obviously, I was sorely tempted, but I felt that, if she really wanted me, she had had her chance. I had had enough of her ambivalence and I was not about to ruin my relationship with Barbara, so I told Susan no. It seemed to me that Susan was ruled by her hormones and just wanted me when she felt horny. I went home to Barbara that evening, having made a decision that love was more important than sex. Barbara and I married two years later.

In 1981, Susan called me from Michigan while I was at work. She had just received her first copy of Medical Clinics of North America. She had opened it to a random page, which happened to be the first page of my article about the evaluation of acute chest pain. We chatted for awhile. She had been right; I certainly was part of her karma. We never spoke again.

CHAPTER 12

SEX AND THE CITY

Manhattan is intimidating for newcomers. I was afraid of being mugged whenever I walked down the street alone. Mount Sinai was located at the border between the Upper East Side and Spanish Harlem. I was starting again at the bottom. Ann Arbor had been easy going, but Manhattan was the center of the Western World, very intense and intimidating. It took two years for me to feel at home, and at that point I fell in love with the place. My time there was divided into two five-year parcels, separated by one year in suburban New Jersey immediately following my fellowship. If I could have afforded to raise a family there I would never have left.

I was still determined to find a mate, although the first year I did little except work, eat, and sleep. I don't remember having a single date for the first six months. I gave up playing basketball and tennis as well. I ate a lot of frozen dinners. An intern's salary, $12,900, did not buy many restaurant meals, and I didn't feel very comfortable asking anyone out on a date. I did have a few dates the second half of the academic year, but none were very successful.

Dating in New York is a lot like the HBO series "Sex and the City." Everyone seems to be looking for "the right person." Everyone you date seems to have at least one fatal flaw that is a deal breaker, just like in the TV show.

After the first year I became more comfortable dating, and soon I began dating about as frequently as I had in Ann Arbor. Casual sex in New York in the 1970's was pretty much the norm, since HIV was still a decade away. One night stands were not uncommon. I never went to bars to meet women because I didn't have the time. Even if I did, I wasn't good-looking enough to be very successful. Mostly I met women in the normal course of my life. Like most single people, I went though dry periods during which I thought I'd never have sex again, and there were times when the opposite was true. Being a single doctor in New York did make me sought after by many women, however, and I would be lying if I said I didn't take full advantage if the situation. However, I never stopped looking for a wife, and I never lied to or manipulated any woman to persuade her to have sex with me.

Like the man in the famous song by the Eagles, "Desperado," I seemed to always want the women I couldn't have. When I fell for someone, I fell hard, and for a long time. It's hard to convey the amount of emotional pain I went through between the ages of 17 and 30 because of my relationships with women. One experience in particular stands out, however, and it was by far the most bizarre I had ever encountered. Shortly after I arrived in New York, I met a third-year medical student named Carla, a disarmingly pretty and extremely charming and even-tempered young woman. As an undergraduate, she had been the homecoming queen at an Ivy League University. She also turned out to be extremely unpredictable and conflicted about men. While Carla was interested in going out with me, she didn't want to have sex; however, she did want to marry me. She was so charming that I was not about to turn her down, and we actually went as far as getting the required blood tests needed to get a marriage license in New York. She was the "dance away lover" that could never be counted on, and I carried a torch for this woman for a full two years although we didn't have sex or even date consistently. Friends of mine who knew her told me I was crazy and that I should forget about her. It turns out that they were right.

During the summer of 1975 I was the senior resident in the ER, and Carla, by then an intern, was working under my supervision. She told me straight up that she wanted to see me, but I was not about to be made a fool of again. I told her I would see her that night but only if she slept with me for the first time. She came over to my apartment that evening and informed me she did not have birth control. I was more than a little surprised, considering how many different men she had been associated with, but I did have condoms.

I will never forget that night. I had never seen her naked, and she was absolutely beautiful. I felt as if I had finally found my home. I was going on vacation the next day, to the Adirondack Mountains in northeastern New York. She asked me who I was going with, and I told her the truth, that I was going with the woman I had been dating, but with whom I was not in a monogamous relationship. I felt that, since I had waited for Carla for two years, she could wait for me for a week. She was very upset. I felt she was being unfair, but she would have none of it and left. Throughout my vacation I could not stop thinking about Carla. I didn't say anything about it to the woman I was with out of courtesy and stopped dating her shortly thereafter. But Carla wouldn't see me after I got back, and I was devastated.

Sometime later, I was scheduled to be chief resident on 3 South for the months of November, December, and January, 1976. This was the main event of the entire internal medicine residency, and I had to be in top form. We got the schedule listing the assistant residents and interns who were assigned to our services a couple of months in advance. If an intern wanted to be assigned to a particular chief's service, the request would usually be honored. When I saw that Carla had gotten herself assigned to my service, I went nuts. I stormed into the department office and demanded that she be moved to a different chief's service. It was obvious to me that she was so insecure with her own abilities that she wanted to be in a position to use my feelings for her to gain special status. I felt strongly that she would offer me sexual favors in return for my doing her work for her. Under no circumstances was I going to violate my ethical principals for sex. If she wanted to have a relationship with me, I certainly would have considered it, but I was not going to be her slave. She ended up being on the service of another chief, a married man. She always seemed to be on call the same nights as he was, and people told me they would sleep in the same on-call room. I don't know if that was true and I didn't try to find out.

After Carla completed her residency at Mount Sinai, she was accepted to a fellowship at one of the Harvard Medical School hospitals. Apparently, she had received excellent letters of recommendation from her professors at Mount Sinai. By now I was back at Mount Sinai on the faculty. The entire faculty received a memo from Dr. Gorlin, demanding that all letters of recommendation written for fellowship applications would have to be approved by him prior to being sent. Apparently Carla had not lived up to her recommendations, and Dr. Gorlin's old colleagues had complained to him. I was told by doctors at Sinai that Carla had gotten her recommendations by performing oral sex on some of her attendings. People told me I was the only one who didn't know what had been going on. Again, I don't know for sure that any of this was true, but I heard this from more than one person, and had no reason to think they would lie about it. The memo from Gorlin was certainly real.

In 1978, before she left for Boston, Carla invited me to her apartment to "say goodbye." I went over to see her. She obviously wanted to have sex with me, but I refused. It had taken me a long time to get over her and I did not want to be suckered in again. I knew she just wanted to keep me in reserve in case things didn't work out in Boston. While I was there, she got a phone call from her current boyfriend, one of the other house staff. I think that was the last time I spoke to her.

I did have one somewhat successful relationship during that time period. I met Fern in 1975 in the elevator in one of the hospital buildings. She was pretty and friendly and we said a few words. I didn't get her name but I later tracked her down on the floor where she worked. She was a nurse on the ob-gyn floor. I was 28 and she was 23. I liked her a lot. My relationship with her was my first monogamous relationship in New York. She was extremely sexual and we got along great. I never cheated on her and I gave serious consideration to marrying her, although she often said she thought she wasn't smart enough for me. I think that was partially true, but we also had markedly different levels of education. She truly loved me, and I tried to reconcile our differences. We were together for nine months. In the end, I just didn't feel right about the relationship. I didn't want her to waste any more time on me and broke off our affair cleanly, without complications. However, this left me feeling frustrated and alone. I just didn't seem to be able to find the right woman. I was very happy for Fern when, a couple of years later, she told me she was getting married.

I dated a lot of nice women while I was in New York, and many of them became good friends. It became clear to me that women doctors and nurses were not suitable for me, so I thought it would a good idea to meet some school teachers. I thought a teacher would be well educated and intelligent and have enough time for a personal life. Deciding that Christmas week in the Caribbean would be a good time and place to meet a teacher, because teachers are on vacation that week and would have enough money to go there, I signed up to go to Club Med in Martinique for Christmas week of 1975.

During the trip down I met two attractive women who offered to spend the week with me. One was 19, the other 24. I didn't feel comfortable with either one and respectfully declined. I had come to look for a mate, not casual sex. When I arrived, I found, to my chagrin, two men for every woman. The first evening at dinner, our table consisted of eleven men and no women. It was there I met Douglas, an advertising executive ten years my senior. He was intelligent, very funny, and more than a little bit crazy. We had a lot in common. The dinner conversation that night centered on all of our frustrations about the paucity of women. After some time had passed, Douglas made me an offer. He had a good friend he had been dating, but both of them had decided to change their relationship to be just friends. He said she was good-looking, smart, and funny. She was 27; I was 30. She was a college graduate who had moved to New York from Minnesota to take a job as an international flight attendant for TWA airlines. Douglas said he would fix me up with her if I fixed him up with two nurses. It was a deal, and we exchanged phone numbers. After a (mostly) chaste week, I was anxious to get home and back to work. I was a very busy first year cardiology fellow at that time. I pretty much forgot about my deal with Douglas, but sometime in mid January, 1977, I got a phone call from a woman named Barbara.

CHAPTER 13

BARBARA

Barbara Blazick was born in July, 1949. (I hope she forgives me for revealing her age.) She grew up in South Saint Paul, Minnesota, a working class suburb of the Twin Cities, where her father worked in a meat packing plant. I'm not sure what her mother did, but later in life she became president of a small life insurance company.

Barbara, the oldest of three sisters, graduated with a degree in Psychology from McAllister College, one of the best liberal arts colleges in the country. On a lark, at graduation, she accompanied a friend to Chicago for an interview with TWA Airlines for a job as a flight attendant. Barbara was driven by the idea of seeing what the world had to offer outside of her experience. Her friend did not get the job, but Barbara did, on the condition that she could get her weight up to 100 pounds. (She was 5'4" tall).

Barbara went for flight attendant training in St. Louis; she wanted to fly international. For the first six months she flew domestic flights before getting an assignment to fly international out of Kennedy in New York. She moved to Manhattan in 1971, at age 21, something few women her age would have had the guts to do. She shared an apartment with one of her college roommates, Mary. Barbara adored traveling and seeing the world. She traveled all over Europe and to Egypt, where she once got deathly ill from some form of infectious disease. She told me that she never realized how food was supposed to taste until she got to Paris.

Before we met, Barbara received her master's degree from the New School in Manhattan. She was not interested in a permanent relationship in those early days, having broken up with a serious college boyfriend who wanted to marry her. She had been dating my friend Douglas but not seriously. Then, at the age of 27, she had made up her mind that it was time for her to have a serious relationship and get on to the next stage of her life.

I never expected anything would come from my deal with Douglas. I was sleeping in the hospital and was on call the night Barbara left a message on my answering machine. She sounded nice and I called her immediately. I was dating two women casually at the time. (One was Karen, a truly beautiful medical resident, and the other was Sally, a Ph.D. audiologist at the Manhattan Veteran's Administration Hospital). I enjoyed their company but I did not want to marry either one.

I felt comfortable talking to Barbara from the first minute. I think we talked every single day from then on for the next twenty years. The night of the famous New York City blackout in 1977, we talked for almost three hours on the phone. The early times of our relationship I have always described as "magical." I simply had never felt so comfortable with anyone in my life. Barbara told people that I was the first man she could talk to in the same way she could talk to her girlfriends. We were both extremely psychologically oriented. We met and got along well with each other's friends. She introduced me to fine foods, something I had no experience with. Shortly after we met, I stopped dating Karen and Sally.

I had been contemplating taking my first trip to Europe with Sally that summer, but instead I went to Europe with Barbara. I remember seeing Barbara's 747 taxiing away from the TWA terminal at JFK, with her waving to me from a window in the first class section. I followed later in coach on another flight. We went to London and Paris on that trip. I was anxious about being in a foreign country for the first time at age thirty. Fortunately, Barbara was the perfect traveling companion, guiding me around like a pro. Everything in London and Paris was very different from New York and just wonderful (except for the food in England, of course). I was enthralled with the shops, restaurants, people, subways, parks, museums—you name it.

New York came into better perspective for me because of that trip. Being in love in New York was just as exciting as being in love in Paris. Barbara knew New York better than I did, having been there two years longer than me and having had a lot more free time. She adored New York, causing my love for the city to grow and grow. To us, New York was not about what the city had to offer; it was about the people who lived there. Once you left that "small island in the North Atlantic," as we sometimes referred to Manhattan, everything was different, especially the people and the culture.

Suddenly, my plans to lead a quiet life as a suburban cardiologist did not seem as attractive. I knew I did not want a career in academics, which would have been the only way I could have stayed in Manhattan and utilized the catheterization skills I had worked so hard to acquire. Only full-time faculty members were allowed to work in the cath labs at the major hospitals in New York City.

When I met Barbara in January of 1977, she had been on winter leave from TWA and was working as a secretary for a small movie production company in Manhattan. She was living in a small but nice one-bedroom apartment in a brownstone building near Central Park on West 90th Street. Barbara insisted that we have an equal relationship, and I agreed. We decided to spend an equal number of nights at her apartment as at my place. When Barbara went back to flying in May, 1977, I really took it hard. She would be away for three days and then home for four, the first two of which she would be terribly jet lagged. I asked her to move in with me. I was able to convince the lady who ran the Mount Sinai housing that I needed a two-bedroom apartment, which became available in October. Barbara and I set up house. Our apartment was on the thirteenth floor and had a balcony overlooking Park Avenue. Living with her was a gastronomical treat, since she was a true gourmet cook. As a second year cardiology fellow, I only had to eat and sleep in the hospital twice a month and made it a point to be home for dinner. It was with a sense of regret that I had to ask her to give up the city to move with me to New Jersey in the summer of 1978.

CHAPTER 14

MY FIRST REAL JOB

In July, 1978 I started a job with a two-man cardiology group at Muhlenberg Hospital in Plainfield, New Jersey. Harrison Fertig was 54 and Esteban Lomnitz was 40. Dr. Fertig, or Hesh as he wished to be called, had been in solo practice for many years prior to Dr. Lomnitz, or Steve, joining him about four years earlier. Hesh was the Chief of Cardiology at Muhlenberg, which did not have a cath lab, though they did have privileges to perform catheterizations at St. Joseph's Hospital in Paterson, New Jersey, about 15 miles north. Steve did cath but Hesh did not. Dr. Russell Brancato, 56, was the director of the cath lab. He was very experienced and was available to back me up in the lab if I had any difficulties. It was an excellent situation in which I could get more experience until I felt comfortable operating on my own.

I had negotiated my own contract without using an attorney. The starting salary was $35,000, or about $120,000 in 2006 dollars. After one year, if all went well, I was to be made partner. My anticipated income after three years would be equal to theirs, $100,000, or about $350,000 in today's dollars. The situation seemed ideal and I was prepared to spend my career there. During the interview process, Hesh and I hit it off famously. Hesh said he knew right away that I was the guy he wanted in his practice. Steve seemed cordial and I didn't anticipate any problems. I had been successful at everything I had done so far in my life and saw no reason to think this would work out any differently.

Plainfield was a community that had recovered from the race riots it experienced during the civil rights movement of the 1960s. Barbara and I found a nice, two-bedroom apartment in a beautiful garden apartment complex in North Plainfield. I was hoping to be able to afford a house in Watchung, a lovely wooded community nearby, but this was not to be the case. Steve seemed to be threatened by my closeness to Hesh, and I felt as if I had become involved in some sort of sibling rivalry. When I would argue with him about a medical situation in the manner that was normal at Sinai, he thought I was being too competitive. Hesh told me that it wasn't important who was right. At the time, I was not able to effectively communicate that I argued not to decide *who* was right, but rather used the back and forth dialogue to reach agreement as to *what* was right for a particular patient or circumstance. This back and forth, so common at Sinai, led to misunderstandings in Plainfield.

The other, and more important, issue was that I didn't like Steve's attitudes. In my naiveté, I was under the impression that grownups treated people with respect. I did not like people who abused their power to harm others strictly for their own selfish benefit. Steve's attitude about women and patients was repugnant to me. I have always felt that if a man cheats on his wife, he will be predisposed to cheat on you. It seemed that everyone assumed Steve had a girlfriend on the side. He once introduced me to a very attractive young woman with whom he seemed to be involved, and he was very proud of the fact.

But Steve's infidelity was only one aspect of his personality. One day in our office, he followed an elderly couple out of an exam room as they walked down the hall away from me. Steve looked back at me and made a kicking motion, as if to kick the couple in the butt. His facial expression at that moment indicated that he expected me to join him in his ridicule of this elderly couple. I didn't say anything but was repulsed by his lack of respect for his patients.

Steve, who was from Chile, also believed in dictatorships and even had a large poster of the Chilean dictator Pinochet on the door to our hospital office. He clearly felt that he was better than other people and was a member of a privileged class that had the right to abuse others. He would also leave papers on the floor and insist that the women working in the cardiology department in the hospital pick up after him. But worst of all was one episode that I will never forget, a form of behavior that I had never seen before or seen since.

Before I recount what happened, a brief description of a cardiac catheterization is necessary. At that time, we did catheterizations via the Sones technique, named after Mason Sones, a cardiologist at the Cleveland Clinic, who had developed the method in 1959. The technique was difficult to learn because the catheter was not preformed to go into the coronary artery. One would insert the catheter into a small incision in the wall of the brachial artery in the right elbow. The catheter would be passed up the arm into the aorta and then down toward the heart under x-ray guidance. The cardiologist would then manipulate the end of the catheter near the heart into a loop and guide it into the orifice of the coronary arteries (the right and left). A clear liquid (called dye or contrast) that blocked x-rays would than be injected with a syringe through the catheter into the coronary artery. X-rays were beamed up from below the patient to a camera above the patient to produce x-ray black-and-white 35mm motion pictures of the coronary arteries. Then the catheter tip would be passed across the aortic valve into the left ventricular chamber. Dye would then be injected with a powerful electric machine into the main pumping chamber of the heart. X-ray motion pictures could then be obtained and assessed for left ventricular function.

The procedure was fraught with potential life threatening complications. One complication that all cardiology fellows were trained to avoid was the possibility of pushing the tip of the catheter into the web-like structures, called trabeculae, in the inside wall of the ventricle. When the power injector forced the dye through the hole at the end of the catheter, one had to make certain that the tip of the catheter was in the chamber and not up against the wall. When the cardiologist was certain that the catheter was properly positioned, he ordered the nurse to push a button to start the injection. If the cardiologist saw the dye going into the wall of the ventricle, he instantly had to pull back the catheter.

Steve was not initially trained in the Sones technique and was learning it under Dr. Brancato's supervision. He had learned the Judkin's technique, in which preformed catheters were passed into the heart from the femoral artery in the groin. In this technique, the catheter passed into the ventricle had the curved shape of a pigtail. This made it almost impossible to push the tip into the trabeculae.

One day Steve did a catheterization on a patient at St. Joseph's. When he brought the film back to Muhlenberg for Hesh and me to view, I was horrified. The tip of the catheter was pushed deep into the wall of the ventricle. The dye was power-injected into the heart muscle and through the wall of the ventricle into the space between the outside wall of the heart and the membrane covering the heart, called the pericardium. No attempt could be seen to pull back the catheter, and the full amount of dye was injected. The patient died shortly thereafter.

As bad as this was, what occurred next was dumbfounding. The patient's family had been at the hospital when this occurred and Steve had not spoken to them after the event to explain what happened. They were returning to Plainfield to meet with Steve to get an explanation. I then got instructions that *Steve wanted me to review the film with the family and explain what happened!* I couldn't believe it. This was totally unethical. I guess that, underneath it all, dictators were nothing but glorified bullies, and bullies were really nothing more than cowards in disguise. Despite his South American machismo, Steve had shown himself to be a real coward. Fortunately, Hesh was in the hospital when I got the instructions, and I told him what had occurred. He said it was just like Steve to behave that way. Hesh gave me permission to refuse to inform the family, so I called Steve in the office and nicely told him I didn't feel comfortable talking to the patient's next of kin. He didn't push me and that was the last I heard about it. However, I was left with the feeling that Steve's behavior had to be improved if I were to continue working with him.

While I rarely lose my temper, it is true that I have always had difficulty hiding my emotions. Ira Gelb, a private cardiologist at Mount Sinai and an assistant editor of the *American Journal of Cardiology*, once advised me that I couldn't continue to wear my emotions on my sleeve. I countered that sometimes I did this for a specific calculated effect. Others have noted that I "get upset when things go wrong." This doesn't mean that I lose my temper; I just can't always mask my expression or maintain a dispassionate tone of voice. I don't know if this is a genetic trait or a result of growing up in a family that never hid any emotions, or a combination of both; it is probably the latter.

Nevertheless, because of the situation with Steve, I soon reached my breaking point. In November of 1978, I lost my temper with Steve and gave him a thorough tongue-lashing over the phone. (I don't recall the reason exactly, but it was related to the way that Steve used the women in the cardiology department to deliver his criticism to me). I knew then for certain that I did not want to work with him unless he modified his behavior at once, and the only way I could accomplish that was to a partner, not an employee.

My contract called for them to give me six months' notice if I was not to be made partner. In December I was given a $5,000 bonus and told I was doing a good job. Steve and Hesh had planned their vacations to occur simultaneously for several weeks in January, 1979, and I was to be left with the sole responsibility for the entire practice for three weeks. I welcomed the opportunity to show I could handle it, which I did without difficulty. But when they got back from vacation, Hesh told me that Steve was reluctant to make me a partner, not because of the immediate circumstances but because he was afraid of what would happen in the future after Hesh retired. Hesh said Steve had agreed to give it another year and give me a $5,000 raise. I was not about to waste another year of my life with these guys and immediately said, "No way." Hesh got back to me a short time later to tell me he couldn't talk Steve into fulfilling our contractual arrangement; in other words, basically, I was out of a job. I was devastated and furious. I had never failed at anything in my life up to that point. I had never been unemployed before, and my anxiety rose to enormous proportions.

Barbara was wonderful about the situation and did everything she could to help me through it. A few years later Barbara told me a story about the husband of one of her colleagues. He was in his early 30's and had been turned down for a partnership at a big law firm in New York. He spent weeks in bed until he got himself together. I never got that bad, but my depression and anxiety were severe. I felt worthless, and I thought that my future was dismal. I saw all my hard work and dreams going down the drain.

Fortunately, I finally had insisted on getting six months' notice, so I still had a job with Hesh and Steve until July, 1979. I pulled myself together, started looking for another opportunity, and I applied for a full-time position at Columbia that was advertised in the *New England Journal of Medicine*. That position turned out to have been filled prior to the ad being placed by a Sinai-trained cardiologist a year ahead of me. This is a frequent occurrence, because federal law requires equal opportunity for large institutions that are the recipients of federal funds.

I called a couple of private cardiologists I knew and soon realized that I needed to get my feet back on the ground before venturing into another private practice situation. I called the Chief of Cardiology at Mount Sinai, Dr. Michael Herman, to see if he could help me. Mike told me the position of cath lab director at Elmhurst was still open, and it was mine if I wanted it. After I thought about it for awhile, it seemed like a reasonable thing for me to do at that point. I had a year's more cath experience and would be more prepared for the responsibility than I would have been the previous year. Besides, it would be a short commute from Manhattan, and Barbara and I were anxious to get back to the city. It turned out to be the right decision.

I had realized that I did not want Barbara to have a career as a flight attendant, since I hated her being away all the time. I knew she wanted to do more with her life, and we had spent a lot of time discussing what she wanted to do. We came to the conclusion that her passion was psychology and she wanted to be a therapist. To do this, she needed to go back to school to get either a master's degree in social work or a doctorate in psychology. Admittance to a doctoral program is extremely difficult and competitive. We decided she should apply for both kinds of programs.

In the fall of 1978, while we were living in New Jersey, I told Barbara that I would support her financially if she took three months off work to devote her time entirely to applying to graduate schools. She did so and was accepted to all the Social Work programs to which she applied, including Columbia. Fortune struck, however, when she was accepted at the Ferkauf School of Psychology at Yeshiva University in the Bronx to a new five-year program leading to a professional degree called a Doctor of Psychology, or Psy.D. for short. After that, all we had to do was find an affordable one-bedroom apartment in Manhattan.

This turned out to be a lot more difficult than we thought. My salary was only going to be $38,000. I had lived in Sinai-subsidized housing as a house officer, so I did not know much about the cost of housing in Manhattan. We walked all over town with real estate agents without much success. We were spoiled and didn't want to live in one of the outer boroughs. Being able to live in Manhattan was one of the main reasons I had taken the Elmhurst job.

Again fortune shined on us. In March of 1977, I had met a patient in the coronary care unit at Mount Sinai who happened to be on the board of trustees. His name was David Paul. He was 37 and a very successful real estate developer in charge of real estate for Mount Sinai. David took an immediate liking to me and we became close friends before Barbara and I moved to New Jersey. David was probably the most brilliant, energetic, charismatic, and creative man I have ever known. We had lost touch after we moved, but now that we were moving back to New York, I called him to see if he could help us find an apartment. Even though I was to work full-time at Elmhurst, I was still a member of the full-time faculty and therefore eligible to live in subsidized hospital housing. David was able to get us a magnificent, large, two-bedroom apartment in the faculty building on Fifth Avenue at 102nd Street on the Sinai campus. Words cannot describe the elation Barbara and I felt at our good fortune.

Several incidents made me feel more reconciled about the situation regarding Steve. First, before we left New Jersey, the nurses from Muhlenberg Hospital gave me a big party at one of their homes. At the party they presented me with an engraved plaque that read "For Outstanding and Dedicated Service." At least I had done something right, I felt.

As a resident and fellow, I had known Jose Meller, a young assistant professor in cardiology, very well. Jose was revered as one of the finest clinical cardiologists at Sinai and, what's more, he was from Chile and had known Steve from medical school there. A few months after I had returned to Sinai, I ran into Jose, who told me that, if he had known I was going to work with Steve, he would have never let me do it.

Years later, in 1998, I was at a dinner meeting with cardiologists at Tavern on the Green in Central Park and just happened to be sitting next to the cardiologist who had replaced me at Muhlenberg. I told him that I blamed myself, in part, for what had happened between me and Steve. He told me repeatedly that Steve had been the bane of his existence and said with absolute certainty that the problems I had had with Steve were definitely Steve's fault, not mine. Thanks to these three events, I was finally able to reach closure on a difficult episode of my life.

CHAPTER 15

MOUNT SINAI, CITY HOSPITAL CENTER AT ELMHURST

When I interviewed with Stanley Seckler, the Chief of Medicine at City Hospital Center at Elmhurst, he told me that a career at his hospital could result in my someday being promoted to full professor, but, if I was interested in making money this was not the place to be. I replied honestly that, at this point in my career, I thought I could help him in my capacity as Director of the Cardiac Invasive Laboratory. I made no pretense to suggest that I was interested in a life-long career at Elmhurst, but I certainly felt a responsibility to do the best job I could for the institution. In retrospect, I kept my word to him.

The City of New York runs a number of municipal hospitals. At that time, private paying patients with private doctors were not admitted to these hospitals. Patients were cared for by medical residents and fellows under the supervision of full-time salaried physicians. The city contracted with the major medical schools to staff these hospitals with faculty from the medical schools. For example: Harlem Hospital was run by Columbia; Queens Hospital was run by Cornell; Bellevue was run by New York University; and Elmhurst was run by Mount Sinai. There were three full-time cardiologists at Elmhurst: Frank Lane; Chief of Cardiology; Jae Rhee, Director of Non-invasive Cardiology, primarily echocardiography and stress testing, and me. My faculty appointment was instructor of clinical medicine at the Mount Sinai School of Medicine. I was appropriately starting at the bottom of the academic ladder.

I was determined to do a good job to advance my career and eventually enter private practice at some time in the future, but, as in any situation, certain obstacles presented themselves. The initial problem that Dr. Lane and I both faced was to keep the cath lab open. The State of New York required all cath labs in the state to perform a minimum of 150 cases per year to stay accredited. This meant we had to average three cases a week, and keeping my job depended on this. Frank was doing a creditable job keeping up a barely adequate number before I got there, but for me the situation posed a serious ethical dilemma. I had been trained never to do unnecessary procedures on patients. This was predicated on two principles: 1) Unnecessary procedures increase the cost of medical care and 2) more importantly, unnecessary procedures exposed the patient to the danger of a complication from the procedure itself. For cardiac catheterization, potential complications included heart attack (myocardial infarction), stroke, and/or death.

Cardiologists are trained intensively to understand in which patients the potential benefits for the patient outweigh the risks of the catheterization. To state it more bluntly: If a patient had a serious complication from a catheterization that was not indicated, it would be considered malpractice. Indications for catheterization change over the years, and cardiologists must remain current about these indications. Of course, there may be honest disagreements about whether or not a cath is indicated in a particular patient. For me to be true to my own values, I always had to place the welfare of every patient above my own personal needs. Put simply, I would not do a catheterization unless I was convinced that it was in the patient's best interest, or another cardiologist persuaded me of this, period. Needless to say, my attitude led to some degree of conflict during the course of my career. In those rare occasions that I violated this imperative, I regretted my decision. As a faculty member charged with the responsibility to train young doctors, I felt only slightly less obligated to teach them the accepted indications for catheterization that were accepted medical practice at that time. At Elmhurst, I was particularly challenged to live up to my standards of care and still satisfy the state requirements for the number of cases we needed to perform in order to stay open.

Dr. Frank Lane was a nice man, but he faced a more difficult problem than I did. He was in his early fifties and had a wife and five children he needed to put through college. College tuition for faculty members at or above the rank of associate professor was paid for by the medical school. If the cath lab shut down, I was young enough to start over somewhere else; Frank was not. I did everything I could to help him find patients that needed cath. Since we had no private doctors admitting patients from their offices, our potential source of patients was limited to those patients admitted through the emergency room at Elmhurst and possibly from the free cardiology clinic we ran in the hospital outpatient department. I would comb the wards to see if the residents had any patients that needed cath. Frank and I arranged meetings with doctors at private hospitals to generate cath referrals. Doctors at private hospitals had a strong financial incentive to send their cath patients where they could admit the patients to their own service at those hospitals and bill for their services, so we were not successful in our attempts.

Frank also was trained in catheterization and performed about half the caths. Problems between me and Frank arose whenever I disagreed with his decision to do a cath on a patient who didn't need one. This conflict would involve the residents and fellows, because I felt a responsibility to teach them the appropriate indications for cath. To do otherwise would have been unethical. I tried very hard to have a good relationship with Frank. I made a point of having lunch with him on a daily basis so I could establish trust between us and keep the lines of communication open. Unfortunately, I was less than entirely successful. Frank told me he had been hospitalized for "nerves," which I took to mean some form of mental illness. He was very rigid, anxious, and fearful, and I think that his fears clouded his judgment. Because of this, tensions increased between us.

One case in particular is illustrative of our problem. A man in his early 30's was admitted to the hospital for a non-cardiac reason that I don't recall. A murmur (a potentially abnormal heart sound) was detected, and when Frank saw the patient, he arranged for the man to have a cath. The patient had a leaky aortic valve but no symptoms of shortness of breath or chest pain, and his echocardiogram indicated that the valve did not need to be replaced. A catheterization would not yield any additional information that would change the patient's management or treatment.

Standard practice was to make the decision for valve replacement based on patient history, a physical exam and non-invasive testing (echocardiography and, if indicated, stress testing). Most patients wouldn't require aortic valve replacement for a leaky valve until at least their late forties. Usual care for such patients would require yearly echocardiograms and careful follow-up as an outpatient. Once a patient developed symptoms and/or significant echocardiographic abnormalities, consideration for valve replacement would be given. A catheterization of this particular patient would expose him to the potentially serious complications without any benefit.

I felt that my responsibilities were to the patient and to the correct education of the residents. I was asked to see the patient at some point and expressed my opinion to the residents but not to the patient. I think I also brought it up with Frank, and I'm not sure if the fellows mentioned it to him. However, this case was emblematic of the tensions that arose between us. We continued to struggle to maintain our numbers in the cath lab for about a year. At that point, I was asked to spend one day per week in the cath lab at Mt. Sinai. Sinai's cath lab was very busy, and I performed between three and five cases there each day. We could then tell the state that the Elmhurst lab was benefiting from my additional experience. After that, we were able to keep the lab open without undue pressure.

Unfortunately, the tension between me and Frank was not ameliorated. One day—I believe it was in '81 or '82—I was called into Dr. Seckler's office. He told me I didn't get along with people and he was going to fire me. This was a serious threat to my future. I knew I was well liked and respected by both the attendings and the residents at Elmhurst. I decided the only way I was going to survive would be to get a petition signed by all the residents, fellows, and attendings at Elmhurst, asking Dr. Seckler not to fire me. I handed him the petition within 24 hours. He changed his mind and made a concerted effort to get me and Frank onto the same page. The three of us met in Stan's office, at which time I reiterated my intention to redouble the efforts I was already making toward this end.

However, things didn't change much, and we continued to muddle through as best we could. Joe Solomito was the chief of all residents that year at Elmhurst. This was an administrative position given to a resident after completing his internal medicine residency. Joe and I were pretty good friends. He told me something that I have never forgotten and which I think defined many of my subsequent professional relationships. Joe said that he told Dr. Seckler: "Richard gets along with good people; he doesn't get along with bad people." I should also mention at this point that I was elected by the attendings at Elmhurst to be the Department of Medicine representative to the Elmhurst Attending Physicians Association.

Despite the problems at Elmhurst, by the beginning of 1980 I felt secure enough to suggest to Barbara that we should get married, and we decided to tie the knot in October. We were able to find a rabbi who was willing to marry a Jew to a gentile.

Planning the party was fun. Our apartment was large enough for a small wedding. I was going to pay for it. We arranged for a gourmet caterer. We were only going to invite people we truly wanted to be there. Barbara felt, correctly, that my mother would not be able to control herself and would completely ruin the wedding for us. As a result, I didn't tell my parents that I was married until after the wedding. My only family members to attend were my sister and my cousin Michael and his wife.

The wedding was on October 11, 1980. It was wonderful, the best wedding I have ever been to. Actually, it was the best party I ever attended. The following weekend we flew to Minnesota where we had another reception for all of Barbara's family. We honeymooned at the end of January, 1981 in Italy for a week. We were able to get first class seats on TWA. We visited Rome, Florence, and Venice. Italy is wonderful in the winter, as the weather is cool and there are no crowds.

CHAPTER 16

STREPTOKINASE

In 1979 or thereabouts, Dr. Peter Rentrop, working with his associates, Dr. Heine Blanke and Dr. Karl Karsch, developed a revolutionary concept in Germany. Dr. Rentrop came upon the idea of not just injecting dye through a catheter into a coronary artery, but administering a medication through the catheter directly into the orifice of the artery. In medical school we had been taught that blood clots forming in the coronary arteries were *not* the cause of heart attacks. This was because autopsy examinations of heart attack victims did not reveal the clots. However, by 1979, cardiologists had shown that coronary angiograms taken *during* a heart attack revealed completely occluded arteries, strongly suggesting the presence of a clot. Dr. Rentrop hit upon the idea that, if clots in the artery caused a heart attack, then dissolving the clot would stop the heart attack and potentially save the patient's life.

Streptokinase, an enzyme produced by bacteria, was known to dissolve clots in humans, a process called thrombolysis. The problem was that it could cause severe bleeding as a side effect. Dr. Rentrop felt that, if he dripped the drug directly into the coronary artery, he could use a very low dose that would dissolve the clot but not cause bleeding elsewhere in the body. The concept of acute coronary thrombolysis was one of the most important breakthroughs in cardiology during the second half of the twentieth century. Dr. Rentrop had done preliminary work in Germany and demonstrated the effectiveness of the concept. The next step was to do a large scale trial of the procedure to prove it would save lives.

Dr. Richard Gorlin, himself a world famous cardiologist, was chairman of the Department of Medicine at Mount Sinai and therefore

Dr. Seckler's boss. Dr. Gorlin wanted Dr. Rentrop to do his clinical trial of intracoronary streptokinase for acute myocardial infarction (the technical name for heart attack) at Mount Sinai. Dr. Gorlin had sufficient funds to support a pilot study with the idea of getting further funding from the National Institutes of Health (NIH), so he offered a position at Mount Sinai to Dr. Rentrop and his associates. Mount Sinai Hospital by itself did not have an adequate number of infarct patients to complete the study. Elmhurst had at least as many infarct patients as Sinai. Belleview Hospital was recruited to participate in the study. The three institutions would collaborate in order to have a sufficient number of patients. As director of the cath lab at Elmhurst, I would play a significant role in the project. I was extremely excited to have such an opportunity and jumped in with both feet. Fortune had again shined on me.

The project was a huge undertaking, but perhaps the most challenging aspect was recruiting patients for the study. At the same time, we would have to explain the procedure to the patients while they were having severe pain during a heart attack. We would have to explain the relative risks and benefits and obtain informed written consent. A cardiologist would have to be on call 24/7 to perform the procedure. To add to the difficulty, the study had to be double blind. That meant that neither the cardiologist nor the patient would know what treatment would be given to the patient. After the patients signed the consent, a sealed envelope would be opened, assigning the patient to one of four treatment groups: intracoronary streptokinase, intracoronary nitroglycerine, a combination of both, or standard medical treatment without any initial catheterization. The cardiologist would not know which medication he was instilling into the coronary artery of any patient. Of course, both the patient and doctor would know which patients received standard medical treatment.

Peter did not initially want a medical control group because he felt that Dr. Kennedy in Washington State had proven that cath during acute MI (myocardial infarction) was safe. Even though I was the junior person in the group of investigators, I felt strongly that we had to have a medically treated control group because Dr. Kennedy had been performing diagnostic caths. We were going to do an interventional cath, which could take longer and expose the patient to unforeseen risks. Peter initially vetoed the idea but was subsequently overruled by the Dean of the Medical School, Dr. Thomas Chalmers. Dr. Chalmers was Dr. Gorlin's boss. He had been one of the pioneers in the development of the concept of prospective randomized clinical trials when he was a professor at Yale.

Peter and I got along quite well and I considered him a friend. Initially he would come out to Elmhurst to do the procedure and train me how to do it. It wasn't long before he felt I was ready to do it independently. I will never forget the first time I saw an artery open up before my very eyes. The whole team was practically jumping up and down and cheering in the cath lab when it happened. We had become a part of the history of medicine.

I totally dedicated myself to the project, even sleeping at Elmhurst during my nights on call, just like a resident or intern. Elmhurst was recruiting as many patients as Sinai or Belleview, and I was quite proud of my contribution. We had to enter as many patients as we could into the pilot trial in order to impress the NIH that we deserved to get a large grant. Peter was doing all the paperwork, preparing the grant proposal. Everyone was involved in setting up the protocol. We had frequent meetings involving statisticians, nuclear cardiologists, hematologists, and all the cardiologists involved. Ultimately we all got on a train to Washington, DC to present the proposal to the NIH in Bethesda, Md. We were awarded a grant of around five million dollars, I believe in 1982. We were able to perform the study and the results were published in *The New England Journal of Medicine* in December, 1984. However, the internal politics involved were very difficult for everyone.

Because of the importance of the study, conflicts arose concerning control and credit, and it didn't take long for Peter and Dr. Gorlin to butt heads over control of the money. I think Dr. Gorlin had expected to use some of the money for other needs in the department of medicine. Peter felt all the money should go only to the project. I really agreed with Peter, but I was too junior to have any say in these decisions. The Dean sided with Peter and sides were drawn. I was also drawn into the fray unknowingly and without being asked.

In early 1983, just before I left on vacation with Barbara to the Berkshires, Valentine Fuster, the Chief of Cardiology at Mount Sinai, and also one of my bosses, called me into his office. Valentine (as he preferred to be called) told me somewhat cryptically that I would go over to Elmhurst when I needed to, implying that he wanted me to come to Sinai to work in the cath lab full time. During our vacation, Barbara and I spent some time discussing what Dr. Fuster meant. I put two and two together and reached the conclusion that Gorlin was going to fire Rentrop and take over the financial reins of the project. I was the only other person trained to do the procedure, so it was logical I would have to go to Sinai and let someone else take over the cath lab at Elmhurst. I did not have much interest in working full time at Sinai because I did not want a career doing research, which was required of all Sinai cardiologists, but I probably would have gone if asked. I was busy trying to plan my future, and that was not what I wanted.

At the first steering committee meeting after I got back from vacation, Peter attacked me in front of everyone. I successfully defended myself but was quite shaken up and incredulous. My supposition was that Fuster and Gorlin had changed their minds about Peter, but that Peter had gotten wind of the plot and thought that I had been part of the conspiracy against him. To make matters worse, I had been trying to recruit Warren Sherman to work on the project with me at Elmhurst. Peter thought I wanted Warren at Elmhurst as part of my plot to take over for him at Sinai. Warren was a great guy and I just wanted to work with him. I had to fight tooth and nail with Peter to get him to let me hire Warren. I was finally successful, but my relationship with Peter was permanently poisoned. Peter and I started to record our phone calls with each other. Gorlin's nefariousness had had a negative impact on all of us.

Peter did, however, throw me a bone, or maybe it was an olive branch. He told me that the higher-ups had asked him how good I was in the cath lab. He had replied: "For diagnostic cath, Richard is as good as anyone." I thanked him for that. I took it as an extreme compliment coming from Peter, as he was not one to throw around compliments. I also knew that he was right; I was as good as anyone doing diagnostic catheterizations. That feeling stayed with me my entire career until I semi-retired in 1997. Our relationship improved somewhat after that and I still consider Peter a friend to this day. I have, however, never forgiven Dr. Gorlin for what he did.

My political problems at Elmhurst did not end when Dr. Seckler changed his mind about firing me. I still had serious problems with Frank Lane's medical decisions. It had gotten to the point that Dr. Peter Nicholas, the chief of infectious diseases at Elmhurst and one of the deans of the medical school, told me he told Seckler that, figuratively speaking, we needed to divide the cardiology division into two parts, one for Frank and one for me. An extraordinary event obviated the necessity for such drastic action. Because Frank was the Chief of Cardiology at Elmhurst and a friend of Dr. Gorlin, he was made principal investigator of the streptokinase study for Elmhurst. I felt this was unfair because I was doing all the work. Peter supported me but could not overrule Gorlin.

At this point it is necessary to describe standard operating procedure in the cath lab. During the procedure, the nurses and technicians record the exact time of each step. For example, the time when the catheter is first placed into the artery is recorded, as is the time when the catheter is removed from the patient's body. The amount of time that the catheter remains in the patient's arteries is called the "arterial time." Cardiologists are trained to use the minimal arterial time consistent with a safe and complete study. The reason for this is simple; the longer the catheter is inside the patient, the more likely it is that a serious complication will occur. (I was very proud of the fact that my skills had advanced to the point that my usual arterial time for a diagnostic coronary angiogram using the Sones technique was approximately 15 minutes). Under no circumstances was the doctor to leave the catheter in the patient and leave the lab to do something else.

Even though Frank did not do any of the streptokinase procedures on any of the study patients, he did do some of the diagnostic caths that each study patient had prior to discharge a week to ten days after admission. One day, Frank was scheduled to do a pre-discharge cath on a middle-aged woman who was entered in the study. He had also scheduled himself to give a lecture at 11 a.m. I always attended all the lectures. Frank was a few minutes late and finished his lecture in about an hour. He then hurried back to the cath lab. Frank had left the catheter tip in the patient's ascending aorta, just above the heart, when he went upstairs to give his talk. During this time, fluid would drip slowly through the catheter to prevent blood clots from forming. Because the pressure in the aorta is high, the bag containing the fluid would be put under pressure with a cuff-like device into which the bag of fluid would be placed. The cuff would be pumped up with air, squeezing the bag and pushing the fluid through the catheter and into the patient.

During a typical cath, only a small percentage of the bag of fluid would be infused into the patient. However, Frank had left the fluid infusing for an hour while he went to give his lecture. There is usually some air on top of the fluid in the bag. While Frank was upstairs, all the fluid in the bag had gone into the patient, and some of the air in the bag had been forced into the patient's aorta. This created a bubble or bubbles in the arteries that supply the brain with blood. The bubbles got stuck in the arteries, preventing the normal flow of blood from the heart to the brain. The upshot: The patient had a massive stroke and died. I was told that, when Frank told the family what had happened, one family member said to him: "How would you like someone to put a bubble in *your* brain?"

I have never seen or read about anything like this either before or since. What happened was not an accident; it was gross negligence and disregard for a patient's life. I did not get involved with any of this and don't know if a lawsuit was ever filed. Because the patient was a study patient, news of the event was transmitted almost immediately to Rentrop, Gorlin, Seckler, and the Dean, Dr. Chalmers. Frank was immediately removed from the study and I was made principal investigator at Elmhurst. A short time later, Frank was fired. Fortunately, he was rehired to run the outpatient cardiology clinic at Elmhurst. That allowed him to keep his faculty appointment and make the tuition payments for his children.

CHAPTER 17

THE SEARCH FOR MY FUTURE

I knew when I arrived at Elmhurst that I was not going to spend the rest of my career there. In retrospect, I'm proud of the fact that I spent five years working for little money in a charity hospital taking care of poor people who couldn't afford a private hospital and doctor. I'm glad I was able to make a contribution to medical science participating in the streptokinase trial. I think I taught the residents and fellows as much as I could. I was able to keep the cath lab open. Also, I had the opportunity to learn an enormous amount about cardiology. I had so much free time I was able to read every issue of the two major cardiology journals and the cardiology articles in the two major medical journals cover to cover in detail. I gave lectures, for which I would study a topic for three months, reading almost all the known literature and preparing slide presentations. I wrote several papers and was a coauthor on several others. I was promoted to assistant professor. I was the first Elmhurst faculty member to be invited to join the Sinai faculty private practice plan and receive the financial benefits it afforded. My cath skills grew because of all the valuable experience I accrued. And I got to live on Fifth Avenue on an assistant professor's salary. I did resent being used as a political football and a pawn of the higher ups, but it was nothing compared to what I had to deal with later in life. I loved my personal life and the wonderful friends I made outside of work.

That being said, I struggled to find a path to the work I really wanted to do: take care of my own patients and secure a financial future for myself and my family. Our apartment was large enough to raise two children, but I came to see it as a gilded cage. In order to stay in it, I would have to stay on the full-time faculty and my life would be under someone else's control. At my 35th birthday party in December, 1981 I remember being quite depressed about my prospects. Barbara's graduate school was going to last until 1984, so I could only look for a position in New York City or the suburbs. I responded to advertisements in the medical journals. I also became good friends with one of the well-respected and very successful private cardiologists at Sinai, Alan Unger. Alan and I became running buddies in Central Park, and we often went out to dinner as two couples. He invited me to moonlight in his office on 86th Street doing echocardiograms. I worked hard to get full admitting privileges to Sinai so that I could join his practice if I was asked. Because of my contributions to the institution, Dr. Gorlin eventually did grant me those privileges.

While I was there, Mt. Sinai was going through some major political struggles. One of the private lung doctors was trying to get privileges to do bronchoscopes at the hospital. Dr. Gorlin wanted to limit the privileges to full-time faculty so as to keep the income from the procedure in his department, to be used to fund other needs. As part of this policy initiative, the board of trustees passed a rule that cardiac catheterization could only be performed by full-time salaried faculty members, such as me. I knew that, if I wanted to stay at Sinai in private practice, I would have to give up cath, but my love of New York and of Sinai made me willing to do so. I even applied for Frank's job as Chief of Cardiology at Elmhurst. Jae Rhee also applied, but Dr. Gorlin wanted someone more senior. He hired John Madias, a really nice man and a bright cardiologist. John and I got along fine, and he definitely valued my presence in the department.

Despite the streptokinase trial, I felt that I did not have the opportunity to live up to my full potential at Elmhurst. I remember walking around the streets in Elmhurst, Queens, feeling isolated and wondering what I was doing there. Life was easy and I was well respected, but my heart just wasn't in it. One day in the cath lab at Sinai in 1983, one of the senior cardiology fellows, Arthur Kennish, told me he was joining Alan

Unger and his partner, Arthur Weisenseel in their practice. Alan had already told me indirectly that Weisenseel had vetoed me. I wasn't surprised since, as much as Alan had respected my abilities, his partner seemed to be put off by my personality. I liked Arthur Weisenseel, but we were definitely not compatible.

Arthur Kennish was a very nice guy and didn't know my aspirations, so I didn't say anything. Once, however, when I was having lunch with him, I began talking about my concerns about my future. He told me how respected I had become and how good I was in the cath lab, adding that they needed me because of the streptokinase project. I explained to him that that was temporary, but I appreciated his compliments and have never forgotten them.

Gus Prichard, the director of the cath lab at Sinai, had trained at the Cleveland Clinic with Dr. Sones, and his skill was widely admired by all the cardiology fellows and attendings. He had trained all the fellows in catheterization. One day, when Gus was having trouble getting the catheter into the left coronary artery of a patient, he asked me to take over the case for him in front of the whole cath lab staff. I was incredibly flattered, and I was able to finish the procedure without any difficulty. So I knew Arthur Kennish's compliment was genuine. I also knew I was ready to go out into the real world. As it turned out, Kennish worked with Unger and Weisenseel for only one year. He told me he had wanted to spend more time at home, and Alan and Arthur Weisenseel wanted to hang around the office after work. I'm sure I would have felt the same way as Kennish, so I was glad that I hadn't joined that practice after all.

In early 1983, Barbara said that I should consider looking for a job in another, smaller city instead of the New York suburbs. I knew she would hate leaving New York, but I also knew she wouldn't have said such a thing unless she meant it. Soon I started answering ads from around the country. I remember getting interest from groups in Greeley, Colorado and Albuquerque, New Mexico, but I didn't travel out there; it just seemed too far away.

Barbara and I went to the Canadian Rockies on vacation that summer. When we returned a message was on my answering machine from a cardiologist in Pittsburgh, Pa. Only 350 miles from New York City, Pittsburgh was an eastern city, and we thought it might be a smaller version of an east coast city. We decided to give the position serious consideration, so I called the guy back. We talked for about twenty minutes, during which I asked all the usual questions. I remember specifically asking him, “How many years to equality?”

He responded: “Three years.” This sounded reasonable, considering my level of experience. I agreed to meet with him in New York, as he had already planned a trip to the city.

I recall two things from that first meeting: I had a small hole in the sole of one of my loafers, and I worried that the cardiologist was thinking that I must be hard up for this job since I couldn’t even afford new shoes. I also remember him saying this about the private practice of medicine: “It’s a business like any other business.” I didn’t agree, but I didn’t say anything. He seemed like a nice enough guy, though, and I agreed to fly out to Pittsburgh to look over the situation.

It was 95 degrees in Pittsburgh in mid September when I arrived there. The practice was centered in a 400-bed community hospital, Jefferson Hospital, in a suburb thirteen miles south of Pittsburgh. The senior doctor had started the practice in 1977 and had brought in another cardiologist in 1979. Both of them were non-invasive cardiologists. He had trained at UCLA, and the junior guy had trained at Emory University in Atlanta. Both of these were well-respected, high-quality training programs.

Jefferson did not have a catheterization laboratory, so their patients were sent to Shadyside Hospital in Pittsburgh for catheterization and bypass surgery, if needed. Shadyside was a 450-bed hospital with a free-standing medical residency program and a cardiology training program. The politics at Shadyside were moving in the opposite direction from those at Mt Sinai. The Shadyside cath lab had been restricted to full-time cardiologists but was now being opened to select private groups. Each group was allowed to have one invasive cardiologist on staff at Shadyside. The group would have to pay the hospital a fee of $50 for each case done. This seemed reasonable to me. The cath labs were up to date, and it seemed like a nice place to work.

I interviewed with the Chief of Cardiology at Shadyside, James O'Toole. Intracoronary streptokinase was still a big deal in 1983, and Dr. O'Toole told me that I was just the kind of guy they were looking for to work at his hospital. Besides, he had agreed to train me to do balloon angioplasty, a procedure I could not do at Elmhurst because it didn't have a cardiac surgical program to take care of the potential complications of angioplasty. I went back home thinking that the situation seemed pretty ideal. It wasn't too long before I received another phone call asking me to come out for a second interview, this time bringing Barbara with me.

Barbara and I met with both doctors, and the senior doctor gave us a guided tour of Pittsburgh. A meeting with a real estate agent was arranged. Barbara and I saw a beautiful old mansion that had been converted into four condominiums with a swimming pool and tennis court situated on two acres. It was built in 1910 and was on a beautiful tree-lined cul de sac near a private elementary school. The ceilings were high and there were three fireplaces. We fell in love with the place. The real estate agent said she had never seen such an emotional reaction to a property in her life.

Everything seemed to be falling into place, that is, until the end of the day. Usually, a second interview for a job means they want you to take the job. This time, at the end of the day, I was told that another cardiologist, Dr. Generalovich, was their first choice and they were waiting for him to make up his mind. We were being put up in the Howard Johnson's Motor Lodge, which was a little unusual, considering that cardiologists usually stay at first-line hotels. I felt sick to my stomach at being used to manipulate another person and had terrible nightmares that night. When I awoke, I told Barbara that I just didn't know what it would take to find a decent job. I left without calling the senior doctor, as I had been asked, because I was pretty disgusted. I left with a bad taste in my mouth. I still wanted the job, since it was a much better situation than any I had seen in the New York area. It also paid a lot. While my salary in Plainfield was $35,000, the Pittsburgh job started at $80,000. I was making $60,000 in New York and the cost of living in Pittsburgh was around 30% less.

Less than a week later I got a call informing me that Generalovich didn't want the job and offering it to me. I said yes. I then received a letter in the mail officially offering me the job. It said that the starting salary was "$80,000.00" and after three years my salary would increase to equal that of the other two doctors at "$150,000.00." I thought at the time that they spelled out all the zeros to impress me. The letter went on to say that "in addition" there were "significant bonuses." I took it to mean around $30,000. It certainly seemed like a lot of money. I didn't know at the time that it was meant to defraud me of hundreds of thousands of dollars.

They wanted me to start as soon as possible. The contract arrived at the beginning of November. I asked my friend Alan, an attorney in New Jersey, to look it over. He said it was mostly "boiler plate" and that I should go ahead and sign it. After my experience in New Jersey, I knew there was a possibility this might not work out any better. It was a calculated risk. I was much more experienced now. I had left Plainfield because I didn't want to fight the "Battle of Plainfield" with Steve and Hesh. It just wasn't worth it, as I really didn't want to live in New Jersey. I figured if Pittsburgh didn't work out, I was strong enough to fight for my survival and win. I certainly was not itching for a fight; I just wanted to get along with everyone.

After I signed the contract in November, 1983, I notified Drs. Madias, Seckler, and Fuster, all my bosses, to let them know when I would be leaving. The people in Pittsburgh wanted me to start January 1, 1984, although I had wanted to start at the end of the academic year in June, 1984. We reached a compromise of March 4, 1984. I told Peter without much regret. I was annoyed that Warren Sherman was being recruited to go full time to Sinai after I had fought so hard against Peter to get Warren to come to Elmhurst in the first place. Also, I was pretty disillusioned with intracoronary streptokinase. The data was showing a mortality rate for myocardial infarction of 15%, no better than the historical rate of death with conventional medical therapy. By doing the study, however, I had become a real expert on myocardial infarction. At Elmhurst, as principal investigator, I had complete responsibility for all the infarct patients in the study. I also had total control of all the clinical decisions made on every study patient, including those in the control group who received conventional medical therapy. Since every patient was part of the statistical analysis, the exact percentage mortality of my medically treated patients was calculated. Very few cardiologists ever have the opportunity to have their actual performance evaluated with such scrutiny. The result I achieved was astonishing: My medically-treated mortality for acute myocardial infarction was only **3%.** I had confounded the data that was supposed to show that intracoronary streptokinase was superior to conventional medical therapy. The number of patients was not enough to be statistically significant: the p value was .07 or .08, with a p less than .05 being required for statistical significance. The study did not have to be stopped and this data was not published, but I did present it at one of the steering committee meetings. This made me even less popular with Peter, and I'm sure he was not unhappy to see me go. In any case, I was certainly dubious of the benefits of intracoronary streptokinase.

One person who was very unhappy to see me go, however, was Richard Gorlin. After he received requests for information about me as part of the routine application process to the Pittsburgh hospitals, he called me to his office at Sinai. Apparently, none of the three superiors I had notified had bothered to tell him I was leaving. Gorlin was an autocrat and was feared by everyone. I guess no one wanted to be the bearer of bad news. I had to sit down with him and the vice chairman of the department while I was raked over the coals for being an ungrateful brat. I was reduced to tears. I told him that I should at least be recognized for having fought so hard to recruit my replacement, Dr. Sherman. When I started to cry, he backed off and wished me luck. Shortly thereafter, Gorlin sent a memo to the entire full-time faculty saying that no one was allowed to quit except on July 1st of every year. I guess he didn't know slavery had been outlawed in the United States. Before I left, I was at some social function when someone asked me, in Dr. Seckler's presence, why I was leaving. Seckler answered for me, saying: "He just couldn't take any more."

PART II

PRACTICE IN PITTSBURGH 1984-1989

CHAPTER 18

INTRODUCTION TO PITTSBURGH

When I called my friend, David Paul, to tell him I was going to move to Pittsburgh, he said he already knew about it. Apparently his brother Bob was related through marriage to the senior doctor in the group I was joining. That doctor, whom I will call Dr. Money (I will not use his real name to protect his privacy), had already bragged to him that I was coming to Pittsburgh. Bob was the Chairman of the Board of Montifiore Hospital in Pittsburgh. Montifiore is a large community hospital located near the University of Pittsburgh Medical School in Oakland. Since that time it was sold and is now part of the medical school complex. I remember talking to Bob at some point, at which time he said he knew Dr. Money and that he was "the most obnoxious human being I have ever met." He said if he had known about it before I signed the contract, he would have advised me not to come. Unfortunately, Bob turned out to be right.

After I signed the contract in November, 1983, Barbara and I bought the condo we had fallen in love with and told all our friends we were leaving town. We had what could best be described as "mixed reviews" about our decision. My close friend Harriet expressed the opinion that "Pittsburgh was death." She was not the only one who said that. I just knew that it was still the right thing to do and did not hesitate. Barbara and I wanted to have a family, and Pittsburgh was definitely a kid-friendly town. I wanted to be in my own business, and this was the promise that was made to me. I got everything in order at Elmhurst before I left. People there were sorry to see me go and gave me a big party before I left, just as the nurses at Muhlenberg Hospital had done.

Barbara was in the last year of her doctoral program, and her internship at NYU was to end in September. I was going to live in Pittsburgh for six months before she could join me. Peoples Express, a low-cost airline, was in business at that time, so we were able to visit each other on weekends. I was on call every third weekend. On the weekends I was not on call, Barbara and I would alternate traveling. This commute was no fun but we survived it.

Full-time academics don't understand how much more responsibility you have and how much more difficult private practice is compared to working in a medical school. Milton Packer once summed up the difference for me at a meeting at Mount Sinai I attended in the early 1990's. After Milton gave his lecture, I went up to congratulate him for an excellent lecture. I said: "Milton that was great. You're so smart."

"No, Richie, I'm not smart. You're smart," he responded. "I only have to know one disease (meaning congestive heart failure). You have to know them all." I was deeply flattered by this remark from such an accomplished man. Milton was right.

When I started in Pittsburgh, I was a little disoriented. While I had enormous book knowledge, I did not know the ins and outs of the intricacies of the totality of patient care. My first week on the job, I spent a lot of time getting oriented and getting to know the nurses and the referring doctors. At the end of the week I told Dr. Money about it and he said that I had been smart to do that. I was off that first weekend. On Sunday evening Dr. Money called me in a foul mood. He started the conversation with: "I'm really pissed off. Here is your work schedule for tomorrow." Apparently the junior doctor, whom I shall call "Dr. R.", had complained to him that I hadn't done much work the first week. I promised to do better. I did not like the fact that Dr. R. had complained about me behind my back rather than talking to me directly about his concerns. What I didn't know at the time was that Dr. R. and Dr. Money had not settled an important conflict in their relationship. As a psychologist, Barbara told me that it was not proper to bring a third man into their group without first resolving their disagreements. Neither of these guys seemed mature enough to have a lot of responsibility. I didn't treat people the way these men were treating me, and I knew I was in for trouble.

Medically, I started to learn the ropes and didn't make any major mistakes. I misread one electrocardiogram in a post operative patient at Shadyside, which did not result in any patient harm. Dr. R. did not hesitate to admonish me for this. Once Dr. R. also admonished me for an anticoagulant order I had written. At Sinai it was drummed into our heads that the coumadin (blood thinner) dose was determined by the blood test 36 hours after a dose, not 24 hours after. I couldn't believe Dr. R. didn't know this and I defended myself in no uncertain terms. He was four years my junior and I did not think he had the right to talk to me in his usual condescending manner. Besides, he had once ordered intravenous salt water on an ICU patient at Jefferson, with a diuretic to be given at the same time. This was equivalent to pumping water from a boat and letting water pour in at the same time. At Sinai no one would have ever done anything so silly. I tried to explain this to him, but he was clueless in his usual self-righteous way. I slowly became aware of the tension between Dr. R. and Dr. Money. Again, I was becoming a political football between two immature men.

In late August I learned that, in early September, Dr. R. and Dr. Money were going to have an important meeting, although I didn't know what the meeting was for. I was doing well in my job, so I didn't suspect it was about me. It wasn't. I wasn't told anything until early November, when Dr. Money called me into his office and informed me that Dr. R. was leaving the group. I was not happy about the idea of being on call every other night and every other weekend. I had accepted the job based on a three-man group and the ability that such an arrangement afforded me to have a family life. Dr. Money told me, "We're going to bring you up to the $97,000 level. Now you will understand the benefits of being number two instead of number three." I had thought we were all going to be equal. I had no desire to live in a pecking order world for the rest of my life. I knew I had an opportunity for personal gain from Dr. R.'s departure, but this did not stop me from going to Dr. R.'s house and practically begging him to change his mind. I knew if he and I stuck together we could resolve his concerns. He then leveled with me (almost) about what had gone on between him and Dr. Money.

Dr. R. told me that he had pushed for a third man in the group because his work load was too heavy and he wanted more free time to spend with his family. He was not a full partner and owned only 20% of the stock in his professional corporation. He said that, although his salary was the same as Dr. Money's salary—$150,000—his year-end bonus was only $100,000 compared to Dr. Money's bonus of $250,000. Their corporate fiscal year ended on August 31st, which was the reason for their big powwow at around that time. Dr. R. wanted equality with Dr. Money, and Dr. Money had told him that he, Dr. R., had not been doing as much work as he had been doing because I was now in the group, picking up a lot of the slack. He pressed Dr. Money on this issue and Dr. Money had said, "Let's vote on it." Of course, Dr. Money had 80% of the voting shares to Dr. R.'s 20%, so Dr. Money called the shots. Dr. R. said that he "couldn't have that." I still felt that if we worked together, we could bring enough pressure on Dr. Money to force him to be reasonable. Dr. R. did not agree. I asked him what he intended to do after he left the group on February 1, 1985, and he said he had no idea.

I found out some time later that this was a lie. I was told that, at a party, Dr. R. had let slip that he was getting a "new partner." Sure enough, on February 1st, Dr. R. joined the practice of a prominent cardiologist at Shadyside Hospital. He continued to work at Jefferson, so now he was in competition with me and Dr. Money. I felt that Dr. R. had been deceitful by not telling me the situation prior to my agreeing to come to Pittsburgh. Clearly Dr. Money had a well-thought-out plan to defraud me into coming to Pittsburgh in the first place. I knew I was in big trouble. I had never experienced such downright dishonesty in my life. At least Steve and Frank did what they did because they felt threatened by me and justified their behavior on the basis of self defense. This situation was based on pure, unmitigated greed. In December, 1984, I hired a lawyer for the first time in my life; it turned out to be the first of many times I needed to turn to the law to defend myself against dishonest people.

I have to point out that Dr. Money and Dr. R. were both excellent cardiologists and good overall doctors. I had no problems with their quality of care and concern for their patients. I enjoyed working with them even if they were a little overly critical of me at first. I did in fact have a lot to learn. At no point did I consider quitting. I was 37 years old and not about to leave Pittsburgh for another city. I was here to stay no matter what happened. Barbara left New York when she completed her internship at the end of September. She was 35. We immediately started to try to conceive. By January she was pregnant. We had a $110,000 mortgage. I was determined to work things out with Dr. Money. After Dr. R. left, Dr. Money and I got along fine, though we both had to work extremely hard. The work load was much greater than it had been when he and Dr. R. were together because I had to spend a lot of time at Shadyside doing caths. Some weeks I did ten or eleven procedures.

Dr. Money was very upset that Dr. R. had quit. Funny thing was, he would never talk to me about any of the issues. He was probably unaware that Dr. R. had spilled the beans on his perfidy. Instead, Mrs. Money was given the assignment of talking to me. She was the office manager for the practice. I had just accepted this situation because I was too naïve to understand her presence would be a seriously disrupting influence. Mrs. Money immediately began engaging me in long-drawn-out conversations about the practice. She told me that her husband had felt that Dr. R. was "ungrateful" for all they had done for him. She said Dr. Money had gone to Chicago to visit his father's grave to complain about Dr. R.'s lack of gratitude. She said that Dr. Money was the "CEO" of the practice. I thought to myself, *I didn't come here to have anybody be my CEO, especially someone who didn't have my skills and credentials.*

I was certainly willing to stay on as long as Dr. Money lived up to the promises he made, but it was not a good sign that he refused to talk to me about anything. He insisted that all communications between us be done through our lawyers. Once he even sent his accountant to my home to negotiate with me. He wanted the accountant to convince me to accept an income that would be $120,000 less than Dr. Money's income indefinitely. This was a blatant indication that Dr. Money had no intension whatsoever of living up to the promises he had made to me. I was not going to be a second class citizen for the rest of my life no matter what, and I told the accountant that I would not accept that arrangement, period.

Dr. Money hired a fancy consulting firm from the Philadelphia area to assess his practice and tell him what he should do. My lawyer told me that these firms got large fees to convince junior doctors to make large financial concessions to the older doctors in the practice. The consultant spent two days reviewing the practice and interviewing me and the other employees of the practice. He made a written report saying that he recommended Dr. Money offer me partnership. He also said that I was being unreasonable in not wanting to pay for "good will." I was willing to accept a large difference in income for a few years, but I was not willing to shell out hundreds of thousands or even millions of dollars. The consultant wrote a separate private letter to Dr. Money, admonishing him for the way he treated Dr. R. I was not allowed to see the letter.

Bob Paul turned out to be correct about Dr. Money, and I came to understand why Bob had thought he was so obnoxious. Dr. Money never had a good thing to say about anyone. He did, however, never miss an opportunity to denigrate just about everyone who came up in the conversation, especially other doctors. He never looked at you when he was talking to you, which I took as a sign of disrespect. His favorite topic was how he was better than everyone else. He judged people on the basis of how much money they had or made. He once said to me, "Everyone has to know their own worth," by which he meant how much money they were worth. Obviously, he was committed to the idea that I was not worth as much as he was. I don't know how any person could take this in any way other than as a personal insult. I knew I was worth as much as he was, and I was not going to work with him except under conditions of ultimate equality of both money and control. I knew I had a tough nut to crack, but I was resolute.

Mrs. Money had made it quite clear to me that Dr. Money felt he was entitled to a percentage of all my work because he supplied the patients. This is a common business model in medical practice. A senior doctor with a large practice will require procedures, such as cardiac catheterizations, to be done on his patients. If the doctor is not trained to do the procedures himself, he will have to refer the patients to another physician to do the procedure. That physician will bill directly for the procedure. The referring doctor will get paid for seeing the patient in the hospital, which is generally a lot less than one gets for the procedure. The doctor who performs the procedure is prohibited by law and by medical ethics from giving a kickback to the referring physician, a process called "fee splitting." To get around this, the senior doctor can hire a physician who is qualified to do the procedure. The practice then bills for the service provided by the junior doctor. The junior doctor gets his salary and the senior doctor keeps any profit. This is entirely legal.

Dr. Money thought that this arrangement was his due. I was willing to accept it for a few years, but certainly not indefinitely, and above all, I was not going to be coerced into taking advantage of a physician younger than me in the same manner. Since Dr. Money and I were both Jewish, we were well acquainted with the Holocaust and the moral vacuity of claiming that you committed a crime because you were following orders. I was not going to be an accessory to fraud by inducing a doctor to join our practice under false pretenses, but that's exactly what Dr. Money expected me to do.

CHAPTER 19

DOING THE RIGHT THING

Dr. Money was probably the most insecure man I have ever met. He seemed to be able only to respect himself when he could put down other people. He had to prove his self-worth by gaining power to subjugate others. Money and power were all he understood. Mrs. Money constantly referred to her husband's father and how much he had learned from him. I guess his father taught him that the reason for the existence of other people was to use them to acquire money and power for oneself. His self-worth was defined by how clever he could be in taking advantage of people.

While he was nice to his patients, he seemed to value them as a commodity to advance his own agenda. He took pride in his ability to keep the patients referred to him by general practitioners, and he wanted to have as many patients in his office practice as he could, since they were the source of his money and leverage over other physicians and the hospitals. He could control to whom his patients would be referred, thereby controlling the income of others. He told me that the doctors who referred patients to him had to do so because, "What choice do they have?" Mrs. Money often voiced the same sentiment.

I tried to accommodate his needs as best I could without compromising my values and self respect. Many years later, one of his then-partners told me that he considered Dr. Money to be the most selfish person he knew. At about the same time, I complimented Dr. Money on the abilities of one of his former associates. He replied: "We've gotten a lot of good work out of him." He was incorrigible.

Whenever I would call him from Shadyside to give the results of the catheterizations I had done on his patients, I would give my impressions. More than once I was able to say, "Good news: Mr. Smith had normal coronary arteries."

His response was invariably, "Did you find a lot of good pathology today?" He didn't seem to be as interested in his patients' well being as much as in the number of procedures he could order to be done on them.

The incident that has stood out most in my memory involved a man in his forties who was admitted to Jefferson Hospital for an infection (endocarditis) of his aortic valve, the valve leading from the main pumping chamber of the heart to the aorta. He was not in heart failure and, at the time, there was no need to consider surgically replacing the valve. He had no chest pain to suggest a blockage in his coronary arteries; therefore, a catheterization would not aid us in his diagnosis or treatment. Even more importantly, an infection of the aortic valve could cause a friable mass called a "vegetation" to form on the valve. Because a catheterization necessitated putting the catheter near the aortic valve, the catheter could dislodge a piece of the vegetation, causing it to travel (embolize) into an artery supplying blood to the brain. This would cause a stroke. In other words, active aortic valve endocarditis was a contraindication to catheterization.

Dr. Money wanted me to catheterize the patient. I explained to him that we had no reason to do so and that it could cause a stroke. He replied, "If you don't want to do it, I will get someone else to do it." This was an oblique threat to my job. I felt I had no choice. I performed the procedure as delicately as I could. The cath results did not change our treatment of the patient in any way. It did, however, cause a stroke (which was fortunately non-fatal). Dr. Money did not even acknowledge in any way that he was responsible. This pattern of behavior was repeated in that, if he made a mistake, he would use his power over people to deflect any legitimate criticism or even acknowledgement of what had occurred. I knew then that any contract I would sign with this man could not allow him to have power over me or any physician who would join our practice in the future. My naiveté was coming face to face with the reality of the business of private practice. I resolved not to give in.

Dr. Money was intent on getting a third cardiologist into the group to replace Dr. R., even though we had not yet reached any agreement on my contract. Despite this, he advertised for another person. I certainly wanted a third person in the group to lower the stress level. He knew this and used it to get my cooperation. He even went so far as to set me up for additional stress. His afternoon off was Thursday. One Thursday morning I was scheduled to make rounds and perform several caths at Shadyside. The actual cath procedures would usually require only about 45 minutes. Reviewing the film, dictating the report, talking to the patient and family, notifying the referring physician, and making arrangements for any further procedures the patient needed (such as bypass surgery) usually required at least another hour. I didn't go to Shadyside every day; on the days I went I would get there before 7 a.m.

That particular Thursday I got back to Jefferson around 4 p.m. Dr. Money had already left Jefferson for his afternoon off and had left me with 35 patients to see, six of whom required full dictations of a consultation or history and physical. There was no way I could do this properly in the time I had, that is, before midnight. I called Dr. Money and explained the situation. He expressed some disdain, but we were able to rearrange things to lessen the load on me. A few days later we were discussing interviewing a new doctor when he said to me in a condescending tone, "We wouldn't want anyone to get overwhelmed." He was putting me down by making it clear to me that he was superior. I vowed not to live with that attitude for the rest of my life.

Dr. Money invited a couple of young cardiologists for interviews. I knew that he would use a third doctor to triangulate and use against me in the same way he had used me to manipulate Dr. R. He probably didn't know that I was on to his shenanigans; even so, he must have thought I was really stupid. I interviewed one applicant in private. I informed him that Dr. Money and I had not worked out our own relationship and, until we did, I could not recommend that he take the job. I knew what would happen to him if he came, and I was not going to participate in this fraud. Afterwards Dr. Money said to me, "What did you say to him? I almost had him." I replied that I thought it would be best if he and I worked out our relationship *before* bringing in a third person. I guess he felt he couldn't force me to lie for him and he was in no position to fire me, so he went along with my request and set about to make me an offer. At no time did he ever talk to me about anything related to our contract. He had no criticisms of my work or of my behavior. The consultant's report criticized the contract he had given me before I came to Pittsburgh and made recommendations for a new contract.

One day Mrs. Money said to me that she was glad that the contract had been worked out. What she meant was that her husband had negotiated with his lawyer and accountant and come up with a plan that he was willing to go along with. They just expected me to be "grateful" and sign it. Dr. Money's lawyer sent the proposed contract to my lawyer in early April, 1985. That evening around 8 p.m., I was getting ready to leave Jefferson to go home, I got a call from my attorney, Jeff Blum (pronounced "bloom"). Jeff asked me if I was in the same building with Dr. Money, and I replied that he was in the office in a separate building attached to the hospital. "Good," he said, "because if you were you would shoot him." He told me under no circumstances would he allow me to sign the contract. Jeff was an aggressive attorney and an associate in a large Pittsburgh law firm. He was young and, like all young attorneys, wanted to be made partner in his firm. He identified with me. I got a copy of Dr. Money's proposal shortly thereafter. I was appalled.

The contract stipulated that after five years I would have compensation of 45% of the corporate profits, compared to his 55%. My ultimate projected earnings were to be $250,000. A third doctor would be hired on a strict salary of $150,000 with no provisions for a raise. I had moved my life to Pittsburgh to work in a three-man group of equals. Jeff did not have to persuade me not to sign.

We decided to offer a counter proposal based on the original offer made to me by Dr. Money. I told Jeff that I wanted to be reasonable because I wanted everything to work out. We decided that a reasonable compromise would be to ask for full partnership after four years instead of the three I had been promised. Any contract for a third doctor would be postponed until our contract was agreed upon. The offer made to me had called for a differential in income between me and Dr. Money of $1.2 million over five years. My counterproposal would have given him $700,000 over four years. I thought this was reasonable.

At the beginning of May, Jeff delivered the proposal to Dr. Money's attorney. Fortunately for me, Jeff and Dr. Money's attorney were old friends. The next day Dr. Money stopped talking to me. I knew something was up but didn't remotely anticipate what was going to happen. Jeff made arrangements for him, me, Dr. Money, and Dr. Money's attorney to meet to negotiate a compromise agreement. The meeting was scheduled to be in our medical office on the Saturday before Memorial Day, 1985. I was looking forward to the first face-to-face discussion with Dr. Money about our business arrangements, but it was not to happen. On Friday afternoon, my afternoon off, I was sitting in our front yard with Barbara when the phone rang. It was Jeff. He said I was fired and had to have all my things out of the office by Saturday morning. He said the only reason I was being informed before the meeting was out of courtesy to him as a friend of Dr. Money's attorney; otherwise it was supposed to have been a surprise.

CHAPTER 20

WALKING THE PLANK

I was shell shocked. Jeff was irate. He was kind enough to offer to drive me out to Jefferson to pick up my stuff, and on the way we discussed strategy. Dr. Money and his lawyer were going to be at the office. Jeff told me to pretend I was not upset but angry instead. He said he was going to threaten to file a lawsuit for "fraud in the inducement" on the Tuesday after Memorial Day. Jeff asked me what I wanted to get in return for agreeing not to sue. We decided the main object of the meeting was to get out of my restrictive covenant so I could get another job in Pittsburgh or even start my own practice.

The look on Dr. Money's face when we got to the office was a look I had never seen on any human being's face. He was staring at me with a snarl, his teeth bared in a distorted grin, like a snarling wolf. The image that came to my mind was one of Adolph Eichmann staring through a window on the roof of a gas chamber, watching his victims die. It was clear he wanted to kill me for standing up to him, but I was determined to get out of this in one piece. Jeff asked me to wait in the waiting room while the three of them negotiated. Jeff came out and talked with me every 15 minutes or so. He said Dr. Money maintained that I had exhibited bizarre behavior in the hospital, and that was his reason for firing me. Of course, this made no sense at all, since we had worked together for more than a year before he had offered me partnership a month earlier. It was a pattern I was getting used to. People would use my personality quirks as a weapon against me when they felt threatened by me. Steve Lomnitz and Frank Lane had used the same tactic. I looked at it differently. Dr. Money was a bad person, and I didn't get along with bad people.

The negotiation was successful. I got a check for four months' salary in lieu of the four months notice my contract had called for. In return, Dr. Money wanted me to continue doing catheterizations on his patients at Shadyside Hospital. He said this was because he didn't want me to suffer from a loss of my cath skills. I thought he just wanted to ameliorate his cost of buying me off by collecting the fees for the caths I did. We shook hands and he said, "Good luck." This was the same thing Gorlin had said to me after raking me over the coals in his office. What was it about these bullies? First they wanted to chop off your head, then they wished you good luck.

As I mentioned, I have always been high strung. At Sinai everyone described me as "hyper." What I always felt was a lot of anxiety. This was a replay of 1979 in New Jersey, only worse because I had a mortgage and Barbara was four months pregnant. I was, however, a lot stronger. I had two years of private practice and five years of academics under my belt. I was determined to do battle if necessary. At first I looked around for another job. I had made friends with one of the young orthopedic surgeons at Jefferson, Norman Krause, the son of the senior partner in a large cardiology practice, Seymour Krause. Seymour wanted me to join his practice but Larry Adler, his partner, vetoed the idea. I called almost every cardiologist at Shadyside, but no one was interested. I did not, however, even consider the possibility of leaving Pittsburgh. Despite all my anxiety and associated depression, I told myself, "This is the chance you've been looking for, a chance to start your own practice."

It didn't take long for me to realize my only choice was to start my own practice, but, in order to do so, I had to keep my hospital privileges at Shadyside and Jefferson. People told me that Dr. Money had tried to use his clout at Jefferson to get me kicked off the staff there. What he didn't seem to realize was that a lot of people at Jefferson wanted more choices of cardiologists. He didn't want to acknowledge to himself that I had made a favorable impression on a lot of people there, including the primary care physicians and the nurses. One nurse told me later that she thought Dr. Money had gotten rid of me because he couldn't stand to work with someone smarter than he was. I was also told that Dr. Money had told people he had fired me for incompetence, while other people told me he had said I left because of mental illness. In retrospect, I did have an illness, an infectious illness, and Dr. Money was the infectious agent. My innate immune system was in the process of cleansing him from my life. No one at Jefferson ever suggested to me that I wouldn't be welcome to stay there.

Shadyside presented a more difficult situation. Initially, I was appointed to the "associate staff." This was a two year probationary appointment prior to being promoted to the "active staff." The medical staff at Shadyside was closed; this meant one had to be invited to join the staff before even being given an application. The bylaws did, however, say that any associate staff member who wanted to be promoted to the active staff was entitled to receive an application to apply. I interviewed with one of the hospital administrators and was in the fortunate position of being able to say that I wanted to continue to work primarily at Jefferson and bring my patients to Shadyside for cath or surgery. I was also able to make it quite clear that I was not quitting Dr. Moncy, nor was I using my association with Dr. Money to surreptitiously gain admission privileges at Shadyside. If I had quit instead of being fired, I might have been viewed as the bad guy.

The most important person I needed to persuade was the Chief of Cardiology at Shadyside, Jim O'Toole. I made four appointments to meet with him, but he didn't show up for any. Finally the administrator for the cath lab whispered to me that the only way to get in to see O'Toole was to sit in his office waiting room and wait for him to see all his patients. I sat there for almost four hours. Sure enough, I was granted an audience. Jim was no stranger to medical politics. He probably sympathized with me, but he had to make sure he didn't go out on a limb for me. I told him I intended to stay at Jefferson and wanted to continue to bring my patients to Shadyside. "Is that all you want?" he said. "I'm a firm believer that once someone is credentialed, they stay credentialed." I didn't know what he was afraid I might say. Maybe he thought I was going to ask him for a job. I left elated. Jim had saved my career. Now I just had to get approved by the credentials committee.

Murray Sachs, a pulmonologist, or lung doctor, was the chairman of the committee. His junior partner was Joel Weinberg. Joel was one of my interns when I was chief on 3 South at Sinai, and we used to jog together occasionally in Central Park. I had been working with them on some of the Shadyside patients, and we were on very good terms. When I told Murray about my predicament, he said, "Everyone knows who is a moneygrubber," referring to Dr. Money.

I was good at walking applications through the administrative hurdles. I had to do it for my full admitting privileges at Sinai. The problem I faced at Shadyside had nothing to do with me. The orthopedic surgeons did not want to create a precedent that would allow their junior associates to quit and go into competition with them. During the week before the credentials committee meeting, I called all of the approximately 30 members of the committee to plead my case. I hoped that by talking to them personally I would become a real person to them rather than just another paper applicant. I was told later that Murray Sachs and Jim O'Toole had gone to bat for me in the meeting, so I was approved. I also learned later that Dr. Money had tried to use his pull to keep me off the staff, but his clout at Shadyside was a lot less than at Jefferson and he had failed.

I felt as if I were walking the plank. My anxiety was all consuming. I had never set up a business before and had no idea how to do it. Not only was I being pushed into the water, Dr. Money had done all he could to put lead weights on my ankles. I was told Dr. Money thought I wouldn't last more than six months. He had told me I wasn't worth as much as he, that I wasn't good enough to have asked for him to have lived up to his promises. I felt like the football team that everyone says isn't good enough to come from behind and win the championship, and I wanted to prove Dr. Money wrong. He was one of the most competitive people I have known. He was happy to compete with me as long as he had the upper hand and we played by his rules. Now the playing field had been leveled. I never felt that I wanted to hurt anyone, including Dr. Money, and I felt no bitterness toward him. I just wanted to beat him at his own game on his home field.

I needed advice, so, on a recommendation, I hired an accounting firm. Sarah Nickel was the junior associate assigned to me. It was the beginning of a professional relationship that has lasted more than 20 years. The first order of business was to find office space to sublet in the Jefferson Medical Office Building. Dr. Money had a lot of power there because of the large number of patients he referred to most of the doctors in the building. Fortunately for me, he also made a few enemies. One was a young orthopedic surgeon who offered me a small space in his office for $600 a month.

Next, I had to hire an office manager who knew what to do, because I certainly didn't. I put an ad in the paper, and the first person I interviewed was Mary Ruth Karnbauer. Mary Ruth had a lot of experience with large practices and wanted $18,000 a year—a lot of money at a time when most doctors' office employees were getting much less. Mary Ruth was emphatic that I needed her and that she was worth the money. I had no income at the time and didn't know if I could afford her. She basically told me I had no choice, so I took a deep breath and said yes. It was a very smart decision on my part. She turned out to be right. Next, I went to the bank to ask for a twelve thousand dollar loan. Sarah came with me. Years later, Sarah told me that the reason the bank turned me down was because I was so nervous. I was definitely not the entrepreneurial type.

CHAPTER 21

STARTING OUT

By the end of June, 1985 I had put together the essentials needed to start a practice. The one missing piece was catheterization privileges at Shadyside Hospital, which required a separate contract with the hospital. Up until that point, only groups had been given contracts, and only twelve cardiologists in total had privileges to do caths at Shadyside. By the end of July I was given a contract. When I made the decision to move to Pittsburgh, I took a calculated risk that, if I got fired, I would be successful keeping my privileges at Shadyside. I had seen the wars at Sinai and I felt this gave me a sense of what I would be up against. In retrospect, Dr. Money had played right into my hands. He had introduced me to the community and then fired me. He overestimated his power to destroy my opportunity in Pittsburgh. This was just another example of bullies almost always overestimating their power to intimidate and destroy.

I spent a lot of time thinking about what had gone wrong. I thought about the whole notion of taking new partners into established medical practices. It seemed to me that, when a young doctor signed a contract, his employer had no risk once a restrictive covenant (a non-compete clause) had been signed. I felt that the young doctor should only have to abide by a restrictive covenant if he quit, but not if he were fired. This would encourage both parties to work out their differences. Also, a separation agreement specifying all the particulars in the event of a breakup needed to be signed. This is similar to a prenuptial agreement prior to marriage. The core issues had to be honestly agreed to in the contract.

The two most important issues in the relationship between or amongst physicians working in a group together were money and control, not necessarily in that order. It seemed to me that the established physician always wanted his income to remain the same while, at the same time, he worked less, or, as in Dr. Money's case, he worked the same amount for more money. Mathematically, this was almost impossible to work out unless the new doctor got screwed. The established doctor needed to determine for himself why he wanted to take in a partner. Did he want time or money or both? In any case, the most important thing was transparency and honesty.

Many doctors compare a medical partnership to marriage: It can only work if there is an establishment of trust. Who in his right mind would want to have a lifetime relationship of any kind with someone he felt was dishonest, untrustworthy, and intent on taking advantage of him? All issues of money and control should be worked out openly and honestly and put into writing. Dr. Money obviously felt that his ability as a businessman was contingent upon being able to trick people through lies and half truths. I think he may have ultimately learned something, because in less than ten years (1984-1994), five different cardiologists came and left his practice. Doctors refer to this type of situation as a revolving door practice. Dr. Money's lack of ability to keep doctors in his practice made it much easier for me to compete with him.

I opened my practice at Jefferson in late June, 1985. Dr. Money was quite surprised to see me there. I would say hello to him and try to be cordial. Once, the two of us were alone together in a hospital elevator. He stared at my crotch with that same menacing snarl he had on his face during the final negotiation. He seemed to be saying to me, "I'm really powerful and I'm going to show you I can cut your balls off." I didn't say any more than hello and then shut up. I was not intimidated.

The one additional ingredient I needed for my practice was patients. I could get a few patients by being on call for the emergency room, but that was once a month at most. I needed primary care physicians and other sub-specialists to refer patients to me, so I set out to meet with every doctor in the medical office building. I used the roster of doctors on the staff to go to all the doctors' offices in the surrounding communities as well. I would bring my curriculum vitae (CV) with me and sit down to chat and ask them to give me a try. At that time, there were only four choices of cardiologists at Jefferson. Of these, Dr. R. was spending most of his time outside Jefferson, working for his new boss; Dr. Money could barely keep up with the enormous work load he had after two doctors left his practice within six months; Krause and Adler, who had a bad reputation at Jefferson, spent little time there. Dr. Money prided himself on being the only choice for referring primary care physicians.

Shortly after I opened my doors, Dr. Bob Milligan and Dr. John Gardill approached me in a hallway at Jefferson. They said they were angry and upset with Dr. Money because he never sent the patients they referred to him back to see them again. They referred to this behavior as "stealing our patients." They told me if I sent their patients back to them they would "keep you busy." I knew from the inside that Dr. Money was indeed stealing as many patients from referring doctors as he could, taking care of all their non-cardiac problems as well. Lee McCormick had a very large primary care practice. He had been forced to do most of his own cardiology because he had no cardiologists he could trust to take good care of his patients and return them to his care when their cardiac problems were under control. I don't think Dr. Money had any idea how much dissatisfaction he had engendered in the medical community.

Dr. William Osler, Chief of Medicine at Johns Hopkins around the turn of the last century, was one of the most famous physicians in history. He is often quoted as saying that the most important constituents of a successful medical practice are, "Availability, Affability, and Ability," in that order. I knew I had to stay at Jefferson almost all the time. My competition did not have that ability. I had to be really nice with all the doctors, nurses, and patients. Most important in my mind was my ability to practice cardiology without making mistakes. I knew I was needed and wanted, but that would mean nothing unless I was perceived as at least as good a doctor as my competition. Because I didn't have many patients at first, I could spend more time with each patient and was able to be meticulous and thorough. Just as important to me, I was not forced to order unnecessary tests or procedures on my patients. When I confronted situations with which I was not familiar, I did not hesitant to ask other cardiologists at Shadyside for their opinions, and would occasionally send a patient for a second opinion in difficult situations. Jim O'Toole was always there for me when I needed his opinion on a tough case.

I knew I also had to get the nurses behind me. Patients and their families always ask the nurses in private who the good doctors are. Nurses worked with all the doctors and were the only ones in a position to compare doctors directly. Nurses care as much as anyone about the welfare of the patients they care for in the hospital. They know which physicians they can rely on to be available at a moment's notice, and which to trust to make the best medical decisions. It didn't take long before I was being recommended.

My biggest concern, of course, was earning enough money to support my family. My accountant told me I needed $70,000 per year after expenses and before taxes to make ends meet. After I submitted a bill to the insurance carrier, it could take up to sixty days to get paid, and I could only hope my money did not run out first. A few patients I had taken care of while working for Dr. Money came to see me, and gradually I began to get referrals from other doctors, from nurses, and from patients. Once I started to work, my anxiety diminished. During the first six weeks I billed for $27,000; of this I could expect to ultimately receive around $19,000, more than enough to pay my practice expenses and support my family. I breathed a great sigh of relief. Once I got over the initial uncertainties, I was in a position to really enjoy my relationships with my patients. I had great joy in helping the patients who put their trust in me. I really cared about my patients and treated each one as if they were a member of my own family. The expressions of gratitude I received gladdened my heart. Having never received any recognition, let alone gratitude, from my parents for trying to help them, I appreciated my patients' expressions of thanks that much more. I had definitely chosen the right profession. I never once turned away a patient because of lack of insurance or inability to pay. Now, all I had to worry about was survival. To me that meant not making any mistakes that would cause anyone to stop referring patients to me.

CHAPTER 22

STRUCTURING THE PRACTICE

I had learned the theory of error analysis and prevention as an undergraduate in physics, so I was able to use that knowledge to develop a system to minimize mistakes in my practice. One of the tools I employed was to set up a system to store information about each patient so that I could easily retrieve it on demand. I needed to be able to retrieve information from office records and from hospital records as quickly as possible. During the day, when my office was open, I could call to have Mary Ruth give me pertinent information on the phone. The hospital records were kept in the medical records department, which was open 24/7. One of the nice things about working in a community hospital rather than a large teaching hospital was the easy availability of the records. If the patient was admitted to the hospital in the middle of the night, the records were always available to the nurses caring for the patient.

I designed my office records with a list of the patients' medical problems on the left side of the folder and a list of current meds under that. The results of important tests were listed with the problems. I updated the list at each patient visit. The purpose of being so organized was to allow Mary Ruth to quickly find the information I needed. If the office was closed, I could go in to quickly review the chart.

Many patients would have repeat admissions to the hospital. On each admission the doctor was expected to dictate a history and physical, or a consultation report. I dictated my reports, including all the pertinent history and physical findings, and dictated all the pertinent diagnoses at the end of each report. I made a point of being thorough so that all a nurse would have to do was read my list of diagnoses to me over the phone if I was not in the hospital when the patient was admitted. Then, when I saw the patient, all I had to do was redictate the old information and add the new information since the last dictation. By using this system, I was able to avoid mistakes that might be made in starting from scratch each time I saw the patient. Not only were mistakes less likely to occur, I could do my work in less time.

My attempts to practice mistake-free medicine led to tension with some of my partners over the years. I think Dr. Money resented me for pointing out his mistakes, while he definitely seemed to enjoy pointing out my mistakes. He thought that trying to practice mistake-free medicine was too time consuming and would decrease one's income. He prided himself on how fast he could go. I was determined to show that a doctor could be meticulous and still earn a good living. It wasn't necessary to skimp on quality in order to generate adequate cash flow. My guiding philosophy was that no doctor should work any faster than he could do so without making mistakes of omission or commission. I was just beginning to learn that not all doctors shared this attitude.

I am a very competitive person. Cardiology in general tends to attract doctors who are highly competitive, intelligent, and energetic. The competition for patients is extremely intense. Unfortunately, the way medicine is structured, too many doctors view competitive success by the size of their practice and how much money they make. *I felt strongly that the only valid way to compete was through the quality of patient care.* I also felt a sense of social responsibility to keep the cost of the care of my patients to a minimum. Even tests that had no potential complications, such as echocardiograms, should only be ordered when needed. I saw too many doctors order tests the patients didn't really need in order to generate more income. Many doctors seemed to focus on ways of getting more money out of the system. This did not necessarily mean they didn't care about doing a good job for their patients; however, financial considerations frequently caused a conflict of interest. I was not entirely immune from this, and sometimes went along for the ride.

The first time I got involved with the business of medicine in this regard was actually before I even opened my doors. After I was fired, in

June, 1985, I got a call at home from Jim Brooks, one of the family doctors at Jefferson, who had a thriving practice located 13 miles south of the hospital. Jim was a nice guy, and we shared a passion for stereo equipment and automobiles. He said he wanted to discuss a business arrangement with me. He said he was impressed with the quality of my work. He wanted me to come to his office one day a week to do cardiology consultations and follow-up care on his patients. He also wanted to form a corporation with me and buy machines to do testing on his patients in his office and share the profits. I was not in a position to say no. This was perfectly legal. We had a prominent attorney draw up the papers. In return, Jim would have me do almost all his cardiology work on his hospitalized patients. I felt I would provide excellent care for his patients and that he would not be shortchanging them by using an inferior cardiologist in return for a share of the profits. I made it clear to him that I was not going to order unnecessary tests and that I would not compromise the quality of care I delivered to his patients under any circumstances. Quality, not profits, was my bottom line. I felt that if I focused on quality, the money would follow in due course.

CHAPTER 23

MD CARDIOLOGY

My formal contract to do catheterizations at Shadyside was not signed until the end of July, 1985. I think I was the first solo cardiologist to be granted such a contract. While I was waiting for my contract, I was taking my cath patients to West Penn Hospital, which was one half mile down the street from Shadyside. West Penn did not have a closed staff. Dr. Money occasionally had patients there, and I had gotten privileges when I joined his practice. West Penn was a good hospital, but I didn't feel as comfortable there as I did at Shadyside. I had been in practice for about three weeks when I ran into Mark Geller, whom I had met when I was in New York. He was an old friend of Warren Sherman. The three of us had had lunch together in New York. Mark had done his cardiology fellowship at Tuft's in Boston, which was a well respected program. Mark had come to Pittsburgh a year before I did. He had worked for an established two-man group at West Penn and left it after about one year. He told me he had joined another group called MD Cardiology Associates. Dr. Mike Danoff was a non-invasive cardiologist with a large practice in Monongahela, Pa., a small town about 30 miles south of Pittsburgh. Mark had developed a following at West Penn and joined Danoff to make a two-man group, incorporating his practice at West Penn. Mark asked me if I might be interested in bringing my Jefferson practice into the group. Jefferson Hospital was only 15 miles from Monongahela Hospital, where Mike's practice was located. We all seemed to hit it off, and I wanted more security than a solo practice could offer. Mike offered me $95,000 to start and I would remain in complete control of my practice at Jefferson and Shadyside.

Mike, who was in his early forties, was a Korean War orphan who had survived by befriending American troops in Korea. He told me that he had severe psychological scars from the experience. He also told me that, to compensate for growing up without a family, he wanted to become the head of a large group of people, so he built a large, modern building in Monongahela to house a huge cardiac rehabilitation facility. He had almost 30 employees. I had learned my lesson from the previous groups I had joined, and I insisted on a formal contract with a pre-arranged separation agreement in case it didn't work out, but Mike didn't want any written agreement whatsoever. Since he didn't ask for a restrictive covenant, I would be able to leave the group at any time and still keep my Jefferson practice, so I really didn't have much downside risk. I officially joined MD Cardiology Associates on August 8, 1985.

As part of the group, I had to join the staffs of four other hospitals in the Pittsburgh area: Monongahela Valley (MVH), Mercy in downtown Pittsburgh, and Forbes Regional and Metro in the eastern suburbs. The group paid for my office in the Jefferson Medical office building. My availability at Jefferson did not diminish because I was always able go back there late in the day or in the evening after having been there in the morning.

Another advantage of being in the group was the opportunity to continue to do balloon angioplasty. This is a procedure in which a small catheter is threaded directly into the coronary artery. A long, narrow balloon on the end of the catheter is centered on the blockage in the artery and inflated to open the artery. I had not been formally trained in this procedure. It wasn't possible to do angioplasty at Elmhurst because the hospital did not have a cardiac surgical program to do emergency bypass surgery in case of a complication during the angioplasty. One of the attractions of my move to Pittsburgh was the opportunity to be trained in angioplasty by Jim O'Toole. During my time with Dr. Money, I had performed 24 angioplasties under Jim's supervision and was to be credentialed after 25 procedures. My cath privileges at Shadyside did not include angioplasty. Mike referred his patients to Mercy Hospital for angioplasty and bypass surgery. Because of my experience at Shadyside, Mercy was willing to give me angioplasty privileges. My practice at Jefferson was not yet large enough to generate many angioplasty patients, but Mike's practice did. As Mark was not trained in angioplasty at all, I was the designated interventional cardiologist for the group.

Mike did not do much care of critically ill patients, whereas Mark and I had extensive training and experience with very sick patients. In addition, I probably had more experience with thrombolytic therapy than any other cardiologist in Pittsburgh at that time. Thrombolytic therapy is treatment of acute heart attacks with a drug, such as streptokinase, that dissolves the blood clot in the coronary artery that has caused the blockage of blood flow to an area of heart muscle. Most cardiologists were frankly afraid of using thrombolytic agents because of the potential side effect of severe bleeding, especially bleeding into the brain, which could be fatal. I was not reluctant because I knew in whom to give the drug and how to use it properly to avoid bleeding complications. Mike would never use it and Mark was nervous about it.

I had given up dripping strepto directly into the coronary artery with a catheter because the intracoronary streptokinase study had not shown any survival benefit. The last time I used the treatment was in early 1985 on one of Dr. Money's patients. Three percent of people do not have a blood-thinning or clot-dissolving response to streptokinase. The last patient to whom I gave it was one of these 3%. Instead of dissolving the clot, a clot probably formed on the tip of the catheter, broke off and traveled to the back of his brain, the occipital lobe, where it caused a stroke that left the patient blind. This would not have occurred if the patient had been given intravenous streptokinase instead of intracoronary, as there would have been no catheter in the patient's body upon which a clot could form. I continued to use IV strepto because research had clearly shown a decrease in mortality for acute myocardial infarction patients from 15% to 7.5% with this treatment. At that time no other similar drugs were available. Intravenous streptokinase is still used widely in Europe today because it is relatively inexpensive compared to other thrombolytic agents and almost as effective.

Mike, Mark and I got along reasonably well except that I found myself again in the position of the middleman. Almost from the beginning Mark would badmouth Mike to me in private, and Mike started to do the same about Mark. I tried to keep peace and was relatively successful. We were able to hire a fourth cardiologist just out of training in Cleveland. His first name was Gerry, but I don't remember his last name. He was a nice guy and a good doctor. With four people in the group we were able to limit the amount of running around to different hospitals we each had to do. The situation was reasonable and within six months Mike gave me a raise to $110,000. What I didn't know was that Mark was up to $160,000 and that Mike's salary was only $180,000.

The quality of care was pretty good, with us younger guys picking up the care of the really sick patients for Mike. In early 1986, I was at a staff meeting at Jefferson. Terry Kostrub (whom I would later threaten to sue for defamation and civil conspiracy) was the administrator of the medical staff services there. At this meeting, she took me aside and privately told me that working with Mike was ruining my reputation. I understood that Mike had once been on the staff at Jefferson and had to leave because of some trouble he had gotten into. But because Mike almost never covered for me at Jefferson, I was not too worried about his behavior there.

As a member of MD Cardiology, I became privy to some of the business enterprises of cardiologists. Mike had a company called "Shared Health," which was run by Monty Nesser, a young businessman. This company was set up to perform echocardiograms in other doctors' offices. The echo machines were hauled around in trucks. These doctors were not cardiologists; rather they were internists and family practitioners. Shared Health paid the doctors about $100 to "rent" the space in the doctor's office to perform the test on each patient, then billed the insurance company for the test, probably around $500. This was completely legal, and Monty had a letter from Blue Shield attesting to this. The trouble was that the doctors ordering the test didn't really understand when their patients needed it. They would find some reason to justify their decision, then Shared Health used that reason when billing the insurance company. Many of the tests were not medically necessary but did result in increased income for the ordering doctor and profit for Shared Health.

As I have explained previously, fee splitting in medicine has always been considered unethical and can also be illegal; Shared Health's fee splitting was legal. The result was rarely improved patient care, but was always a drain on the country's health care budget. Mike went so far as to buy a large building across the street from Shadyside Hospital in which he would house Shared Health and offices for all the doctors in the group. My role in all this was just to read the echocardiograms and cough up a few thousand dollars to purchase a limited partnership in the building. Shared Health was not the only business in Pittsburgh doing mobile echocardiograms. Krause and Adler had a company called Cardiac Rehabilitation Institute (CRI). After I opened my solo practice, Seymour Krause asked me to read echoes at CRI. This just required a few hours per week. During the month I worked there I was able to earn $5,000, for which I was extremely grateful. Now, as part of MD Cardiology, I was in direct competition with CRI.

I was pretty content being in the four-man group. For the first time in Pittsburgh, I had time for my family. My son Ben was born in September, 1985. I had complete autonomy in my practice at Jefferson so I could insure the quality of care I expected of myself. The money was not a lot but it was enough for me. I had a nice home and a new car, which was all I really needed. I also liked the people I was working with. They treated me with respect, and I had fun working with them.

Unfortunately, around March of 1986, the floor fell out of MD Cardiology. I now knew what Terry Kostrub had been talking about. I did not witness this personally, but it became general knowledge among all the employees of the practice. Apparently, Mike had been found curled up in the fetal position on the couch in his office in his underwear, totally inebriated from alcohol. This type of behavior clearly was not tolerated in cardiologists, so Mike went off to a rehabilitation center in Ohio. We all felt bad for him, and Gerry, Mark, and I resolved to hold the practice together in Mike's absence.

Prior to these events, I had only had one seriously bad experience while a member of MD Cardiology: I violated one of my own rules, and a patient paid the price. Mike would sometimes have me schedule one of his Mon Valley patients to be catheterized by me at Shadyside Hospital. Sometimes I wouldn't actually see the patient until the morning of the cath when the patient might arrive by ambulance at Shadyside. This was common practice. One morning Mike sent me a man in his seventies who had a history of a heart attack in the bottom (inferior) part of his heart. Mike was concerned that he might have other blockages but hadn't done a stress test to assess for other blockages before ordering the cath. When I spoke to the patient, he said he had had no recent chest pains. In the absence of a positive stress test or recent chest pain, I knew there was no good reason for a catheterization, but the patient had come 30 miles by ambulance to have the procedure, and I felt an obligation to do it. I figured he was unlikely to have a serious complication because he was clinically stable. I noticed that he appeared somewhat gaunt and undernourished, but I didn't think that made much difference. I had never seen or read about a serious complication from a cath due to underweight.

During the procedure, I used the femoral approach with the preformed Judkins catheters. The left coronary catheter popped right into the left coronary ostia (the opening of the left coronary artery into the aorta), but shortly after the first injection of dye, the patient's blood pressure began to fall. On the fluoroscopy (x-ray) screen I could see a tear in the left main coronary artery. I knew the catheter had caused it and that the man would likely die as a result. I put in an intra aortic balloon pump as fast as I could and sent him to the operating room for emergency bypass surgery. As I had feared, the patient died on the operating table. The surgeon told me that all the patient's coronary arteries were paper thin. I had never seen this before or even read about it, but I immediately realized that his paper-thin arteries were due to his emaciated condition. The artery wall was so thin that it could not withstand even the mild amount of pressure placed on the wall from the relatively soft catheter.

I felt terrible. I knew the cath wasn't indicated but I did it anyway for reasons of expediency. Again, I had done a catheterization to please my boss, and the patient paid the price. That was absolutely the last time I ever did a cath that I didn't think was necessary, regardless of who wanted it. Mike was great about the incident and drove 30 miles to the hospital to talk to the family. He had a wonderful bedside manner and was able to get us all through the emotional trauma. There were no repercussions, because a coronary dissection was a known complication of the procedure, and I had informed the patient before the cath that there was a risk of death. (In future chapters I will elaborate on how unnecessary procedures are common and how they increase the cost and reduce the quality of patient care.) I knew that Mike had probably ordered the cath, in part, to satisfy my need to do cases, rather than for any sort of personal gain. I never lost another patient in the cath lab.

CHAPTER 24

BREAKING UP THE GROUP

While Mike was away at rehab, we all worked very hard to keep the practice intact, out of a sense of responsibility; however, Mark went on a campaign to get me and Gerry to break off from Mike and start our own practice. I initially resisted the idea because of my innate anxiety and the idea that there was security in numbers. I was certainly concerned about Mike's mental status, partly because of an incident that happened before he left. He had called me at home one night. I could tell he had been drinking and had diarrhea of the mouth. I think by this point he was concerned about how Mark had been bad-mouthing him and wanted some moral support. I did not like all the backbiting by Mark and was sympathetic to Mike's concerns, but then he started talking about Barbara and how attractive she was and how that he wanted to "rape her." I know he didn't mean it literally, but that was simply something one does not verbalize. I knew then for sure that Mike was not really trustworthy. Mark had also told me he learned that Mike told the office manager to write him a check for $25,000 from the practice over and above his salary to pay for his kid's tuition. I also knew at that point that I was generating more than double my salary for the practice. Mike was so driven by the idea of being in charge of a large group of people that he had run his practice overhead up to 70% of gross receipts. From a purely business standpoint I couldn't afford to stay in his practice, the damage to my reputation from his drinking notwithstanding.

Mark and I had fun running Mike's practice and talked daily about the situation. I told Mark that, if we left the group, I would have to give up angioplasty because I would not have enough cases from my own practice to maintain adequate skill. I had to make a decision: I could be an interventional cardiologist working for someone else, or I could be a clinical cardiologist and still do diagnostic catheterizations. In general, only one patient in five on whom I performed a diagnostic cath would require an angioplasty. Since diagnostic cath was much easier than angioplasty, I would have no trouble keeping up my skills in the simpler procedure.

Eventually, Mark persuaded me that we couldn't work with Mike any longer. I hoped that Gerry would join us so that my dream of a stable three-man group would become a reality. We waited until Mike came back to work to let him know what we were going to do. We arranged for Sarah Nickel to be our accountant and Jeff Blum to be our attorney. Mike had the same prominent attorney as Jim Brooks. Mark, Mike, the two attorneys and I met at Jeff's office one evening to work out the legal terms. Mike was adamant that Geller was "fired" but he wanted me to stay with him. I was flattered but felt I had no choice but to leave.

Gerry was not happy with the situation and went back to Ohio. I think Mark may have been triangulating with Gerry against me, and I don't think Gerry wanted to be caught between the two of us. Mark and I made a pretty smooth transition to our own business. We each put in $20,000 to fund the corporation. I had to borrow the money from my father. We hired Cindy, the daughter of Mike's office manager, to be our office manager. Mary Ruth stayed on as the Jefferson office manager, Mark had a physician's assistant, George, who worked with him at West Penn, and we hired a secretary as well for the West Penn office. I took over the lease on the Jefferson office and kept my office with Jim Brooks, while Mark kept his office with a large internal medicine group at West Penn. Nothing really changed in the actual practice at Jefferson and West Penn Hospitals. We had a couple of very busy primary care physicians who wanted to continue to refer patients to us at Mon Valley Hospital because they were not happy with the care their patients had been getting from Mike. We continued to take the patients from Mon

Valley to Mercy Hospital for cath and bypass surgery. We continued to go to both Forbes Hospitals until we got a feel for where we stood. We didn't miss a beat.

Mark and I formed a corporation called "Cardiovascular and Critical Care Associates," a name that Mark came up with. I insisted that we be equal partners and each have equal compensation. Mark had more gross income from West Penn than I did from Jefferson, but his overhead was about $100,000 a year more than mine. He was paying $4,000 month rent for his office space to a medical group run by Frank Kush. This was far over market value, but Mark got all of the group's cardiology referrals in return. Mark also had the cost of George's salary. I was in charge of the business aspects of the practice because I had more knowledge and experience in this area. I was more nervous than was Mark, but after our first week in business, I was reassured. That first week our combined practices had billed for $20,000, which translated into more than one million annually.

CHAPTER 25

PRIVATE PRACTICE, THE EARLY YEARS

My father was very happy for me to finally be in my own practice, and he was confident we would be successful. I think it finally put his mind at ease. I put his advice to always do a good job into practice. In business, one is never on an even keel. At any point in time the business is either getting larger or smaller. When you hit a soft patch, you worry about going out of business, and when business picks up, you worry about not being able to get all the work done. At Sinai, Peter Rentrop had said of me: "Richard is insecure and overly cautious." I think this was true from his perspective as a risk-taking innovator, but my insecurity and cautiousness motivated me.

I was now in direct competition with Dr. Money and his new associate, Dr. R.'s new group, and Krause and Adler's group, Cardiac Medical Associates. I knew my competitors were excellent doctors, especially the first two. My success was totally dependent on the medical outcomes of my patients. I had gained credibility with many of the referring physicians. As the new kid on the block, I knew my results would be carefully scrutinized. I structured my life and practice around one central idea: no mistakes. I also continued to read the cardiology literature, although I didn't have the time to read as much as I did in New York. What I found was that the five years I had spent in academics gave me a foundation of knowledge that none of my competitors could match. Of course, this meant nothing unless I could effectively use it to increase the survival benefit for my patients. To do this, I felt I had to be totally meticulous about all the details of each patient's care.

Mark was a very intelligent and competitive man who constantly compared himself to me and wanted to come out on top. He worked faster than I did and generated more income. He would argue that my being so meticulous was less important than working faster. Of course, Mark's referrals were guaranteed by his business relationship with Kush, whereas mine, except for those from Jim Brooks, were from completely independent physicians. Because of this, I felt Mark had more leeway in making mistakes at West Penn than I did at Jefferson and Shadyside. Since our practices were almost completely separate, his quality of care only affected my practice when he was covering for me. We only covered for each other on every other weekend and during the one week twice a year when we were out of town for vacation or conferences. Other than that, we each covered our own practices every day and night. I think we both liked this arrangement because the calls we would get at all hours of the night would be mostly for patients that we knew well. This continuity of care is extremely important, but unfortunately, our current system of care in this country is sorely deficient in promoting this continuity.

Mark and I had a lot in common: We were both New York born and raised Jewish men; we were both argumentative and verbal; we both got 1500 on our SAT, and we were both a little crazy. But basically we both considered ourselves excellent cardiologists, hardworking and dedicated to our patients, and most of the time, we got along very well. Actually, I think Mark was even more insecure than I was in some ways. He would call me frequently to discuss his fears about the future of our practice, and I would spend hours reassuring him that things were going to be okay. We were good friends, but when we argued in private it was at very high decibel levels, which few people not from New York City would be able to tolerate.

Mark and I were able to structure the practice in a way that suited both our needs. Other than cross-covering on weekends, I would do caths at Shadyside and make rounds there and at West Penn every Monday. Mark would go to Jefferson on Mondays, and our patients would have their surgeries at West Penn or at Shadyside. I hadn't had much experience with post-operative care at Sinai, either as a fellow or an attending. Mark, however, was a real expert in post-operative care, and I learned an enormous amount from him and relied on him for advice. I got pretty skilled at it after a while, and I don't remember making any serious mistakes in post-operative patients in my career. I developed a system in which I would meticulously go through all the patient information each morning when I made rounds in the cardiothoracic ICU. The nurses respected Mark and me for our ability and dedication, even if our personality quirks, such as being blunt and demanding, were sometimes nettlesome for them.

One of the great pleasures of my practice was the exceptional quality of cardiac and intensive care at Jefferson Hospital. We had a higher percentage of major university-trained cardiologists than any other hospital in the Pittsburgh area. The ICU nurses had enormous experience and had learned high quality care from the cardiologists. Jefferson also had the advantage of not having any interns, residents, or cardiology fellows. This meant that every problem that arose in a patient required the nurse to call me rather than a house officer. An experienced nurse, I found, could give me more accurate information and make better judgments about the clinical status of a sick patient than all but the very best and most advanced cardiology fellows. At Shadyside and West Penn, where there were residents and fellows, the nurses called them first for any problems. Because the house officers could write orders on our patients without having to call us first or even notify us about what they ordered, they would frequently make serious mistakes. At Jefferson, the nurses could not write orders themselves; they had to call us for every problem. And because they were usually able to assess a patient better than the residents, the patients got better care. More often than not, if a house officer had made a decision at night without discussing it with me first, I would have to undo the damage to the patient the following morning when I found out what had occurred.

It also became exceedingly apparent to me that cardiologists who practiced cardiology in a community hospital, rather than in a large teaching hospital, were far and away much better overall clinicians than their academic counterparts. I knew this first hand because I knew I was a much better clinician after two years of practice than I had been as a full-time medical school cardiologist. Of course, this makes perfect sense when you consider that practicing cardiologists essentially spend all their time taking care of patients, whereas academic cardiologists spend the majority of their time doing research, teaching, or working in a narrow field of their particular sub sub-specialty. We practicing cardiologists had to deal with every problem afflicting our patients, not just patients with one particular group of diagnoses. For example, Peter Rentrop was a great invasive cardiologist, but I felt that he had a very limited understanding of the more clinical issues. Also, the practicing cardiologists at Sinai had much better clinical acumen than the brilliant researchers who came from Harvard to run the division of cardiology at Mount Sinai. Without question, those in practice at hospitals where the private cardiologists did all the critical care became far more capable than even the private cardiologists at Mount Sinai. At Sinai, they were prohibited from doing any procedures on their hospitalized patients and frequently did not make any of the clinical decisions on their post-operative and ICU patients. For example, at Sinai, a full-time cardiologist was assigned to do the cardiologic care on the cardiac surgical post-operative patients. That was why I had to learn so much about post-op care from Mark. Another example is the University of Pittsburgh Medical Center, in which cardiology professors only spend four weeks per year in the coronary care unit; I, on the other hand, took care of ICU and CCU patients every day and night, all year long. In short, I was very, very happy about the quality of care I was able to offer my patients at Jefferson.

As I've mentioned previously, I would try to devise tests for myself to see if I was living up to my own standards. One test I used in the early years of my practice was my mortality rate for acute myocardial infraction (heart attack). Once I stopped giving intracoronary streptokinase, I used intravenous instead. Because I had been so deeply involved with thrombolytic therapy, I knew exactly in which patients it should *not* be given. For example, if the drug was given to a patient who had had a stoke in the past, it could cause bleeding in the brain, which was invariably fatal. Over the course of about two years, I kept track of my results.

I was able to take care of 52 consecutive infarct patients, whom I treated with IV streptokinase, before I had the first death. (Of course, I never withheld streptokinase from those at high risk of dying from their heart attack.) This was not just because I knew all about thrombolytic therapy, but also because, while I was at Elmhurst, I had educated myself about all the potential complications of heart attacks in general. I did this not by learning from "experts," but rather from reading almost all the pertinent articles in the literature, past and present, about myocardial infarction and drawing my own conclusions from the scientific data directly. Very few cardiologists have the opportunity or time to do such a thorough review. By comparing my results to the published mortality figures (i.e., without thrombolytic therapy), I learned that my 3% mortality for medically treated infarct patients at Elmhurst and my less than 2% mortality at Jefferson for patients treated with streptokinase were far better than the accepted mortality of 15% and 7.5%, respectively. Although I knew I was "overly cautious and insecure," I was far more aggressive using thrombolytic therapy than most cardiologists at the time because of how much study I had put in. So, while Mark was teaching me about post-operative care, I could return the favor by teaching him about thrombolytic therapy.

During the first year our patient population steadily increased and we continued to run around like crazy to all those different hospitals. The busiest day I had was one Sunday when I started work at around 6 a.m. and finished at 11 p.m. I saw a total of 51 patients in six different hospitals, including six new admissions and consults. I was exhausted and elated at the same time. Being in one's own successful business is intoxicating; I was not only living my dream, I was also becoming somewhat of a workaholic. My desire at the time, however, was to get enough business so that we could take in a third partner, and this time I had a say in how the group was to be structured. I insisted that any new doctor would become a full partner after a few years and that all the legal issues would be handled honestly and transparently in advance. I wanted more free time for Barbara and Ben, and I was willing to make less money in order to accomplish this. During the first fiscal year of our practice, May 1, 1986 through April 30, 1987, Mark and I each took a salary of $110,000, which was more money than I had ever made. In addition, we had enough money left over for each of us to take a $65,000 bonus. After taxes, I was left with a bonus of $42,000. To me, this was an enormous amount of money to have at one time. Mark and I and our wives celebrated with dinner and champagne at a fancy restaurant. Pittsburgh was treating me very, very well, and I was optimistic about our future.

CHAPTER 26

THE PRACTICE EVOLVES

Once Mark and I felt a little more established, we confronted the challenge of how to keep the practice and make it grow. My idea was to focus on quality. We were going to six hospitals, and maintaining quality over such a wide geographic area was difficult. I wanted to increase our business at our core hospitals of West Penn, Jefferson and Shadyside. Mon Valley Hospital was almost 30 miles from my home in Pittsburgh and even further from Mark's house in a northern suburb. When I suggested to Mark that we stop going to the Valley, he said, "I would rather give up my right testicle." When I asked him why, he said it was because we were billing for $120,000 per year from that hospital. I replied we could easily make this up by adding to our business at the closer hospitals and spending less time driving. Availability was essential, and the fewer hospitals we went to, the more time we could spend at any one hospital. This would increase our business and quality of care at the same time. Eventually, I just had to tell Mark that I wasn't going to go to the Valley anymore, so he would have to handle it by himself. He said that was impossible and finally gave in. I turned out to be correct. Our practice continued to grow even faster.

I loved working in the Shadyside cath lab because the expertise of the staff and the quality of the equipment were excellent. At first, I was criticized for my technique of pausing between dye injections to avoid toxicity from dye. (Before the advent of better contrast agents in the late 1980s, fully half of what I did in the cath lab was to prevent adverse dye reactions). I let the heart recover after each injection. I was criticized for being too slow and taking up too much lab time, thereby interfering with other cardiologists completing their procedures. During the summer of 1985, the administrator of the lab undertook a study of how much actual time each doctor used to complete his cases. I felt that, by avoiding dye reactions, I was actually using less time overall by limiting complications, especially congestive heart failure. When the data was released, my average overall cath lab time in the first month of the study was only 45 minutes per patient. This was the actual time from when the patient was put into the laboratory until he was wheeled out after the procedure. None of the other twelve cardiologists working in the lab at that time had a shorter average time. This was another objective parameter I could use to evaluate my own performance.

In 1986, Jefferson Hospital changed the regulations about who could have privileges to perform and interpret non-invasive testing done in the hospital. Now each cardiologist on staff was allowed to interpret, and bill for, all tests done on his own or referral patients. Also, each non-cardiologist who ordered such a test could designate which cardiologist was to interpret the study and dictate a report. I actively recruited referring doctors to designate me for all or some of their testing. The list of referring doctors and their preferred cardiologist was posted in the cardiology department, and my list quickly grew to be the largest of any cardiologist. Patients without a designated reader would still be read only by those groups with a hospital contract, i.e. Dr. Money and Drs. Krause and Adler. Among the physicians who designated me were Dr. Stanley Wetschler and Dr. Howard Lang, the senior physicians of the largest internal medicine group, Brentwood Medical. (I mention this because it relates to my ultimate forced retirement from medicine 15 years later.)

Mark was extremely competitive with me. Each month, our staff printed out a breakdown of billings and collections for the practice, and I found out that Mark always told our office manager, Cindy, that he wanted to "beat" me. In this way, doctors frequently competed with members of their own groups. This was how Dr. Money justified his total control of his group and his larger income. Years later, Dr. Wetschler told me that he would tell his partners, "You have to do what I say because I bring in more money than you do." This culture of power and money was frequently diametrically opposed to efforts to improve patient care. Cardiologists in general are very competitive people and even more so with other cardiologists, both inside and outside of their own groups. Dr. Money criticized me for not being as "productive" as he was. He used this as a weapon against me to justify his demand for more money and control than me. It's very important for the reader to understand this basic aspect of medical culture.

Larry Adler once said to me: "Power and money is what people want, don't they?"

I replied, "Power and money are a poor substitute for love and trust." This may seem Pollyannaish to many people, but I truly believe it. To me, my love of my patients was manifested by doing my absolute best for them. Trust was their gift to me in return for their realization that I always put their welfare first and foremost.

Because of my beliefs, I always said that quality of care, not money or power, was the only legitimate way to compete. I certainly did not dismiss the importance of money in life, but I felt that if I provided the best possible care, the money would follow me and I wouldn't have to chase it. I was driven to prove that Dr. Money was wrong in his assessment of my "worth." I wanted to prove that being meticulous and perfectionistic would not result in lost income, but rather could actually increase one's income.

It was because I was a perfectionist, not in spite of it, that my practice grew so quickly. I treated my referring doctors with the same love as my patients. This was manifested by always living up to the trust that the doctors put in me, not just to take good care of their patients, but also to respect their relationship with their patients by not trying to steal patients from them, as Dr. Money had done. By 1988, Mark and I each took home almost $400,000 before taxes, at a time when the average income for cardiologists in the United States was only a little over $200,000. It was also a lot more than the $250,000 that Dr. Money said I wouldn't be worth until 1990.

Despite the fact that I was extremely competitive, I was also a team player. I believed that money and control should be distributed equally among all members of a group. Of course, I knew that a new doctor in any group would have to "pay his dues" for a few years before reaching equality. Mark struggled with this concept and would chastise me repeatedly for demanding equality with him. He would rail at me that he was doing more work than I was. While it was true that he billed for more services than I did, I produced more net income because his overhead was $100,000 per year more than mine. I didn't have a physician's assistant or pay $4,000 a month in rent to maintain a base of referrals, as he did with Frank Kush.

These issues caused a lot of conflict between us but were not the ultimate reason we eventually broke up. However, Mark did seem to be obsessed with the idea of "beating" me. Mark told me he harbored a lot of resentment toward his father for neglecting him as a child, and the sense of rejection he carried led to low self-esteem. He would often tell me that making a lot of money was a way he would prove to his immediate family that he was better than they gave him credit for. Because I was five years older than he was, I think he projected a lot of his resentment of his father into his relationship with me. (His tarnished self-image may also have been the reason why he grew to hate Mike Danoff so much). I tried to make Mark realize that, even though he billed for more work than I did, I was working very hard to build relationships with referring doctors. These relationships were generating more net income because I was not essentially giving kickbacks to a large percentage of my referring doctors in order to assure their referrals.

I wasn't perfect in this respect because I maintained my relationship with Jim Brooks, and this relationship became a real sore point with Mark. He began a relentless campaign to have me change my agreement with Brooks. Since my deal with Brooks started before I joined MD Cardiology, Mike had been agreeable to my keeping the corporation Jim and I had formed. Monty Nesser, the administrator of Shared Health, had sold us a used echocardiogram machine for $24,000. (A new machine, at that time, cost between $150,000 and $200,000). Mike lent me $12,000 to pay for my half of the machine. But my corporation with Brooks only generated about $6,000 profit in its first year. I would order echos on Jim's patients when they were necessary, but not when they weren't. In addition, the quality of the studies produced by the second-hand machine was not up to my standards. The performance and interpretation required a lot of skill and training. I had moonlighted as an echo technician and interpreter for Alan Unger when I was at Elmhurst. Also, as a cardiology fellow at Sinai, I was required to perform the test myself, not merely read a study done by a technician.

Most of the scientific papers written about echocardiography used meticulous measurements to help make important clinical decisions about patients. For example, the correct decision about when to do heart surgery for valve disease was dependent on exact and accurate measurements of the size of the various chambers of the heart on the echocardiogram. I knew I could not take proper care of my patients unless the echo results were totally reliable and accurate. I simply could not provide adequate care of Jim's patients if I relied on the sub-standard echo machine Jim and I had purchased.

Because of this, as well as Mark's constant pestering, I finally agreed to get rid of my separate corporation with Jim. Instead, I offered him $800 a month rent to use his office as my satellite office. I pointed out to him this would be more than he was currently getting from our corporation, and he grudgingly agreed. I also got Monty to buy back the machine from us for $5,000. I told Jim he could have the whole $5,000 in return for all the trouble I had caused him. I don't think Jim trusted me on this because he refused sell the machine. I told him he could keep it, as I had no use for it, and I know he kept it in his office for many years after that. Unfortunately, years later, I was chastised by Dr. Thomas Schaefer, a family physician, for how I had "screwed" Brooks in my business dealings with him.

Even more intense than our competition with each other was the sense of competition between us and the other cardiology groups with which we were vying for business. Mark and I never tried to set up a business just to increase our number of patients. For example, John Gardill and Bob Milligan, the two older family doctors who asked me to do their cardiology work because Dr. Money was stealing their patients, approached me a year or two later and said they could no longer send me patients. The reason, they said, was that Dr. Money was twisting their arms. Apparently, Dr. Money had set up some sort of radiology business that they had invested in. In return for referring their patients to this facility, they received a share of the profits. They said that Dr. Money was going to cut them out of the deal if they continued to send me their patients, and they felt they had no choice but to comply, because they needed the money. They said they were going to help me out by suggesting to a new young family doctor that he send me his cardiology work.

The physician, Dr. Thomas Schaefer, became one of my biggest referral sources. I was only going to compete on the basis of the quality of services I provided to them and their patients, not by creating businesses in which I could do a legal form of "fee splitting." Tom ended up sending me many more patients than John and Bob ever did. This is not to say that I didn't sometimes participate when I was offered an opportunity to invest and make money. Jim Brooks created a medical blood testing laboratory that received investments from many physicians. We would send the bloodwork from our office patients to the lab and, in return, receive a monthly check for our share of the profits. I received up to $1,000 a month. This was completely legal at the time as long as we paid our taxes on the income. After about a year, a law was passed prohibiting such labs, and the business was closed.

I was rapidly learning that doctors were gaming the system simply to make money. I saw the handwriting on the wall. We were in the process of killing the goose that was laying the golden eggs. I began to rebel by telling my colleagues that, if we continued to do this, we would begin to bankrupt the system that was insuring the large sums we could earn just by providing needed patient care. Of course, no one listened, and the rest is history. We got what we deserved: managed care.

One thing Mark and I fundamentally agreed upon was that we wanted to be the best cardiologists in Pittsburgh. I felt that, as long as we aspired to this, we would always prosper. Mark was beginning to rebel emotionally against his deal with Frank Kush. We both wanted more independence. I felt we should bring a third cardiologist into our group.

I wanted to hire someone who had been formally trained in angioplasty, someone I could trust to do high quality work for our patients. We put ads in some journals and even interviewed one candidate. We also hired two cardiology fellows at the medical school to moonlight for us on weekends. I hoped that one of them would want to join us when he finished his fellowship, still refusing to give up on my desire to have a three-man equal group. Ultimately, disagreement about the third man led to our breakup.

CHAPTER 27

QUALITY OF CARE

The decision by the hospital to allow me to interpret and bill for Holter monitors (24 hour ambulatory EKG monitoring), echocardiograms and treadmill tests solved a huge problem for me. Many cardiologists purchased equipment to perform those tests in their offices. In 1978, when I was interviewing for a job after fellowship, I visited a cardiologist in southwestern Connecticut who proudly showed me his new echo machine. He said once he had done several hundred tests, the machine would be paid off. "Then the rest is yours," he added. I didn't take the job. I did not want to do unnecessary tests on patients just to pay off a machine costing over $100,000.

There are two parts to the billing of services for an echocardiogram. The technical component is billed by the owner of the machine, who also pays the salary of the technician who performs the test. The professional component is billed separately by the physician who interprets the pictures and writes the report. So, because Jefferson Hospital paid for the machine and for the technician's salary, I was not burdened by having to do the extra work that would have been required to meet these costs. At the time, third-party payers were paying almost two hundred dollars for the professional component. While I could spend 30 minutes reading a complicated echo, the average time was 15 to 20 minutes. By reading three or four studies per hour, I could earn $600 to $800 without any overhead. Because I thought that this was a huge amount of money for an hour's work, I felt a responsibility to provide a totally accurate report. Mark was quite surprised that I actually used a caliper to make all the measurements myself instead of using the (usually inaccurate) measurements obtained by the echo technicians. Years later, when I applied for a part-time position at the University of Pittsburgh Medical Center, I was told by the director of the echo department, Dr. John Gorcsan, that I was not qualified for the position because he could read an echo in five minutes, and I would be expected to spend a lot less than 15 minutes per study.

I came to realize during my first couple of years in Pittsburgh that the quality of the echo reports left a lot to be desired. The pictures taken by the technicians were frequently too poor to do accurate measurements. When the studies were adequate, the technicians usually did not measure the dimensions of the heart accurately. Because the results of an echocardiogram are so important for diagnosis and treatment, I insisted that I read all the studies on my patients myself. The same was true for interpreting 24-hour monitors and *performing* treadmill tests. At Sinai, we were trained how to get the patients to safely achieve 100% of their maximum predicted heart rate (MPHR) on the treadmill. This requires a lot of training and experience. A treadmill test in which a patient achieves 100% of the MPHR is far less likely to produce a false negative result than if a lesser heart rate is achieved. In Pittsburgh, all the cardiologists I knew had been trained to only go to 85 to 90%. Most of my colleagues expressed the opinion that it was too dangerous to go up to 100%. I felt I had no choice other than to do all my patients' stress tests myself.

A big advantage to doing my tests in the hospital was the quality of the equipment and the technicians. The hospital could always afford to buy the newest and best echo machines, which cost around $200,000. The senior echo technician at Jefferson was a woman by the name of Irene Travis, who really knew what she was doing. We developed a close working relationship. If I had a tough case, I would call her and discuss exactly what I was looking for. We would frequently review the study together. This was the only way I could depend on the data to make potentially life-and-death decisions on my patients. Even in later years, when I was in a large group, I maintained separate tapes on which the technicians would put all the studies on my patients, and I asked my partners to leave all my studies for me to read. Without question, by doing all my own studies and knowing the details of the clinical history, I was able to practice the highest quality of medicine. Very few cardiologists have the opportunity to practice such one-on-one medicine with their patients. Cardiologists who practice in large medical centers do not have the opportunity to do all these different kinds of tests on their patients personally. In large institutions, tests are performed by cardiologists who are highly specialized in that one particular area. Besides, I was never forced to do studies to "feed the machine" in order to pay the overhead.

One area in which I had little control was caring for patients without health insurance. Unless the patients were very poor, they could not qualify for Medicaid, the federally funded health care insurance. Patients over the age of 65 were covered under Medicare, so they did not face this problem. I never turned away a patient without insurance; I would take care of them for free. I was making so much money that I couldn't justify denying my services to anyone who needed my care. However, I could not provide the testing or surgical procedures they might require, so I saw people die because of lack of insurance. These experiences are one of the main reasons I am writing this book, and why I feel it is simply immoral not to have universal health insurance in this country.

One case stands out in my mind, a woman in her early fifties who was admitted to Jefferson with symptoms of congestive heart failure. I determined she had a severe narrowing of the valve between her left atrium and left ventricle, the mitral valve. This usually did not require emergency surgery and responded well to medication, but she certainly needed to have valve surgery in the not too distant future. Although she did not have health insurance, she was able to get a policy from Blue Cross/Blue Shield. However, the policy did not cover pre-existing conditions for one year. Her family doctor preferred that he follow her as an outpatient, rather than having her see me in the office. I felt he would be able to recognize any deterioration in her condition in a timely manner.

I didn't see her again until eleven months later when she was admitted emergently to Jefferson. She still had one month to go until the insurance company would pay for her surgery, which would cost about $50,000, but I did not think she could wait. I called the insurance company office in Harrisburg and pleaded with them to allow her to be operated upon immediately. I was able to get them to agree. Because of her age, she required a catheterization before her operation. The surgeons needed to know if she had any blockages in her coronary arteries in addition to the valve disease. They would also need the data from the cath to exclude any other associated heart problems that might need to be addressed during the surgery.

Her insurance required that her catheterization be done at West Penn, where she was taken by ambulance. When I saw her in the preparation area, before anything had been done, she stopped breathing, though her heart was still beating. We were able to stabilize her by placing a breathing tube in her trachea and attaching her to a mechanical ventilator. I went ahead and did the catheterization, since I knew we had to have the information in order to save her. I got everything I needed as quickly as possible. It was clear to me she could probably not tolerate open heart surgery in her condition, so I called a cardiologist I knew at the medical school who had been doing a new procedure called valvuloplasty. This was a procedure in which a catheter was passed across the mitral valve. A large balloon was attached to the catheter and, when it was in the proper position straddling the valve, the balloon was inflated. This would force the valve to open enough for her to be able to survive until she was stable enough to have the valve replaced with a prosthetic valve.

The cardiologist agreed that this was the correct course of action, and the woman was taken immediately by ambulance to the cath lab at the university, where she was met by the cardiologist. He successfully crossed the valve with the catheter. Because of her severely narrowed valve, the heart muscle of her left ventricle was very thin. Unfortunately, the catheter penetrated the wall of the left ventricle and she died on the table.

The only reason this woman died was because she didn't have health insurance. If she had had insurance, or if she didn't have the pre-existing condition exclusion, she would probably have lived another couple of decades. She was a victim of the dysfunctional healthcare system in this country. I also remember a 60-year-old man who came into Jefferson with a heart attack. His chest pain had occurred a week earlier, but he had not sought medical care because he was uninsured. By the time he got to us, he developed a severe complication and died. I knew that, had he come in promptly, he would almost certainly have survived.

I have seen other cases in which patients died because they did not have health insurance, but these stand out. The statistics in the medical literature are definitive when they describe the marked increase in deaths rates in people who do not have health insurance. I am convinced that many people who die under these circumstances die without ever having seen a physician and are not included in these statistics. No other developed country allows its citizens to suffer such a fate.

CHAPTER 28

THE HOME FRONT

Barbara moved to Pittsburgh in early September, 1984, and the move was extremely difficult for her. She felt as if she "fell off a cultural cliff." We had naively assumed that we would meet people and make friends in the same way we had in New York, but we were wrong. Pittsburgh had more in common with Midwestern cities than east coast cities. We met people and socialized quite a bit, but the intimacy we had experienced with our friends in New York could not be reproduced. The same lack of "intensity" that I had lamented in Ann Arbor was just as prevalent in Pittsburgh. Barbara became clinically depressed. Although she did not require medical treatment, she started to spend money to fight her depression. Since one of the reasons we had moved to Pittsburgh was to take advantage of the lower cost of living to start a family, spending our money was not a wise thing to do. Still, Barbara showed enormous inner strength in building a new life for herself, and fought off the depression. I missed our friends and the city as much as she did, but I was consumed by my work.

Barbara's mood had improved by January, 1985, when she found out she was pregnant. When Dr. Money fired me, Barbara was four months pregnant. She was very supportive of me, and I used her strength to help me get through this very difficult time. Once I got back on my feet, she concentrated on her pregnancy. I did too. I've read that some men shy away from sex in the later months of their wife's pregnancy; in retrospect, I think that was true of me. Barbara didn't really address the issue with me until years later when she told me that the lack of sex had bothered her. I think it's hard for some men to conceptualize their wives as being simultaneously a lover and a mother.

I went to all the Lamaze classes with her and was very responsible with regard to my role in the delivery. Because Barbara was 35, she had an amniocentesis to rule out certain birth defects, so we learned the baby was going to be a boy. Barbara went into labor three weeks early, and Ben was born in late September, 1985. My parents came to Pittsburgh for the circumcision. Ben had been a pretty calm baby until the circumcision, but afterwards he became quite anxious and cried a lot. Ben's difficulties put a lot of stress on both of us. Barbara became depressed again after the delivery. She did not have much regard for antidepressant medications at that point; she would spend a lot of time in bed and got little exercise. The weight she had gained during the pregnancy did not come off. After a couple of months, I persuaded her to join the gym and start exercising, and she felt much better once she started to exercise regularly.

Once I started to get a salary again, we had no money problems. I had some money left over from my settlement with Dr. Money, so I decided to use some of it to give us a little Christmas present. We arranged to have a Christmas party for eight adults and their three young children at the Plaza Hotel in New York. The Plaza had a half-price special for Christmas Eve night, and I was able to get a large suite for only $400. We arranged for a dinner to be served to all of us in the suite, which had a beautiful view of Central Park. We joked that the party was on the house and paid for by Dr. Money. It was fitting compensation after all the trouble he had caused us. We were resolved to maintain at least some of our life in New York.

After Ben was born I began to feel that I had lost my wife. I had been the focus of her life, but now, of course, Ben had to be that focus. I read that this happens to many couples after the birth of their first child. Barbara and I loved each other very much, but we were on somewhat different wavelengths when it came to sex, and the presence of an infant did not help matters. Ben had a great deal of difficulty falling asleep in his nursery (formerly a bathroom, transformed by a custom-made crib built over the bathtub). The room was just outside the door to our bedroom. He would cry and scream for more than an hour every night. Barbara consulted all the books she could find without much success. I wanted him to sleep with us, but that was considered a no-no by the so-called experts at the time. Our sex life suffered, and I began to rely more and more on my own inner sexual fantasy life.

During the summer of 1986, the year Mark and I started our own practice, my father developed heart trouble and was hospitalized at Mount Sinai. We went to New York to see him and visit friends. I brought Ben with me to the coronary care unit to visit my father, and I was glad that he was able to see his year-old grandson at the same time he knew I was establishing my own practice. I had referred my father to a private cardiologist I knew. I chose him because I trusted his judgment and knew he would not do any needless dangerous procedures. We didn't know exactly what was wrong with my father's heart, but we did know his echocardiogram showed a left ventricular ejection fraction of only about 30%, with normal being greater than 55%. My father had type 2 diabetes and borderline high blood pressure and had smoked more than a pack a day for 40 years. He was okay and left the hospital after a few days.

As my job situation had stabilized, Barbara and I planned to have my 40th birthday party at a fancy restaurant in New York in December, 1986. We rented out a whole room and arranged for a sit-down dinner for the thirty close personal friends we had invited. I was certainly a lot happier with my life than I had been on my 35th birthday. I just loved the idea of having all the important people in my life at that time in the same place. Barbara, Ben and I were going to spend the night at the Plaza. However, about a week before my birthday, I got a call from my mother early in the morning. My father had collapsed unconscious at home. The ambulance had taken him to the local hospital. I called the emergency room immediately and spoke to the ER doctor, who said he was trying to resuscitate my father as we spoke. I tried to give him some guidance, but it was useless. My father died shortly after I placed the call.

I went to Jefferson to make rounds, not knowing what else to do.

Mark was busy with his morning obligations and I couldn't just abandon my hospitalized patients. I was able to see the few patients in intensive care. Then I called my friend George Heymach, a pulmonologist, and asked him to cover for me. I trusted George, a kid from the Bronx, to get my patients through the day until Mark could help him out.

Barbara, Ben and I got on the first flight to New York. I was devastated. I hadn't realized how traumatic the death of a parent could be. I wasn't depressed; I just had a sense of overwhelming loss, apprehension, and powerlessness. I felt terrible for my father. He had been such an important part of my life for so long and had done so much good for me.

The funeral was small, with just our extended family attending. The death of my father meant that I was on my own. I now had to be the pillar of the family. I also came much closer to the reality of my own mortality. I was going to be next; I just didn't know how long I had. I became even more driven to be successful in my practice. I was glad that my father got to meet his grandson and see his son in his own practice before his death. My birthday party was scheduled for a few days after the funeral, and Barbara and I felt it would be best if we didn't cancel it. It was the right thing to do, try to celebrate life even in the presence of death and grief. I found that I was still able to enjoy the party.

The busy schedule of our two-man practice made it very difficult to spend any time in New York. Work became all consuming. When I had patients at Shadyside, which was most of the time, I would make rounds there before heading south to Jefferson, where I had to be by 7:30 to do my first treadmill test. I would frequently pass Seymour Krause on my way out of Shadyside, just as he was arriving. He prided himself on being a hard worker, and I took pleasure in him seeing me finishing at Shadyside before he even showed up. I wanted to get a reputation for being a hard worker too, since his opinion of me mattered.

I usually finished my treadmill tests at Jefferson and completed my morning rounds by noon. Then I went to the office to see patients, manage the business side of our practice, do paperwork, and make return patient phone calls until around 5:30 p.m. Then I went back to the hospital to read echos and Holter monitors, see any new consults, make a second visit to sick patients who needed more intensive care, and check the emergency room to see if any patients I didn't already know about needed to be seen by me. In addition, we were required to attend at least 50% of the medical staff meetings in order to keep our hospital privileges. I built in fail-safe systems to minimize mistakes. My office staff was instructed to call me immediately if they received a call from home from any patient who called the office with complaints of chest pain or shortness of breath. These symptoms could indicate a life-threatening emergency. I would then call the patient myself to evaluate the situation and make a decision about changing medications and/or referring the patient to the ER or seeing the patient myself in the office. I had to build in an hour or two during the day over and above the amount of work I knew I had to get done, in order to be available for any emergencies.

Cardiologists have no control over when a patient might need an emergency consultation. A sick patient admitted at 5 p.m. to the ICU could require an hour or two of my time to be stabilized enough so that I could safely go home and manage the problem over the phone with the ICU nurses. I also left room in my office schedule so that I could see any new patient within 24 hours if necessary. In short, I made myself available to my referring physicians as much as I could. They needed to know that I would be there for their patients whenever they needed me. In addition, many of my referring doctors wanted me to manage the non-cardiac problems on their hospitalized patients for whom I was consulted for a cardiac problem. Obviously, the amount of time I had to spend working detracted from my home life. I made a point of getting home by 9 p.m. to say goodnight to Ben before his bedtime. The only time during off hours that I did not spend with my family was the two or three times a week I went to the gym. Exercise was essential if I was going to stay mentally and physically healthy.

Between my work schedule and Barbara's child-care responsibilities, we had little time to spend alone. I did everything I could to ease Barbara's schedule. I was able to afford a full time nanny and people to do most of the chores at home, and I encouraged Barbara to find part-time work and spend time during the day with her girlfriends. I also arranged for Barbara and me to spend the night at a nearby hotel once a month. Barbara did not feel comfortable leaving Ben with someone for more than one night, so the nights at the hotel made a huge difference in out relationship. From my perspective, we were able to make progress on some of the sexual frustrations and differences we had.

I needed to have some balance in my life. Even though I didn't have much spare time, I truly felt that our marriage was moving in the right direction during the late 1980's.

CHAPTER 29

A RELATIONSHIP HAS TO KEEP MOVING OR IT DIES

Mark and I agreed on many fundamental aspects of our practice. We both felt it important to treat our employees well. For example, my office manager at the Jefferson office was paid $22,000 at a time when the going rate was around $16,000. The employees received full health insurance and a pension plan. Our accountant wanted us to delay vesting in the pension plan until the employees had been with us for five years. The idea was that if an employee quit or was fired, Mark and I would get to keep their money in the pension plan. I felt this was tantamount to theft. How could I possibly justify taking money from people who were making so little money? I insisted on vestment from day one. It was their money, not mine. For our office Christmas party, we took our four employees to Ruth's Chris Steak House where we treated them to Dom Perignon and steak or lobster.

Mark and I also agreed on providing the highest quality medical care for our patients. We referred our open heart surgical patients to the best surgeons at Shadyside and West Penn hospitals. I referred all my angioplasty patients to Jim O'Toole at Shadyside simply because I thought he was the best interventional cardiologist. Mark and I discussed difficult patients in depth and sought out other opinions from our colleagues and competitors. When we were still unsure, we would get outside assistance. For example, one of my patients at Jefferson, a woman in her early seventies, was referred to me by Tom Schaefer for symptoms of congestive heart failure. The echocardiogram revealed a severe narrowing (stenosis) of her aortic valve. She definitely needed to have the valve surgically replaced. However, her situation was complicated by the fact that I discovered a large aneurysm in her abdominal aorta. The aneurysm was 11 cm (about four inches) wide compared to a normal abdominal aortic diameter of less than 3 cm (about 1¼ inches). Both of these conditions were invariably fatal. We didn't know for sure which problem to treat first or whether they should be treated simultaneously. We also didn't know if we should do an aortic valve balloon valvuloplasty first to get her through the aneurysm surgery and then do the valve replacement. Aortic valvuloplasty was an experimental procedure at that time, and indications for its use were in the process of being developed. We spoke to several cardiac surgeons and other cardiologists, but no one was sure of what to do.

Instead of just making an educated guess, we chose to get more input from outside Pittsburgh. Mark knew a faculty member at Tuft's, where he had done his cardiology fellowship, who used computer analysis of the medical literature to help make clinical decisions. Mark contacted him and we asked him to evaluate how we should proceed. (The patient was stable enough to wait a week or so.) We received a prompt reply, a ten page analysis, which indicated that, with 80% probability, the best course of action was to surgically replace the valve first, wait three to four months for her to convalesce, and then do the aneurysm surgery. We followed his recommendations, and the patient survived both procedures and did extremely well. Years later when I told this story to Larry Adler, he replied: "You did that! If I was a referring doctor and you did that for one of my patients, I would never send another patient to any cardiologist but you."

I also felt that I had an advantage over my main competition at Jefferson, Dr. Money and Dr. R., who were both excellent clinicians but did not do cardiac catheterizations. They tended to look down on invasive guys as lacking clinical acumen and just being "cath jockeys." But I always considered myself a clinician first and an invasive cardiologist second. I knew that I had a much better understanding of hemodynamics (pressure, volume, and flow relationships of the cardiovascular system) than most non-invasive cardiologists. Invasive cardiologists did more than just take x-ray pictures of the heart; we also had to measure pressure, volume, and flow in patients with complex cardiovascular disease. We also measured these under different forms of interventions, including exercising patients during the catheterization and administering fluids and different medications. I thought that "being inside the heart" gave me a much better understanding than I could ever get by just studying the literature. True, every cardiologist is trained in the cath lab as a fellow, but doing it as a career was on a different level. This increased knowledge translated into a better understanding of how to manage fluids and drugs in very sick patients in the ICU and in post-operative patients. In addition, my years of studying physics and mathematics allowed me to understand hemodynamics at a deeper level than most cardiologists.

I mention this now because my clear understanding of fluid management, while leading to excellent outcomes for my patients, led to my being driven out of medicine by a group of pulmonologists many years later. It was not uncommon for us to be taking care of the same sick patients in the ICU when they would tell me a patient was going to die and I disagreed. Sometimes I was able to send such patients home. The most difficult case of my career was that of Mr. C. Although his case did not involve this pulmonary group, it is an excellent example of the demanding work I was doing at the time.

Mr. C., 74 years old, had severe coronary artery blockages. While I was catheterizing him at Shadyside, his blood pressure dropped precipitously as a result of the primitive dye we used in 1986. I put in an intra-aortic balloon pump as quickly as I could and sent him to the operating room for emergency bypass surgery. I blamed myself for what had happened and I was determined to prevent his death. After surgery, he was alive but in very bad shape. His respiratory system had failed and we had to keep him on a ventilator. He developed congestive heart failure, as well as failure of almost every organ system. I made sure I saw him at least every day, and most days, morning and evening, or even more than that. I also made multiple calls every day to discuss his status with the nurses caring for him in the ICU. If there was a serious problem and I was stuck at Jefferson, I would ask one of the other Shadyside cardiologists to see him and give me a call, something they were always willing to do.

Mr. C. went through kidney failure and required dialysis. He had bed sores. His liver became inflamed from IV Zantac and was on the verge of failing. He had gastrointestinal bleeding. His mental status was severely impaired. He developed a fistula (channel) between his trachea and his esophagus, which was due to malnutrition and almost always fatal. (It can be quite difficult to give intravenous feedings or tube feeding into the stomach in a person with heart failure because the fluid can exacerbate the heart failure.) I had five or more consultants to help me with all the other organ systems. Every morning I listed each organ system and its status and what needed to be done. I kept in constant contact with my consultants. Occasionally someone would say I was wasting my time trying to keep Mr. C. alive because he was surely going to die soon. Sometimes, I even had to threaten a consultant if he refused to care for an acute problem in the off hours, although this was quite rare. Sometimes I had to change consultants.

Nurses and doctors got used to seeing Mr. C. in the ICU. He was there for about four months before it was safe to let him go to another room. When he woke up, he was able to play cards with his wife. He never got back to his prior state of health but he was able to leave the hospital and live for another year; I know his family was very happy to have that extra year with him. After he left the ICU, people I hardly knew at Shadyside came up to me to congratulate me on the job I had done, as no one thought he would get out of the ICU alive. I still blame myself for what happened to him, but at least I know the catheterization was absolutely necessary because he had severe coronary disease, which likely would have resulted in his death had it not been treated with revascularization.

Mark also got a little frustrated with me spending so much time on Mr. C. because Medicare didn't compensate us for all the extra time I had to devote to his case. Although I felt that I had no choice but to do what I did, there was an underlying bone of contention between Mark and me: the division of labor and monetary compensation. Mark would repeatedly indicate that just because I was more meticulous than he was did not justify my getting a salary equal to his. I would always remind him that my net income after expenses was more than his, but he continued to feel abused because he was billing for more than I was and consequently felt he was doing more work than I was. Sometimes he would actually yell into the telephone at me: "Work, work! It's about good, honest work."

I wanted to work less and have more time for my personal life, and I was willing to make less money in return. Mark always seemed to feel deprived and wanted to make even more money. He often said that the large sums of money he earned would prove his sister and parents wrong about him. He continued to resent what he perceived to be neglect on the part of his father. It seemed to me that I represented a father figure to whom he could prove his self-worth by making more money than me. It wasn't long before Mark was creating a war between the Jefferson office and the West Penn office. He just didn't seem to be happy unless he was in a fight. But he was willing to cut corners and break the rules of engagement.

One anecdote that indicated this inclination occurred while Mark and I were still working for Mike. We were both heading to Forbes Regional for a staff meeting, having a lot of fun talking to each other on our cars phones, which very few people had in the mid eighties. We decided we were going to race each other to see who got to the hospital first. Mark had a large off-road vehicle and I had a small sports coupe. I had no trouble getting to the hospital first. As I waited for the gate at the parking lot to open, Mark came up and drove over the curb to get into the parking lot before me. I considered this cheating.

Mark also justified any person's lack of marital fidelity to me on the basis of, "One person cannot take care of all of your needs." As I mentioned before, if a man cheats on his wife, he will be predisposed to cheat on you. I came to believe that he cheated on me in his behavior during our attempts to hire a third cardiologist. Even in the midst of interviewing, I got the impression that he was trashing me to the prospective candidate behind my back. I thought he was doing the same thing with the cardiology fellows who moonlit for us. I think the reason Gerry went back to Cleveland was because Mark tried to use him to triangulate against me in the same way Mark tried to use me to triangulate against Mike.

Mark also wanted me to participate in a dishonest dealing with Medicare, involving nasogastric tubes. A nasogastric (NG) tube is a small tube passed through the nose into a patient's stomach. These tubes can be used to feed the patient or to remove fluid from the GI tract in patients with intestinal or gastric obstruction. Mark placed one in one of our patients, a procedure for which Medicare paid about $60. Cindy, our office manager, inadvertently used the billing code for gastroscopy instead of the correct code. (Gastroscopy is a procedure in which a surgeon or gastroenterologist uses a fiber optic scope to look directly into the stomach. This is much more difficult procedure than passing an NG tube and requires special training in order to get hospital privileges to do it). Medicare sent us a check for $600 because of Cindy's mistake. She asked me what to do, and I told her to send the check back or repay the money and then resubmit the bill to Medicare using the correct code. Mark insisted he wanted to keep the money. Why on earth anyone making as much money as we were needed an extra $540 was beyond me, and I told him I was not going to risk going to jail to satisfy his greed. We sent the money back. Good thing too, because it wasn't long after that that Medicare did a full investigation of our clinical and business practices.

One thing that I learned from Mark, Mike and Dr. Money was that people who use money to compensate for their low self-esteem never feel they have enough. I suffered from low self-esteem as well, but I tried to handle it by being a perfectionist in my practice of cardiology and by trying to be scrupulously honest in my dealings with others. Mark and I had increasing difficulty reconciling our different points of view about the future of our practice. Just like a shark, our practice had to move forward or it was going to die.

CHAPTER 30

PRELUDE TO THE BREAK-UP

My concept of how the practice should grow involved the hiring of a third cardiologist. Since Mark and I had no real formal training in angioplasty, I wanted to hire a young doctor with extensive angioplasty experience who also wanted to practice some general cardiology. To attract a good candidate, we would have to have enough angioplasty patients to keep an interventional cardiologist busy enough to maintain a high level of skill, and I thought our combined practices would generate enough legitimate cases to accomplish this. On the other hand, Mark wanted me to allow him to do angioplasty on my patients. I was not going to refer my patients to someone who was not formally trained, regardless of the financial implications. I was content to allow Jim O'Toole to do all the angioplasties on my patients. The most experienced angioplasty person at West Penn was Jeff Garrett. For my patients whose insurance required they be treated at West Penn, I was comfortable with letting Jeff doing the procedure. Mark felt allowing another group to do our cases was "suicide," but my ultimate responsibility was to my patients, not to Mark. I felt I did not have a choice.

Another difficulty arose when Mark wanted to join the Shadyside staff. Jim O'Toole, as chief of cardiology, had the final say in this matter. I pushed hard to get Mark admitting privileges at Shadyside, but it was a closed staff and Jim had the final word. Mark had a well-established reputation as being difficult to work with, even worse than mine. The Shadyside cath lab staff worked in a very high pressure environment, and Jim told me that he did not want to place added stress on them by having Mark in the lab. But Mark was my partner and I saw no reason why

I shouldn't advocate for him. Needless to say, Mark was not very happy with this rejection. It just added to the strain in our relationship.

To complicate matters, I was not very happy with some of the care I was involved in at West Penn. During early 1989, a 36-year-old man was referred to Mark by his biggest referral source. The patient, a very difficult case, was having blood clots in multiple arteries in his body. Fortunately, none had gone to his brain yet and he was mentally intact. We did every imaginable test and consulted numerous physicians, including neurologists, but over a period of about two weeks in the hospital, we could not find the source of the clots.

The only thing we had to offer this man was the empiric use of the blood thinner (anticoagulant) coumadin. The use of this medication required the man to undergo frequent blood tests as an outpatient to monitor the thickness (coagulability) of his blood. If his blood got too thin he could have life threatening bleeding. If it became too thick he would certainly have more blood clots. He seemed to stop having clots in the hospital after we got his coagulation tests into the therapeutic range. When I was at Mount Sinai, we were trained to follow the blood tests for thinness very closely, especially immediately after the patient went home. I can honestly say that no patients in my career—when I was personally responsible for managing their anticoagulation—ever had a serious episode of bleeding or a serious blood clot.

About two weekends after the patient was discharged, I again made rounds at West Penn. The young man was back in the hospital, this time with a major stroke. On his admission, his blood test showed that his blood had been allowed to get too thick. Mark was not managing the patient's coumadin, so I had no complaints about him. The anticoagulation was being managed by the referring primary care physician, and I was appalled at that doctor's negligence. I had witnessed other, more minor mistakes, but allowing a young man to have his life ruined by negligent care was too much for me to take.

There was nothing I could do but blow off a little steam to calm my outrage. In my opinion this stroke was totally avoidable. Of course, it was entirely possible a stroke might have eventually occurred, even with perfect anticoagulation. I had a little hissy fit in the hallway, which was not understood by the poor neurologist standing there with me. When I explained to him what was upsetting me, he was unfazed and thought what had happened was not unusual. He asked me what I wanted him to do, and I replied, "Share my outrage." He just thought I was crazy.

I had a lot of pent-up frustrations about the care I witnessed at West Penn. On some level I did not want to work with the people responsible for such negligence. After my little scene, the nurses complained to Mark. On the other hand, of course, I got constant complaints from almost everyone that Mark came in contact with at Jefferson. I felt I had to put up with the situation because I saw no alternative for myself, but it just increased the strain on my relationship with Mark. I had still not given up hope of getting a third cardiologist.

CHAPTER 31

CARDIAC ARRHYTHMIAS AND THE DRUG COMPANIES

Sometime during the late 1950's, Bernard Lown, an academic cardiologist and professor at Harvard Medical School, described a classification of ventricular premature beats. These are not normal heartbeats. A normal heart beat occurs when an electrical impulse stimulates the heart muscle to contract, thereby pumping blood to the body. Normally, the impulse is generated by cells in the upper chambers of the heart, called the atria. The impulse is carried by the electrical conduction fibers to the lower chambers, the ventricles.

Sometimes an abnormal electrical stimulus is emitted by cells in the lower chambers, which causes the ventricle to contract before the impulse from the atria gets to the ventricles. These premature beats are called "ventricular premature beats" or VPBs. A heart attack almost always causes VPBs to occur. Dr. Lown stipulated that, if a patient had more than six VPBs in one minute, he had a higher probability of dying. Dr. Lown drew the conclusion that giving medication to prevent the premature beats would increase the patient's chance of survival. This dogma persisted until 1989 with the publication of the Cardiac Arrhythmia Suppression Trial, or CAST study.

Prior to that, in 1979, while I was at Elmhurst, I was assigned to give a lecture to the residents and fellows about ventricular arrhythmias. My perfectionist's nature meant that I did not want to embarrass myself by providing false information or by not being able to answer all the questions I might be asked. I was quite familiar with the teachings of

Dr. Lown, but I had never had occasion to review the topic in depth, so I went to the medical library and started a literature search. I read a recent article and used the listed references to expand my search. I then used those articles to find other articles, until I was satisfied that I had reviewed essentially all of the pertinent research done on this topic. My review took me to articles concerning the presence and treatment of VPBs for all the conditions in which they could occur. These include heart attacks, lung disease, thyroid abnormalities, and numerous other maladies. I read and read until I was satisfied I had left nothing out. This was prior to the streptokinase trial, so I had a lot of free time to pursue the topic. I worked almost constantly on the assignment for a full three months prior to giving the lecture. I copied most of the pertinent articles and made slides of almost 50 different charts, graphs, tables and diagrams to present to the audience as I spoke.

What I learned astounded me and appalled me at the same time. I could find no good scientific data that medications used to treat the VPBs in patients with heart attacks in any way caused them to live longer or better lives. Of course, I discovered good data to suggest that treatment of VPBs due to other conditions, such as hypertrophic cardiomyopathy (a condition found in some young athletes), was probably beneficial. But for most diseases, chronic treatment of VPBs with medication was not helpful.

I recalled a case when I was an assistant resident rotating through the coronary care unit at Mount Sinai in 1974. The patient had frequent VPBs. I was involved in his care but was not in charge of his case. I don't remember the underlying diagnosis. At that time, we had only a few antiarrthythmic medications that could be given by mouth, including quinidine, procainamide (Pronestyl), and possibly Inderal (propranolol, a beta blocker). We started with low doses and increased the dose gradually, and needed a week or so to achieve complete suppression of the VPBs. We were satisfied that we had done a good job. The next day the patient's heart stopped suddenly and he died. You never forget something like that. I had learned first hand that antiarrthythmic medications could be deadly.

After my literature review in 1979, I came to the conclusion that I could do more harm than good by treating VPBs in a heart attack patient after the first few days post attack. I continued to treat heart attack patients with intravenous lidocaine only for the first few days. Very few cardiologists at the time adopted this attitude.

During the mid 1980's, new medications came on the market. These drugs, called type IC agents (flecainide, encainide, and propafenone), were much more effective than other available oral drugs in suppressing VPBs. They became known as "VPB killers." The reason I am relating this story is to convey how drug companies sometimes market unsubstantiated claims to doctors. Mark became a victim of the marketing of these new drugs.

When I first came to Pittsburgh, the representative of the drug company that made and marketed streptokinase asked me to give lectures on the drug. I did not get paid to do this. I did it to market myself to referring doctors. I gave an honest talk in which I said that intracoronary streptokinase should not be used, but that *intravenous* use of the drug was very effective in carefully selected patients. Once my practice got big enough, I thought my time was better spent taking care of my patients than giving talks at other hospitals.

Mark, on the other hand, embraced the idea of being paid by drug companies to give talks advocating use of their products. Pharmaceutical companies would set up "speakers' bureaus" consisting of doctors who would go to various hospitals to give talks. Mark prided himself in being a member of these bureaus and became involved with the makers of encainide. I kept telling him there was no proof that these agents helped heart attack patients, but my words had little effect on him.

At one point the drug company flew Mark to a conference for their speakers, and he came back lecturing me on the new classification of VPB's and when they should be treated in heart attack patients. They had convinced him that these new drugs were so effective in suppressing VPBs that it was intuitively obvious that they would prolong life for these patients. I continued to maintain that there was no scientific data to support such a contention. I'm sure Mark wasn't the only cardiologist who was won over by the drug company. They claimed that the drugs had to prolong life since patients who had more VPBs after a heart attack had a worse prognosis than those with fewer VPBs. Therefore, the converse must be true: Using a drug to decrease the number of VPBs would naturally improve the prognosis. Of course, anyone with even a basic understanding of the principles of logic knows the converse of a true statement is not necessarily also true. Because of the drug companies' marketing skills, the use of type IC agents grew during the late 1980's.

The drug companies were so sure their products were safe and effective that they went along with a scientific trial to test their hypothesis. This test required what is called a prospective, randomized, double-blind study of thousands of patients, the same principle Dean Chalmers had insisted we use for the streptokinase trial, since this method eliminates subconscious prejudice in the investigators. The name of this trial was the "Cardiac Arrhythmia Suppression Trial," or CAST for short. This was the first and only scientific trial of oral antiarrhythmic medications in patients after a heart attack. The dogma initially started by Dr. Lown was so ingrained that most cardiologists assumed that the medications would prove to be beneficial. To the contrary, the CAST trial was stopped prematurely, in 1989, because the patients receiving the drugs were dying at a much faster rate than those not receiving the drugs. This result stood much of the cardiology world on its head.

The reality was that VPBs were not the cause of death but were more frequent in patients with more heart damage. It was the more extensive heart damage, not the VPBs, which caused the patients to die. The VPBs were just a marker of the amount of heart damage. The type IC agents actually weakened the heart muscle, even while they were suppressing the VPBs, which caused more deaths.

The point of this story is that doctors need to study the scientific literature before prescribing medications. This is called practicing "evidence-based medicine." Unfortunately, few doctors have the time or inclination to actually review the scientific data. Drug companies too often rely on this when they market their products to doctors. Drug companies today (2007) spend more money on marketing than they do on research. Two recent examples of similar occurrences are the use of hormone replacement therapy in women and the use of Vioxx for the treatment of pain.

I experienced drug company marketing efforts constantly while I was in practice. Highly paid "drug reps" came almost daily to my office, making claims for their products that were not justified by the available scientific evidence. They would always ask me what they could do to help my patients, and I would almost always reply, "Lower your prices so my patients can afford your medicine." In 1998, I was treated to an all-expenses-paid trip to New York City, for me and my girlfriend at the time, which included dinner at Tavern on the Green. All I was expected to do was spend a few hours attending a presentation about their product. I still refused to prescribe their drug, which I considered to be inferior to the competition. I never accepted another free trip from any drug company. This was at a time when many of my Medicare patients had to choose between medications and food or rent.

CHAPTER 32

THE MEDICARE INVESTIGATION

During the 1980's there was a lot of fraud and abuse in the Medicare program. Doctors would bill for a more intensive level of care than was actually provided, and they would also frequently perform tests on patients who did not actually require those tests for clinical reasons. These practices have continued even in the present day, despite serious attempts by third party payers to prevent them. One of the ways Medicare has tried to curtail this practice is to investigate doctors whose billing practices seem to be excessive. If the investigation reveals evidence of systematic overcharging or performing unnecessary tests, Medicare extrapolates the percentage of over-billing to all the charges billed to Medicare during the period in question. The doctors are then required to reimburse Medicare for all the overcharges. For example, let's say a practice bills Medicare for one million dollars over a period of two years. If Medicare examines 10% of those billings, $100,000, by actually looking at those patents' medical records and finds that the doctors overcharged or performed unnecessary tests accounting for 10% of the total billed, Medicare requires the practice to reimburse 10% of the one million, or $100,000, not just 10% of the $100,000 in billings that were actually investigated. Only a small percentage of practices are investigated by Medicare.

In December, 1988, to the best of my recollection, we received a letter from Medicare indicating that they wanted to investigate our practice. The letter came to the Jefferson office, but I did not get to see it. In January, 1989, the letter was found unopened behind a file cabinet. I estimated that we had billed Medicare for nearly a million dollars since

Mark and I started the business in April, 1986. If we were found to have been dishonest in our billing practices, I thought we might have to return more than $100,000 to Medicare. It was a scary situation. It might also lead to us not being allowed to care for Medicare patients. This was not likely for a first offense, but it could potentially be career-ending.

I was confident that we had not been over-billing or doing unnecessary testing, so I thought the problem occurred because Cindy had been using the incorrect codes for the services we provided. Billing codes are supposed to represent the amount of care rendered for any particular visit, either in the office or hospital. (To simplify matters, I will call the visits small, medium, and large.) We had printouts from Medicare indicating what the average reimbursements were for the different levels of service in our geographic area. Medicare was paying $55 for a large, $40 for a medium and $30 for a small visit. However, if a doctor billed only $50 for a large visit, Medicare would not pay the usual fee of $55, but only the $50 that the doctor actually charged. Despite my entreaties to Cindy that she had been using the wrong codes, she refused to change, stipulating that she was using the same codes her mother was using when billing for Mike Danoff. However, we were only billing $35 for a large visit, so Medicare was actually paying us five dollars less for a large visit than it was paying other doctors in our area for a medium visit. I suspect the Medicare computer flagged our practice because so many of our visits were large. In reality, I estimated that only around 10-15% of our visits qualified as large.

The letter asked us to supply Medicare with copies of 60 charts, including 15 each from the West Penn and Jefferson offices and 30 from inpatients at West Penn, Shadyside and Jefferson hospitals. We had 60 days from the date on the letter to comply. Of course, the letter was behind the file cabinet for five weeks, so we didn't have much time left after we found it. In addition to the charts, we were allowed to submit a cover letter. This letter was due by the deadline, and any further correspondence after the deadline was prohibited. I immediately called our attorney, Jeff Blum, who said that one of the attorneys in his firm specialized in this type of case. I explained to Jeff that we had an absolute deadline to submit the letter. In the past, Jeff had always explained his tardiness to me by saying that "lawyers are slow," and now I was concerned that he wouldn't meet the deadline. Our employees worked overtime to get all the charts ready. However, they excluded the list of diagnoses, tests, medications, and weights that were on the left side of our charts. I thought we had to show how thorough we had been in our patient care. I had seen other practices' completely disorganized charts, so I felt that our charts, if complete, would make a good impression. The staff was not happy with having to go back and copy the additional pages of each chart, but they did.

We were able to get all the information ready prior to the deadline. Federal Express was scheduled to pick up all the boxes at 11 a.m. one morning in February, just inside the deadline. The day before, I called Jeff to ask for the letter from the attorney in his office to send with the charts, but his secretary said he was in court in Harrisburg. I called his Harrisburg office and was told Jeff could not be disturbed because he was in court. I was outraged by this incredible display of negligence on Jeff's part. I had no choice but to write the letter myself, along with a full explanation of what had occurred. I included all the documentation that we had previously gotten from Medicare concerning the average reimbursements in our geographic region, and I pointed out that we had in fact been undercharging Medicare for our services. Mark and I also included a brief explanation of why we provided the services rendered for each and every hospital chart, including that of my patient at Shadyside, Mr. C., the patient who had spent four months in the ICU. We finished everything just in time for the Fed Ex pick up. I knew we hadn't done anything deliberately wrong. I hoped Medicare would see it the same way.

About two weeks after we submitted the data, Jeff Blum called me, saying that the lawyer in his office was ready to work on the letter. This level of incompetence was beyond my comprehension. I told Jeff I had already written the letter myself because of the absolute deadline. Jeff said that I was reckless in writing the letter myself, and that we were going to get into big trouble with Medicare because of it. I thought that, if he felt that strongly about it, why hadn't he completed the letter on time? It wasn't long before our relationship with Jeff came to an end.

All Mark and I could do now was wait. We heard nothing for months.

I recall that, in August, 1989, I received a call from Cindy, who said that a representative from Medicare was in the West Penn office with her. The representative had made a special trip to our office to tell us we had received a commendation for "excellent care." I read the written evaluation from the cardiologist who had reviewed our practice and recall it stating: "The quality of care rendered by Cardiovascular and Critical Care Associates was excellent. There was no utilization of unnecessary testing." He did indicate that we had made a few "documentation errors" in billing for Mr. C., so we had to pay back $400. I have no way of knowing how often a Medicare investigation results in a commendation for excellent care, but I've never heard of it happening to any other doctors.

That same year, 1989, Jefferson Hospital evaluated all its physicians as to the length of time each physician kept his patients in the hospital after an admission diagnosis of congestive heart failure. At that time, hospitals were reimbursed for a specific diagnosis, not for each day in the hospital. Medicare had instituted payment by Diagnosis Related Grouping (DRG for short) several years prior. Since hospital costs depended on the number of days a patient spent in the hospital, the hospital would lose money if the patient stayed in the hospital too long. Complicating matters, Medicare continued to pay doctors for each day the patient was seen in the hospital. This resulted in a conflict of interest between the hospital and the doctors. The longer a patient was kept in the hospital, the more money the doctors would earn and the more money the hospital would lose.

The hospital calculated the average length of stay for congestive heart failure for every doctor that admitted patients to the hospital with this diagnosis, and we each received confidential reports indicating our patients' average length of stay and comparing it to the average for all the doctors. My patients' average length of stay was 5.5 days, compared to a 10.5 day average for all the heart failure patients admitted to the hospital. The hospital administrators were very nice to me after this data was released, although I was just practicing what I considered to be good medicine. I never discharged a heart failure patient before I felt that he or she was ready to go home from a medical standpoint.

CHAPTER 33

THE BREAK-UP

Throughout May, June and July of 1989 my relationship with Mark came under more and more stress. We were pulling in different directions, and he grew more and more resentful of me. I began to feel that I was controlling Mark rather than negotiating with him and reaching common ground, and I didn't like that feeling. I wanted to be in a group that reached consensus and was not controlled by any one person.

Mark's resentment fueled his desire to hurt me. He planned for a move to break free of me and take over my practice at Jefferson. At about 11 p.m. on a Friday night in late July, I was in my car driving home from Jefferson. I was to be off that weekend and I had stayed late to make sure all the patients were stable so Mark would not have to deal with left-over problems on Saturday morning. I called Mark from the car to give him sign out for the weekend. By giving him a short synopsis on each of my hospitalized patients, I would save him a lot of time and make his weekend easier. I don't remember what we actually started to fight about, but as usual we were soon yelling at each other. Suddenly Mark said that he was breaking up the group. I was stunned. He also said he was very close to breaking off his relationship with Kush.

When I got home and told Barbara about Mark's news, she was as shocked as I was. I was in disbelief. I had thought we still had a chance to expand with a third doctor, but now I felt my future slipping away.

Mark and I had several conversations that weekend, during which I tried to convince him to change his mind. I just didn't think I could practice solo and still have any time for my family. Mark had the advantage that his wife was a practicing radiologist, so that he was not the sole support for his family, as I was. We finally decided the break-up would officially occur around August 24, 1989, and we would meet with our lawyers beforehand to define the distribution of practice assets. I developed that same sinking feeling in my stomach that had occurred in 1979, 1981, and 1985, and I began to think there was something very wrong with me.

Barbara and the kids and I went to the Chautauqua Reservation in western New York State for vacation the first week in August. It was the worst week of my life. I had been depressed many times before, but this was different: I felt totally worthless and helpless. I saw no way to get my life back in order. The more I thought about what to do next, the more hopeless I felt. I thought about suicide constantly. I looked into the dark waters of Lake Chautauqua and just wanted to be at the bottom. The pain was so intense that words do not do it justice. At the time, a friend asked me how it felt. I said: "It feels like someone is pulling your brain out through your nose." I thought about buying a handgun and blowing my brains out. One day by the lake, Ben, who was almost four, asked me, "What's wrong, Daddy?" I told him I wasn't feeling well and that I was very sad. Underneath all my pain, I knew suicide was not an option because of Ben and my daughter Sarah, who had been born that January. I had a million dollars in term life insurance at that time and wondered if Barbara and the kids would be better off without me. That was very dangerous thinking.

Barbara tried to be supportive, but she had to care for two young children and was not in a position to give me the same level of psychological support that she had during previous crises. She just advised me that my only real choice was to wake up every morning and put one foot in front of the other. By the end of the week I had made a decision. I realized the only morally and ethically correct course of action for me was to stay with my patients, because I knew they really needed me. God had gifted me with the trust of these people. It was this gift and knowing that I was needed that saw me through.

After we returned from vacation, I was prepared for the worst, since I knew I had let Mark cover my practice while I was away. I knew he was going to trash me as much as he could at Jefferson. He couldn't do this at Shadyside because he wasn't on staff there. Jim O'Toole's group covered for me there. Mark cruelly told me he was going to take my practice away from me and that I was *not* the best cardiologist in Pittsburgh, a claim I had never made. This did not stop him from telling some of my referring doctors at Jefferson that he, not I, was the best cardiologist in Pittsburgh. I knew this because Stan Wetschler and Les Levy, two of my referring internists, told me the story about how Mark had seen them in the hospital and how he had gone through a complicated song and dance, telling them he was the best cardiologist in Pittsburgh. They asked me if he was crazy, and asked if Mark didn't know that they were friends of mine.

Amazingly, people in almost every part of the hospital, especially the ICU, emergency room, and cardiac step down unit, started congratulating me. I knew Mark was difficult and I had had numerous complaints about him, but I had no idea the extent to which he was disliked. People had a huge sense of relief that they would no longer have to put up with him. This sense of support was good, but it didn't help me solve my problem.

Mark and I always remained on speaking terms. Shortly after we broke up, Mark gave me a gift that I considered priceless. I was driving to work while I talked to him on the car phone, although I don't remember the exact context. Out of nowhere he said, in a sincere tone of voice, "You're the best cardiologist I know." I thanked him and told him that was the nicest thing he could possibly say to me.

"It's true," he insisted. Coming from someone who hated my guts at the time made the remark even more meaningful.

In the days that followed, I did what Barbara had suggested: I got up every morning around five and just put one foot in front of the other, although I remained severely clinically depressed. I would pass a gun shop on the way to work, and every time I went by I thought about the coward's way out of my intractable pain. To keep going I kept repeating one word to myself: "Courage." I had to carry on regardless of how bad I felt.

I couldn't eat or sleep very much, and soon I lost 12 pounds, bringing my weight down to a measly 132. I cried out to myself: "My brain is broken. Please, someone help me fix my brain." I woke Barbara at 2:00 one morning to ask her to help me, but she was approaching her wit's end. "It's going to take you at least six months to get back to normal," she cried, clearly frustrated with my illness.

Fortunately I was able to function well at work, and none of my patients ever suffered from my state of mind. I was determined to go it alone. I was not going to demean myself by asking any other cardiologist or group to work with me. I knew I had built up a large, wonderful practice, and if anyone was interested in working with me, they could approach me. I set about trying to arrange some coverage for weekends. I was clearly not on good enough terms with Dr. Money or Dr. R. to ask them. The only other group at Jefferson was Cardiac Medical Associates, Krause and Adler's group. I was pretty friendly with their two younger associates, Gerald Myers and Vasantha Madhavan, so I spoke to them about covering me on some weekends. Gerry actually asked me if I would give him a job. I knew they were not being treated fairly by the owners of their group. Both had been in the group for about eight years, and promises to make each of them a partner had been repeatedly broken. Madhavan had even confided in me that Krause and Adler were "dishonest." Nonetheless, I was dismayed when Madhavan got back to me and said that their group's lawyers and accountants had advised them that legalities made it impossible to arrange a cross coverage system. "What am I going to do?" I lamented to him. I didn't have an answer.

By mid August, Barbara had had enough; I woke her up in the middle of the night once to often. She started to pound the bed, yelling, "I can't take it anymore. You have to get professional help."

Western Psychiatric Institute and Clinic, WPIC, is part of the University of Pittsburgh School Of Medicine. It was a world leader in the pharmacologic treatment of mental disorders. In the morning, after Barbara's outburst, I made a completely cold call to WPIC to ask for help. The person I spoke with asked me if I was having suicidal thoughts. Within 24 hours I was in the office of Steven Carter, PhD, a clinical psychologist with expertise in treating severe depression, including depression in physicians, and he seemed confident he could help me. Steve explained he wanted to try to keep me out of the hospital and was willing to try a course of outpatient treatment combining talk therapy with medication. I was reluctant to take medication because, in New York, medication was not favored by the mental health professionals. Still, I knew I had no real choice; I was very ill and desperately needed help.

Because Steve was not an MD, he wanted me to see a psychiatrist to prescribe and supervise any medications. I was given a choice between Prozac (on the market for only a year at that time) and imipramine (Tofranil). Anxiety was an even bigger problem for me than depression. Steve said imipramine was better for anxiety, so that's what I chose. I saw Alexandra Kreps, MD, the day after I saw Steve and began taking imipramine immediately afterward.

Imipramine is a difficult drug to use properly. It was the first antidepressant, having been put on the market in the mid 1950s. As with many medications, it was discovered by accident. The chemical formula for imipramine is similar to many decongestants taken for the common cold. During drug trials, patients receiving it for symptoms of congestion noticed an improvement in their general sense of well-being, so it was dropped as a cold medicine and investigated as an antidepressant.

The drug must be started at a very low dose, 50 mg daily, and increased no more often than every three days. Like all antidepressants, its beneficial effects begin three to five weeks after initiation of therapy. My dose was gradually increased to 250 mg daily. The side effects were brutal: I had a very dry mouth; I sweated profusely; I became constipated, and I had retrograde ejaculation and sexual dysfunction. The latter two didn't affect me very much because I had little interest in sex.

Amazingly, I continued to work effectively. As soon as Mark and I separated, my business dramatically increased, and I received a lot of support from my colleagues. The number of consultations referred to me went through the roof, making me busier than ever. Even though I remained severely depressed, this support helped keep me going, and the quality of my work did not deteriorate in any way. I was a little surprised by this, and I realized that I was a lot stronger than I thought I was.

At the end of September, Cammy, my office manager, put together my first solo monthly financial report. I couldn't believe my good fortune. During the five weeks from August 24, when Mark and I officially separated, until the end of September, I had billed for more than $92,000. Considering I usually collected about 70% of billings, this translated into a great deal of money. I had never done so much work in any similar period of time prior to that. I began to entertain the idea of hiring another cardiologist, but I knew I would not be able to attract someone who would be comfortable with my practice style. Not only had experience taught me that the chances of success for a new relationship were less than 50%, the published data indicated that more than half of all new doctor partnerships didn't last very long. I did not want to go through another bitter "divorce." Fortunately, I was presented with another, unexpected opportunity.

PART III

PRACTICE IN PITTSBURGH 1990-2001

CHAPTER 34

A NEW AND BETTER WORLD

Certain moments in one's life can stand out and be remembered for a lifetime. Such a moment for me occurred on the morning of November 9, 1989 as I was driving to work, listening to NPR and learning that the Berlin Wall had fallen. I thought: *Hey, this could be a lot better world than you thought. Maybe I'll stick around.* The imipramine had suddenly kicked in, and my depression lifted at that very moment. It had been a very long three months.

Around September 12th I got a call from Seymour Krause. I knew Seymour liked me and was impressed with my work habits, so I wasn't surprised with the call. He said a coverage arrangement was not practical but asked me if I would consider joining their group. Since I had serious doubts about the honesty of their business dealings and the quality of care they provided, I did not jump at the opportunity but told him I was willing to get together to talk about it. I wanted to delay the meeting until I had my first financial statement.

I met with the four members of their group—Seymour, Larry, Gerry and Madhavan—in early October, and we discussed our general philosophy of practice. I showed Seymour the full computer print-out of the work I had done those first five weeks on my own. He said, "I didn't know anyone could do so much work." And I did it while in the depths of depression. I felt pretty good about myself. They said that, if we could work out a deal, my base salary would be $250,000 plus bonus and retirement contribution, amounting to about $400,000 a year *to start.* I also knew that I was giving away all my angioplasties and nuclear cardiology tests to other cardiologists because I was not qualified to provide those services. If I joined the group, I would be generating even more than I had on my own, since Madhavan would get my angioplasties and Gerry Myers would get my nuclear work. I couldn't believe my good fortune. Not only would I be making more money, I would also have a lot more time for my family and myself. They had made me an offer I truly couldn't rationally refuse, and I couldn't wait to get home to tell Barbara. I wanted her to congratulate me for having survived my illness and ending up a lot better off than before Mark and I broke up. I knew she had gone through a rough time with me, and I was glad to feel that I could make it up to her. Unfortunately, it was going to take a lot more than good news to make her happy again.

As I had suspected, Seymour and Larry had a rocky relationship. Larry had to work for Seymour for 13 years before he was made a partner. Seymour had problems with Larry's behavior and vice versa. Seymour was 70 and getting ready to sell out his share of the practice and stay on as a part-time employee, only working in the office seeing patients, but not making rounds in the hospital. Seymour had run the business end of the practice and had concerns about Larry's ability to take over. By then I had had a lot of experience running the business end of my practice, and Seymour wanted someone who knew how to do that in his absence. He was also concerned about the interpersonal relationships, because their practice had been divided into two opposing factions. Seymour and Gerry had a very different outlook from Larry and Madhavan. When Seymour left, Gerry would need a friend.

I had two basic concerns about joining the practice. First and foremost was the quality of care. They did not have a good reputation. Shortly after I actually joined the group, one of the nurses in the Jefferson ICU asked me, "How does it feel to be working with a bunch of incompetents?" The next most important concern was to develop a system to create stable relationships within the group. I had spent a lot of time during the previous twelve years thinking about how to structure a practice to ensure long term stability.

I wasn't too concerned about the quality of care at Jefferson because

I would basically be in charge of most of the clinical decisions for all the group's patients at that facility. I was more concerned about Shadyside, specifically with angioplasty and post open heart surgery care. I quietly asked the nurses in the Shadyside cath lab about Madhavan's ability. I knew he had eight years' experience doing angioplasty, which was a lot more than Mark or I had. The nurses told me Madhavan was as good as just about all the other interventional guys. I also discussed the issue directly with Madhavan. We talked about the number of cases he was doing per year, his results, and his philosophy. I had to be sure that I was referring my patients to a highly-skilled person for a potentially very dangerous procedure. The risk of death from an angioplasty was ten times the risk from a diagnostic catheterization. I became satisfied that Madhavan was going to give my patients excellent care. I turned out to be right.

Dealing with the interpersonal relationships within the group was not as clear cut. I knew I had a lot of bargaining power because I was going to bring a lot of new business to the group. I guess that's called being a "rainmaker." Granting power to rainmakers in the practice of medicine is one of the biggest causes of the poor quality of care in American medicine, but at the time I felt empowered to set down some ground rules for them to agree to before I joined the group. I insisted that Gerry and Van (his preferred nickname) be made full partners. I insisted that any new members of the group be made partners after three years. They were already giving equal bonuses to everyone; I also wanted to equalize the total compensation among the doctors after a period of time. I wanted to make sure that Gerry and Van viewed me as a friend and not as a threat to them. Larry was 15 years older than me, so I knew my long-term stability was dependent on my relationship with Gerry and Van because they were both a few years younger than me.

By December I was satisfied with the arrangements, so I met with Larry and the group's lawyer to finalize the deal. Larry agreed to meet my requests, and I was to officially start on January 1, 1990. I would keep my corporation and work as an independent contractor to the group for three years. On January 1, 1993, I would trade my practice for stock in Cardiac Medical Associates (CMA). Simultaneously, Gerry and Van would be made partners and purchase an equal percentage of the shares in CMA, 16-2/3%. Van's cousin, Ramesh Chandra, was a cardiologist finishing his cardiology fellowship at Shadyside on June, 30, 1990. He was already scheduled to join the group on July 1, 1990, when Seymour originally approached me. I insisted that Ramesh be made partner after three years, i.e. July 1, 1993.

Despite having reached agreement with me about all these issues, Larry did not have a contract for us to sign before I started. I just let it slide because I didn't feel I needed the contract for my own security. My security was my patients and referring doctors. As long as I wasn't cheated out of any money, I would have no problems working without a contract. What I didn't really understand at the time was that Larry would routinely agree to something without the slightest intention of doing what he said he would do. This level of dishonesty is what eventually led me to have to leave the group in 1997 and to the break-up of the entire group in 2004 in what I heard was a flurry of recriminations and lawsuits between Larry and the other three remaining members of the group.

CHAPTER 35

PICKING UP THE PIECES

My illness had created real problems for my marriage. Sarah was only six months old when I got sick. Having to deal with two small children and my illness simultaneously put enormous stress on Barbara. (The spouse of a depressed person usually does not experience the full effects of a mental illness until the person has recovered and the spouse can breathe a sigh of relief). Barbara withdrew from me emotionally, and I felt she didn't love me anymore. I tried to reinstitute our monthly night alone in a hotel, but her feelings were just not there. Of course, I felt this was my fault and therefore also my responsibility to make it up to her and to put things back together.

Our condominium was lovely and spacious but had only two bedrooms plus the small nursery. We needed a third bedroom for Sarah after she became too big for the nursery. We had a large unfinished basement that I thought we could finish as a bedroom for Ben. I thought he might like this, but Barbara vetoed the idea. I wanted to live in the condo indefinitely because doing so would keep down our cost of living and allow us to save more money. I had always been able to live on less money than I earned. But Barbara wanted a house, so I told her to start looking for one. Since I would have an income of $400K, I told her we could afford a house in the price range of $400-500K. That was a lot of money for a house in 1989 in Pittsburgh.

Barbara looked at many houses without finding anything she liked, until she finally found an older house a few blocks from the condo. The house was built in 1893 as a spec house. Only three families had occupied it over nearly 100 years. It was 2½ stories with a finished attic, totaling around 5,000 square feet. It did not have a garage. Barbara absolutely fell in love with this house, saying that she couldn't sleep because she was thinking so much about it. It was on a nice street, but near the edge of Pittsburgh in Point Breeze, a middle-class part of town. The house had just come on the market at $500,000. The next most expensive house on the block was around $300,000. In addition, I knew we were going to have to build a garage and do renovations. I hoped that by getting her the house she would love me again. In my system of values, love was more important than money. In January we closed on the house for $475K. People on the block thought we had paid far too much, but I didn't care; I just wanted Barbara to be happy and love me again.

Barbara started therapy to help her cope with my disease. Her therapist's name was Elaine, which was also her mother's name. I don't remember the timing and exact sequence of events, but I think Elaine irreparably damaged our relationship. Elaine told Barbara that one of the reasons I was having so many problems at work was because she was "enabling" me. Now Barbara felt she was responsible for my behavior as well as her own. This was a prescription for catastrophe. Barbara told me that she considered me to be another child in the family. She said I was like another patient to her as well. One of Barbara's personality characteristics was an overly-developed sense of being nice to people to gain their favor, a pattern she developed when dealing with her mother. I guess Elaine thought Barbara had to stop feeling this way so she could stop enabling my behavior, and she started Barbara on Prozac. Soon Barbara felt a lot better and said that the drug allowed her to feel less desire to please others. Unfortunately, this included me. Now I was officially Barbara's *problem*, not her lover and husband.

Prozac is notorious for destroying the libido, especially in women. I had a fair amount of experience with the drug, as I used it to treat depression in my heart patients. I had always had the stronger libido, and the Prozac exacerbated the difference. Simultaneously, I had recovered from most of the sexual side effects of the imipramine. While I was no longer multi-orgasmic, the actual pleasure of intercourse increased dramatically. I could have had sex every night, but Barbara was becoming far less interested.

Our sex life had been a problem for us from the very beginning. I was frustrated with her inability to let go. She told me that she was afraid of me in bed. (I tended to be a lot more adventurous and uninhibited than she did). Prior to my getting sick, during the late 80s, I felt we had made a lot of progress. Our nights in the hotel had allowed us to become more intimate sexually. I was very happy and satisfied. However, the current situation caused us to lose all the progress we had made. We had gotten to the point where we had sex precisely once a week at precisely ten o'clock every Saturday night. There is no reason to go into any further details, but two things stand out. Barbara would not allow me to kiss her on the mouth during intercourse. She also said she did not want me to put a lock on our bedroom door because, she said, "Who wants to be locked in with Attila the Hun?" I never asked her exactly what she meant by this. In some ways, I thought of myself more as "Attila the Honey."

We decided to try marriage counseling. Simultaneously with all this, my mental state changed significantly after I recovered from my depression, and the fundamental dynamic of our relationship changed as well. For years, I fulfilled the role of a strong father figure in her life, a role her father couldn't play. She fulfilled the role of a loving, supportive mother, one that my mother couldn't do. Now, because of the imipramine and my successful survival, I felt a lot more confident in my ability to take care of myself. I didn't feel very much in need of a mother; I needed a wife and lover.

Barbara and I discussed this openly, both at home and during counseling, but we could not reach a resolution. Barbara didn't seem to be able to shake the notion that I was a child and a patient. These circumstances are not a prescription for long-term stability in a marriage. The worst part was the constant reply she gave me when I asked her what she wanted me to do: "You just don't get it." I asked this question for years and always got the same, unhelpful reply. In his book *Passionate Marriage* (1997), David Schnarch describes the reasons why, in any couple, the person with the lesser sex drive controls the couple's sex life. This was certainly the case with Barbara and me. At one point, Elaine suggested to Barbara that she should negotiate with me to have sex two or three times per week, and Barbara agreed to this. However, despite this agreement, we still only had sex twice in one week on only one subsequent occasion, and never three times in one week. All this was going on while I was reaching the greatest level of success of my professional career.

I was still in therapy with Steve. We discussed my sexuality at great length, and Steve didn't think I was in any way abnormal. I started to evaluate my sexuality and human sexuality in general, although I don't remember exactly when I began to do this. I read a fair amount about the topic. One book in particular stands out in my memory, "Female Perversions" by Louise Kaplan (1990), which was not about "kinky" sex. It is a serious book about female sexual problems that manifest in symptoms such as "delicate self cutting," eating disorders, and the inability to be intimate during sex. The model used by Dr. Kaplan was the fictional character Madame Bovary. I tried in vain to use some of the insights I gained from the book to help us.

Elaine did say one thing that helped me a great deal in the years ahead. When Barbara told Elaine about my ideas of a mature adult sexual relationship, including the idea of incorporating sexual fantasy, Elaine said, "That's a very high level of functioning." Years later, in 1997, I was accused by Dr. Eric Hedberg and Dr. Penny Zeigler, of the Farley Center in Williamsburg, Virginia, of having delusional and unrealistic thoughts of "ideal love." Elaine's words helped me to understand that I was not unrealistic; rather, I had high aspirations for my relationships. (I will discuss this in detail in a later chapter.)

Unfortunately, Barbara and I didn't make a lot of progress during our first course of marriage counseling. Instead, we settled into a pattern she was comfortable with and took up the task of renovating our new "old" house. Despite this diversion, my frustration grew. I divided my sexuality in two. One part was the limited intimacy I shared with Barbara. The other part was my sexual fantasies, which I was forced to keep to myself. I did discuss my dilemma with Steve and, while he understood and commiserated with me, he could not offer any solutions.

CHAPTER 36

STARTING WITH THE GROUP

I started working as an independent contractor for Cardiac Medical Associates on January 1, 1990. The transition was seamless. I kept my own office and my own staff and was able to maintain the higher salaries of my employees because the CMA employees had no way of knowing they were earning far less. My days were not much different than they had been, except for rounding on the group's patients as well as my own. I now spent one full day, Wednesday, at Shadyside to make rounds and do catheterizations. Within a few months I was also rounding at the group's other hospital, Braddock General, on Tuesday mornings. My days were sometimes shorter than they had been because Gerry would come to Jefferson on some afternoons while I was in the office. He would finish rounds and read the group's Jefferson echocardiograms. (I continued to read the echoes on my own patients.) My days would frequently end at 6 or 6:30 instead of 8 or 9 o'clock. I had a lot more time with my family.

To my way of thinking, I had two goals. The most important, of course, was the quality of patient care. The second most important was to get along with everyone in the group. I needed to set an example of impartiality, honesty, and concern for the welfare of all members of the group. I wanted everyone in the group to know that I was concerned about the problems each of them faced. I was largely successful doing this, but the problems I faced were frequently difficult. Almost immediately I began to experience the same problems with triangulation that I had experienced previously. I knew the most difficult relationship for me was with Larry, since I assumed he would be intrinsically distrustful of me. Logically he would consider me a threat to his control of the group after Seymour bowed out. I tried to bend over backwards to make Larry comfortable with my presence, and we talked frequently after hours. During those times, Larry tried to recruit me to help him with his problems with Gerry and Seymour.

Larry and Seymour were in the process of negotiating Seymour's buy-out, and I was put directly in the middle. I had considerable experience dealing with doctor's interpersonal business conflicts, although I soon saw that Seymour and Larry seemed to me to be at each other's throats. My sympathies were with Larry because he was the junior partner, and he and I spent untold hours discussing the negotiations. I wanted to reach an agreement that was fair to both of them because I liked Seymour and knew he had bailed me out of a difficult situation. Larry's attorney was Paul Titus, and Seymour's attorney was in the same firm as Jeff Blum. Seymour's attorney was of the same generation as Seymour and had a reputation for being extremely tough-minded and money-oriented. I spoke to Paul Titus frequently and worked very hard with him to talk some sense into Larry and Seymour. Larry knew I was trying to protect his interests, and this brought us closer. I began to establish the trust with him that I knew was needed if this relationship was going to survive long term. These negotiations lasted for the better part of two years; I don't think I am giving myself too much credit by saying I played a crucial role in getting Seymour and Larry to the point they could agree on a buy-out that they both could feel good about.

I didn't mind Larry triangulating with me and Seymour because Seymour was as interested in reaching an agreement as was Larry. The situation with Larry and Gerry was more problematic. Almost from the first day, Larry began to complain to me privately about Gerry's work. I had just as much at stake in my relationship with Gerry as with Larry, so I took the only tack I could. Every time Larry complained to me about Gerry, I told him the same thing: "Larry, you really need to discuss these problems directly with Gerry." Gerry would also complain about Larry's behavior and felt that Larry was overly critical of him. I tried to support each of them and express my understanding of their concerns. Each of them did have legitimate problems with the other, but I knew neither was equipped to change their underlying personalities.

Gerry did make mistakes more often than Larry did. I knew I could not talk to Larry about the mistakes I saw Gerry make. Instead, I called Gerry and discussed the problems with him directly, which is what I told Larry he should do. I told Gerry that I was not going to mention any of his mistakes with any other member of the group, especially Larry. Gerry acted like a real gentleman during these discussions. If appropriate, he would apologize for making a mistake, ask what he needed to do to rectify it, and thank me for calling him. In return, Gerry paid me the most sincere form of compliment, calling me whenever he had a tough clinical problem and asking me what I thought he should do. When Gerry's wife became acutely ill while skiing in Colorado, he called me directly to ask what he should do. I told him that she probably had a sudden rupture of one of the supporting structures of her mitral valve, which was causing a severely leaking valve. I told him she would probably need open heart surgery to repair the valve. She was in no immediate danger but needed to take certain precautions. Not long afterwards she went to the Cleveland Clinic to have her valve repaired, and, to my knowledge, she has been fine ever since.

(The best compliment one doctor can give another is to refer a family member. Years later I relied on this bond from the President of the Medical Staff, Dr. Stanley Wetschler, who had referred both his father and his wife to me, to protect me from attack. I was sorely disappointed. Stanley was directly responsible for my forced early retirement from medicine in 2001).

Gerry and I reached a firm understanding. I would help him clinically and he would help me get home in time to see my family. Gerry always said, "Richard and I complement each other."

My second goal, quality patient care, was just as challenging as the interpersonal relationships. For the most part, the quality of patient care rendered by CMA was within the normal range, but a few glaring problems soon became evident. When I rounded on patients who had been in their practice for some time, I routinely reviewed the entire hospital record to get a better understanding of the patient's history. I frequently discovered that a patient's diagnosis was not supported by the available evidence. A phrase I commonly found on the chart was: "The patient carries a diagnosis of congestive heart failure." The problem was that the patients frequently "carried" the diagnosis even though I didn't think that they actually had congestive heart failure. I would often spend up to an hour reviewing extensive patient records to determine the correct diagnosis, or if none was evident, I would start from scratch, doing my own history and physical and ordering the necessary diagnostic studies. I would usually call the doctor who saw the patient in the office to discuss the case. Invariably the patient's doctor was agreeable and appreciative of my efforts. I don't remember any serious conflicts concerning these conversations.

One of the reasons I liked working in a group was that I always had another member of the group look over my hospitalized patients and find my mistakes. I always expressed my appreciation to anyone who helped me correct a mistake I had made on any patient. Even if something turned out not to be a mistake made by me, I welcomed the opportunity to discuss the issue with one of my partners. I explicitly told everyone in the group that I wanted to be notified if they thought I had made a mistake. When one makes a mistake, it behooves him to acknowledge it and learn from it. I was determined not to make the same mistake twice.

When I disagreed with someone's acute diagnosis or treatment, I always tried to speak to him directly. Larry was a very good clinician having spent a year at Mount Sinai as a cardiology fellow under Dr. Charles Friedberg, the Chief of Cardiology at Mount Sinai in the 1960s. At that time the definitive textbook on cardiology was written by him, and Dr. Friedberg was universally revered at Mount Sinai as a brilliant clinician. Many of the attending cardiologists at Sinai were trained by Dr. Friedberg. Larry had clearly benefited from this training and was considered one of the best clinical cardiologists in Pittsburgh. That did not mean, however, that he never made a mistake, and I don't think Larry was always very happy to get calls from me pointing out his mistakes.

One occurrence I remember very well, one which disturbed me quite a bit at the time and still does, happened shortly after I joined the group. Tom Schaefer referred a woman in her sixties to me. She required heart bypass surgery and was certainly in good enough shape to tolerate the surgery. I recall that she had her surgery on a Friday at Shadyside, and I made rounds there on that Sunday. She tolerated the surgery well and was having no chest pain, shortness of breath or impaired mental status when I saw her. However, her lab data indicated kidney dysfunction. I had seen this many times and learned that most patients would survive this problem if treated soon enough with hemodialysis (treatment with an artificial kidney machine). The kidneys could fail completely after surgery and still recover enough function within a period of weeks to allow the patient to live without chronic dialysis or a kidney transplant. So, on that Sunday I ordered a consultation with a kidney doctor (nephrologist) for the patient.

I realized that I usually wanted dialysis before many doctors would consider it necessary, but I knew from experience how to diagnose incipient kidney failure very early in its course. As I was not scheduled to make rounds at Shadyside again until that Wednesday, I also knew I would not be seeing the patient again for three days, and I wanted to get the ball rolling before it was too late. It didn't even cross my mind that Larry would disagree with me because I knew he was an experienced clinician.

When I returned to see the patient on Wednesday morning in the ICU at Shadyside, I was shocked to see what Larry had done. The renal consult done on Sunday indicated that the patient did not yet need dialysis, yet no one had notified me about this. I think Larry saw the patient the next two days and did not push for dialysis. Instead, the nurses told me, the patient was allowed to go into full-blown kidney failure. To make matters worse, Larry had decided that she was too sick to dialyze and made the determination to let her die. I was told that he spoke to the family and had them sign a form indicating that the patient would be allowed to die without dialysis.

By the time I got there on Wednesday, it was too late for me to save her, but there was no way I was going to be persuaded that this woman's life could not have been saved. I had seen many similar patients and almost all had survived. I was devastated. I recalled the Jefferson nurse asking me, "How does it feel to be working with incompetents?" and I questioned my decision to join the group. Yes, joining the group was the right thing for me personally, but was I justified now that I truly thought the only reason this woman had died was because I had joined this group?

I was sad and embarrassed to tell Tom Schaefer his patient had died after surgery. I can't recall any other patient that Tom referred to me who had died from any procedure during the four years or so that we had been working together. I asked Tom to keep me informed of any problems he had with our group. He did, and sometimes it was not pretty. I'm sure these events contributed to his decision to change cardiologists in 1993.

Seymour was still in charge of the group. He made the fundamental decisions that determined the quality of medicine practiced by the group. Unfortunately, it seemed to me that Seymour was much more concerned with money than with patient care. (He had grown up during the Depression, as my father had). The following are some of the facts that led me to this conclusion.

First and foremost was the basic structure of the group. For the most part, the volume of work was too great to allow most cardiologists to adequately care for the patients. Dr. Money had come to Pittsburgh to work with Seymour and Larry. Either Dr. Money or his wife told me that Dr. Money abruptly quit the group after being given his work schedule one day. I was told that he remarked, "No one can do this much work." This was despite the fact that Dr. Money was a very fast worker.

Cindy Isador was the registered nurse working for the group at Braddock Hospital and occasionally at Shadyside. When we would make rounds together at Braddock, she expressed to me her strong disapproval of Dr. Krause's work habits. She said Seymour would make rounds but never make any decisions on the patients. She told me that he always said to her, "Let's leave this for them (the other members of the group)." The reality of this attitude was patently obvious to me as I made rounds at Shadyside and Braddock. I felt the group was being dishonest by billing for Seymour's services when it seemed to me that he was not actually providing any service. Larry told me on more than one occasion that one of his main roles with Seymour had been to cover for the man's clinical inadequacies.

Quite often when I was asked to see a long-time patient of Seymour in the office, the patient would have no heart disease whatsoever and would tell me that Seymour would see him in the office every three months to check his heart. Other members of the group told me that they had had similar experiences. The patients told me that they kept coming back because Seymour had convinced them they needed to be checked that often. In addition, Larry once confided in me that Seymour was being investigated by Medicare for over-coding the level of service he provided. I don't know if this was true or not, and I never heard of any results, but I recall Larry telling me something to the effect that the group had to pay back some money to Medicare.

Occasionally, I felt I was being asked to work faster than I thought was prudent. I remember telling myself on more than one occasion that I refused to sacrifice the quality of care I provided to patients for anyone, including Seymour and Larry. In fact, the group was sued for malpractice during the time I was working as an independent contractor.

As I recall, the man, who was in his late sixties or seventies, was admitted to Jefferson Hospital for complaints of lower back and abdominal pain. He was not on a bed with a cardiac monitor and, for the first few days in the hospital, he was seen by other members of the group. I was on call that weekend and saw the patient for the first time on a Saturday morning. His son was in the room and expressed concern for his father's persistent pain. I did what I usually did when I saw one of the group's patients for the first time in the hospital: I started from scratch to piece together the correct diagnosis.

At Jefferson, the old medical records were very easy to get on a moment's notice from the medical records department, or were kept by the patient's room and were immediately available. I never admitted a patient to the hospital without reviewing the old records. Sometimes this required more of my time. It was obvious to me that the other members of the group did not always take the time to find and review the old records. In this instance, the patient had been in the hospital for about three days, but there was no indication I saw that the old records had been reviewed, even though they were right in the cupboard by the patient's room when I got there. In less than two minutes of review, I knew the probable cause of the patient's pain. Prior to this admission, the patient had been hospitalized for some other condition. During that hospitalization, a CAT scan of the abdomen had revealed an aneurysm of the abdominal aorta. At the time of the previous discharge, the patient had been instructed to see one of the doctors in the office. He never did this, so no follow-up on the aneurysm could be done.

When I saw this information on the old chart, my jaw dropped in shock and surprise, although I tried to hide my emotions from the patient's son. I knew the most likely cause of his pain was a small rupture of the aneurysm and bleeding into the surrounding tissues. This type of rupture can cause almost immediate death from severe blood loss. I immediately transferred the patient to intensive care and got an emergency surgical consultation. The patient was taken to the operating room and had a successful repair of the aneurysm. Unfortunately, the patient developed kidney failure after the operation and required dialysis. After a rocky clinical course, he died in the hospital several weeks later.

Not long afterwards the son filed a malpractice suite against the doctors in the group. I was not named as a defendant because I was an independent contractor and was not accused of negligent care. The case was not initially settled and was scheduled for trial. As is quite common, a settlement was reached on the morning of the trial, and I got a phone call from the group's lawyer to tell me what had transpired. I told the lawyer that I thought the problem had been that the group did not always review the old records on newly hospitalized patients. She replied that this information offered her an opportunity to save all the doctors from having a malpractice settlement on their records. Instead she was able to shift the blame to the corporation for its policies on old records. I think the group resented me for mentioning this to the lawyer, but I had bailed them out of a serious situation.

Despite these issues, the group prospered during my first three years. Seymour and Larry were able to reach an agreement. Gerry and Van were happy with me, and so was Larry. I successfully negotiated the contract for Ramesh Chandra. Dr. Madhavan and his cousin, Dr. Chandra, were both excellent, concerned physicians. I thought that the quality of care provided by the group had improved markedly.

By December of 1991, however, I became very concerned that we had more patients than we could adequately care for. At one point we had one hundred and ten patients in the hospital at the same time. At a practice meeting, I insisted that we hire another cardiologist, believing that we had to divide the work in order to have enough time to do the job properly.

During those first two years, everyone had made a lot more money than they had before I joined, and this good fortune was credited to me. At one meeting, Van stood up and made a toast, saying something to the effect of, "Here's to Richard for all the success he has brought to the group." At one of the Christmas parties for the entire group, including spouses and employees, Connie, our registered nurse at Jefferson, got up and said, "Now that Dr. Schneider is with us, we are going to kick some ass at Jefferson." I got up and made a toast to Larry for having brought the group together, but it worried me that he did not seem to appreciate my toast or any of the compliments I received. I had been rock solid on the imipramine and thought I had finally found a home. Unfortunately, the home was not permanent, as my concerns about Larry ultimately proved justified.

CHAPTER 37

THE GROUP EVOLVES

My first year with the group, 1990, was a huge financial success. Except for Ramesh, everyone received a bonus of $120,000. In addition, I collected the accounts receivable for the work I had done in my practice before joining the group, so my gross income before taxes that year, including pension contribution, was $500,000. I also helped Larry get our billing practices in order, including adopting the use of computers. The following year, 1991, the practice did even better; I earned $500,000 *without* any income from my old practice. In 1992, I earned $600,000, which in today's dollars is probably more than one million. By this time I told Barbara that I thought it was more money than I deserved. I was able to rationalize this by thinking I was being paid back for all the years I had spent working in a charity hospital for relatively little. Needless to say, everyone in the group was very pleased with how well they had done financially since I joined, even Larry and Seymour, as they earned almost $700,000 in 1992.

As I mentioned, in December, 1991, I convinced the group to hire another cardiologist, and Dr. Stuart Tauberg joined us in July, 1992. Stuart was completing his cardiology fellowship at Allegheny General Hospital. He was a physics major in college, as was I, at the University of Pittsburgh. He had gone to med school and done his internal medicine training at Pitt as well. Seymour was no longer in the picture, so Larry was the one Stuart had to negotiate his contract with. Again, as I had done with Seymour and Ramesh, I acted as intermediary. Stuart, Larry and I sat down one day at Larry's house and spent a few hours working out the details. Larry, who had no experience in this area, seemed reluctant to sign anything, but Stuart and I convinced him, and both parties appeared to be pleased with the result. But again, Larry had no intention of abiding by the contract.

For some reason, Larry seemed to feel that people were out to get him, and therefore did not want to commit to anything or anyone. His personal life exemplified this. He had been married, had two sons, and had lived alone, except for his children, for many years. He did, however, have a real reputation as a ladies' man. As Gerry once told me, "Larry has hit on every nurse at Braddock Hospital." I can only describe Larry's attitude as paranoid. Years later I read an article that stated, "Paranoid personality disorder is present in 4.4% of the population." I wondered if Larry was afflicted with this malady, as it would have explained a great deal about his subsequent behavior.

I felt I had made a contribution to the group by successfully negotiating Stuart's contract. Seymour's retirement was effective the same day Stuart started working with the group: July 1, 1992. Gerry, Van, and I, however, still had no written contracts, but I was confident that Larry would keep his word to us. I still believed this when Larry invited me to his home in December, 1992. (I was scheduled to become a partner on January 1st.) Larry told me he thought everything was going well and wanted to proceed with the stock transfer. I said I agreed and we shook hands. Gerry and Van were supposed to become partners simultaneously with me. All that was left to be done was to have the lawyers draw up the papers and have everyone sign. I truly felt I was in a stable long term situation in which I would spend the rest of my career.

January 1st came and went with no contracts. Over the next few weeks I asked Larry repeatedly to get the papers drawn up, and he kept reassuring me that he would. By February I was getting impatient, as were Gerry and Van. I told Larry that the contracts were very important to all of us. He then informed me that he was not even going to discuss the issue with me again. By now the three of us, Gerry, Van, and I, were talking about the problem almost on a daily basis. I devised a plan in which Gerry and Van would talk to Larry about the contracts on alternating weeks. I knew Larry needed someone to triangulate with. By denying him anyone to turn to for emotional support, I thought we could eventually wear him down.

After a few months, the lawyers had drawn up everyone's contracts, including Larry's, and the new corporate papers and bylaws were also prepared. Still, Larry absolutely refused to sign anything. Finally, in October, 1993, I surprised Larry at a practice meeting in his house with all the papers and asked him what he wanted in order to sign. He said he wanted to stop taking night and weekend calls by 1997, and I hand wrote this into the contract. Gerry, Van, Ramish, Stuart and I were all sitting in his den, urging him to sign. We initialed the clause he wanted and had to practically force him to sit on the floor with us amid the papers before he finally—reluctantly—signed.

This was hardly the end of the story. Ramesh was scheduled to be made partner in July, 1993, but, not surprisingly, Larry refused to give Ramesh what he had been promised. Ramesh had a wife and children and needed the contract for their security. Larry's behavior was by now driving everyone crazy. I got frequent phone calls from Ramesh, imploring me to help him. I distinctly remember him pleading with me, saying, "Richard, you have to help me. Please!" I was completely on his side, and the situation was tearing me up emotionally. Since I had negotiated his contract with Larry, I felt responsible for making things right. As I have mentioned, I do not like it when powerful people abuse their power to mistreat the powerless. Larry was starting to fall into the category of "bad people" with whom I did not get along. I did everything I felt I could do to help Ramesh. I don't remember exactly what happened, but I think Larry tortured Ramesh with his behavior for about two years before he finally made Ramesh a partner.

Stuart was scheduled to be made a partner on July 1, 1995, and again Larry refused to live up to his promises. Stuart had a signed, witnessed legal contract that Larry just refused to recognize. I told Larry that if he was so unhappy with Stuart, he should try to fire him. Of course, I would not have voted for this, nor would Gerry and Ramesh. Larry was stuck and just continued to stonewall. At some point Stuart hired a lawyer, but I continued to offer him advice and support. In 1999, after I had left the group, Stuart said to me, "You know, Richard, I really value your friendship because of your honesty. With you, what you see is what you get." He also told me that he would tell others, "If Richard says it, it's true."

I replied, "You mean, 'I *think* it's true.'"

"No," he answered, "I mean if you say it, it's *true*." When he said this, Larry had still not reached an agreement with Stuart, and never would.

CHAPTER 38

HOW HOSPITALS WORK

Before I can tell the rest of my story, I need to explain how the medical staff of a hospital works. Academic and community hospital staffs work under different rules. Academic staffs are employees of the hospital and/or medical school; usually these staffs are organized into group practices. The clinical work these doctors perform is billed to the insurance companies, and the income is divided between the hospital, medical school, and the doctors. Doctors in community hospitals usually have their own solo or group practices, which bill independently for their professional services and keep all the money. The hospital bills independently for its services. The relationship of the private physicians and the hospital is governed by the "Bylaws of the Medical Staff." In Pennsylvania, these bylaws constitute a legal contract between the doctor and the hospital. Certain hospital-based doctors, such as radiologists, pathologists, and anesthesiologists, can have separate contracts with hospitals that allow one particular group to have a monopoly for their services in that particular hospital. These contracts usually have to be renewed every few years. If the hospital is unhappy with one of these groups, it can hire a different group when a contract expires.

The bylaws are a long document written by the hospital staffs with the assistance of attorneys. Bylaws enumerate the rights of the doctor and his responsibilities. At the start of a doctor's relationship with a hospital, he applies to the hospital for admitting privileges and for privileges to provide certain services for his patients in that hospital. For example, a cardiologist will apply for privileges to do stress tests, echocardiograms, and cardiac catheterizations in the hospital. The credentials committee evaluates a doctor's credentials to determine if a particular clinical privilege is to be granted. Every two years or so, every doctor on the staff must reapply for privileges. Privileges can only be denied under certain circumstances, which are delineated in the bylaws. If a hospital violates the bylaws to the detriment of the physician, a doctor may seek legal redress in court. Some hospitals require doctors to pledge not to sue the hospital if their initial application for privileges is denied. This does not apply once a doctor has privileges and is just going through the biannual reappointment process. A hospital cannot prevent a doctor from suing a hospital for violating its own bylaws in the reappointment process or in disciplining a doctor already on staff. The hospital cannot abrogate the legal contract, the bylaws, with a doctor unilaterally. If hospitals agree to this contract, they cannot invalidate it as part of the routine reapplication process. All this was explained to me by one of the top healthcare attorneys in Pittsburgh, Michael Cassidy.

Jefferson Hospital, sometime during the 1990's, mandated that a doctor who submits his routine two-year reapplication must sign a form stating he will not sue if his reappointment his rejected. Jefferson Hospital hired the law firm of Horty and Springer to deal with its medical staff relations. The hospital claimed that no doctor already on staff could sue the hospital under any circumstances for violations of the bylaws or for any other violation of civil law.

My attorney, who happens to be Michael Cassidy, represents doctors, not hospitals. He told me that the hospital cannot claim exemption from all and any lawsuits by doctors for any violations of civil law. Mike said, "If the hospital can do that, then what are the bylaws for?" For example, the hospital cannot take away privileges from a doctor without any reason. Also, if a hospital violates a civil law, say one against defamation or discrimination, the hospital cannot claim immunity against state or federal laws.

In order to maintain patient safety, laws have been passed to take away privileges from doctors who are incompetent, impaired, or engaged in criminal behavior. These laws, called Peer Review laws, protect medical staff officers and hospitals who take action against these doctors for specific violations. The purpose of these laws is to protect patients from bad doctors. Unfortunately, too often these laws are turned on their heads and are used to punish good doctors who try to protect their patients from negligent or incompetent care by the hospital or other physicians. In 2003, Steve Twedt, an investigative reporter for the *Pittsburgh Post-Gazette*, published a five-part series called "The Cost of Courage." It was about doctors around the United States who have been punished for trying to protect their patients from negligence or incompetence. Dishonest hospitals and doctors retaliate against the complaining physicians to destroy their careers and to set an example to other doctors who might stand up and fight for their patients. At other times, political enemies of doctor can use political clout and the peer review process to destroy a doctor simply for becoming temporarily ill.

At a community hospital, the medical staff elects its own leadership. At Jefferson, these elected positions are for a two-year term and include the president, vice president, and secretary-treasurer. In addition, the chiefs of the major departments, such as Medicine and Surgery, are also elected to two-year terms. The primary purpose of the medical staff leadership is to ensure quality care and patient safety. Occasionally, unscrupulous doctors will be elected to these positions and abuse their power to protect their own financial and/or professional interests. In 1997, I am totally convinced, I was the victim of Dr. Lawrence Adler, who, I believe, used my illness to try to destroy me and take over my patients. Extensive circumstantial and written evidence indicates that he was assisted in this endeavor by his friend Therese Kostrub, the hospital administrator in charge of medical staff, and Dr. Arnold Fingeret, then President of the Medical Staff. However, I believe Dr. Fingeret was the unwitting dupe of Adler and Kostrub. I only became aware of this behavior after I conducted an extensive investigation in 1999 and 2000. In 2001, I believe I was the victim of Stanley Wetschler, then President of the Medical Staff, who tried to destroy my career under false pretenses and for then unknown reasons. I only discovered this after an intense investigation in 2002, 2003, and 2004. I mention this now in order to put events into context to make it easier for the reader to follow the events described in the following chapters.

I do not consider myself a politician. In fact, I'm the last person I would consider suitable for a public office. I did however maintain very good relations with almost all of the doctors at Jefferson. I would not have been able to build a successful practice if I did not get along with the other doctors and their patients. In the 1980's I participated in a few hospital committees, but I never considered running for office. After I joined Cardiac Medical Associates, Larry Adler wanted me to get involved in hospital politics. At first I demurred. By 1992, I decided I owed it to Larry to do what he asked in return for all the benefits I had received by being a member of the group. Besides, my work load had been lessened by the group, so I had more time to engage in political activities. Perhaps Larry felt that obtaining political power was necessary to protect the group's interests. I decided to run for Chief of Medicine, and asked some of my friends to support my election. I was elected to the position for the term of 1993 and 1994.

The job of the Chief of Medicine was to oversee the quality of care in the department, conduct department meetings, and occasionally get involved in disciplinary actions. I also had a seat on the executive committee of the hospital, which included the senior hospital administrators and dealt with all major hospital business and patient care issues. During my two years, I reviewed hundreds of cases regarding quality problems. I was very lenient and focused exclusively on education, not disciplinary actions. There was not a single complaint registered against me by any member of the medical staff. I learned about how the hospital functioned during this time and worked fairly closely with the medical staff administrator, Therese (Terry) Kostrub. Once, I was asked to attend a medical staff leadership conference in Naples, Florida with Terry and Sister Nancy, a vice president of the hospital. The President of the Medical Staff, Kris Gopal, went with us. On the return trip, flights were cancelled due to bad weather, and I got a standby seat on another flight. Out of courtesy, I gave my seat to one of the women. I thought Terry and I had become friends during that trip, but I was to be proven wrong.

One day, during my tenure, Terry called me to inform me of an unfortunate occurrence with one of the doctors on staff at the hospital. A female doctor, an internist about 40 years old, had attempted suicide by sitting in her car with the engine running in her garage with the door closed. I was friends with this doctor and was very concerned about her situation. She survived, but the hospital had to get involved. Terry told me I had to call the Physician's Health Program (PHP) in Harrisburg to report the incident and refer her to the program. I had never heard of this organization. Terry gave me the phone number. She said most of the time these events with doctors usually involved drug or alcohol abuse by the physician involved.

Lee McCormick was the doctor involved with substance abuse at the hospital. Lee subsequently was elected as President of the Allegheny County Medical Association and then President of the Pennsylvania Medical Society. He was one of the main supporters of my practice after Dr. Money fired me in 1985. He also chose me as his personal cardiologist. Lee came to see me the same day Terry called me to also tell me that I had to call the PHP about the doctor. I hesitantly did what I was told I had to do in her best interests. The next day I received an urgent call from the office of the CEO of the hospital, Bill Jennings. I was summoned to his office. When I arrived, Bill and Terry were there with some other administrators, though I don't recall Lee being there. I was told that the doctor had come to Bill's office with her husband and a lawyer, threatening to sue the hospital because I had reported her to the PHP.

I informed everyone that Lee and Terry had told me to call. With an absolutely straight face, Terry lied to Bill in my presence and denied she had even spoken to me. I was astounded. Now I knew why the people who worked for Terry complained to me about her. I had dismissed those complaints when I first heard them because she had always been so nice to me. Her behavior was a portent of things to come.

CHAPTER 39

THE PULMONARY GROUP (PART I)

A pulmonologist is a specialist in lung disease. To become a pulmonologist, a doctor must first complete an internal medicine residency, which usually takes three years. Then he applies for a pulmonary fellowship, which usually lasts at least two more years. (In recent years, some physicians have begun to specialize in a relatively new sub-specialty called "critical care.") When I arrived in Pittsburgh in 1984, most of the pulmonology practiced at Jefferson Hospital was done by two physicians, P. David Laman and George Heymach. Both these gentlemen were very bright and trained at university hospitals. As I mentioned before, Dave Laman and I became good friends. David was born on the same day of the year as me but two years earlier, and we occasionally celebrated our birthdays together. David and I were so close that we even went together to the consumer electronics show in Chicago in 1988. David had originally come to Pittsburgh to work with Murray Sachs at Shadyside Hospital. I got along pretty well with Dr. Heymach as well. He was also from New York, and had attended Bronx High School of Science.

The only area of disagreement with them, at first, was over a procedure called "thoracentesis." This is a simple procedure in which a needle is put into the chest to remove fluid from the space between the lung and the chest wall. This space is called the pleural space. In healthy people, very little fluid is present there, but in various disease states, fluid can accumulate in this space. Sometimes a small amount of fluid is removed and sent to the laboratory for testing to determine a diagnosis. The presence of a large amount of pleural fluid can impair a person's ability to breath, in which case it may be necessary to remove almost all the fluid.

At Mount Sinai all the medical residents were trained to perform thoracenteses, and I probably did hundreds of these procedures before coming to Jefferson. Excessive pleural fluid can accumulate due to congestive heart failure. In my heart failure patients at Jefferson, I would perform my own thoracentesis when indicated. George Heymach took issue with this, basically accusing me of stealing work from them, and insisted that I consult them to do all the thoracenteses on my patients. I did what he requested, as it meant less work for me, and I certainly did not need the small amount of extra money. A few of my referring doctors did not want the pulmonary group to see their patients except when absolutely needed, so on those patients I continued to do the procedure as a courtesy. This is an example of how the politics of medicine plays out in actual patient care. Money seems to be the issue that too often drives doctors. At that time I didn't know that, years later, the pulmonary group would often refuse to do a thoracentesis on my patients for whom I felt it was absolutely necessary. (Later, I will explain how this situation contributed to my forced retirement.)

In 1985 or 1986, a third doctor, Emil Deliere, joined David and George. Emil had gone to Columbia University and was a champion wrestler, a huge, powerful man. He had been on the full-time faculty at Johns Hopkins for two years. When Emil got to Jefferson, he announced to many of the ICU nurses that, "Lasix should be a controlled substance." Lasix is a powerful diuretic that was revolutionary for the treatment of acute congestive heart failure. Apparently, Emil's experience at Johns Hopkins led him to believe this medicine was overused, and he was correct in assuming that too much Lasix could decrease the amount of blood flow. In patients in respiratory failure on a ventilator, a drop in cardiac output and blood flow to the lungs could reduce the amount of oxygen that the blood could get from the lungs. Also, diminished cardiac output could decrease the amount of oxygen delivered to the muscles that moved the chest in and out in order to breath. Emil would often give additional fluid to a patient to increase the cardiac output, which, I was convinced, worsened that patient's congestive heart failure.

Emil began his campaign against diuretics and never let up. Many of the cardiologists at Jefferson told me that they thought Emil was preventing them from adequately treating congestive heart failure, but no amount of reasonable discussion could affect Emil's seemingly almost religious belief against diuretics. David seemed be neutral about this issue. Emil was very smart, and I thought that he wanted to assume the intellectual leadership of his group. On the other hand, George began to call Dr. Deliere "Dr. Delirious" in his conversations with me. George repeatedly told me that Emil would never be a partner in his group because he wasn't a high-enough caliber of physician. I have never heard something like that said by any physician about one of the doctors in his own group, but I could understand George's frustration. Emil never seemed to talk English. He responded to any questioning of his opinion by writing complex equations about respiratory physiology, which no one, including me, seemed to be able to fully understand.

Everything I knew about congestive heart failure told me that Emil's approach was worsening the heart failure in some of my patients. Emil seemed to think he understood congestive heart failure better than me, and I thought this represented incredible arrogance. Apparently he believed that his two years on the pulmonology faculty at Johns Hopkins made him more of an expert in congestive heart failure than I was, with my five years on the cardiology faculty at Mount Sinai. I repeatedly spoke to David about this, but I had to be extremely strong-willed to protect my heart failure patients from Emil.

We eventually reached a state of accommodation. In 1992, however, some events caused me to reach a tipping point. I don't remember the particular cases, but I went on a full-fledged campaign to point out that all the excess fluid Emil was giving patients was exacerbating their heart failure. I had kept up a dialogue about this issue with Joel Weinberg, who was director of the Medical Intensive Care Unit at Shadyside Hospital and Murray Sachs's partner. As I mentioned previously, Joel and I had been friends at Mount Sinai, and we completely agreed on this issue. I asked him for references from the medical literature to give to Emil. I copied ten or so articles, including several from a Dr. Schuster in St. Louis, but Emil absolutely refused to discuss these with me. Later that year I went to a one-week course in Chicago, given by the national

Critical Care organization, most of whose doctors were pulmonologists. I spoke in private to Dr. Parillo, the president of this national group, about these issues, including proteins in the blood and their relationship to congestive heart failure. We did not disagree about anything. When I tried to discuss these issues with Emil, he refused to listen.

One day, Larry Adler and Jim Brooks told me I had to meet them for breakfast at a Denny's near Jefferson. There, they informed me that I had a defective personality because I always thought I was right, and I had to stop acting this way. It was like sitting with a couple of theologians from the 16th century telling me to stop saying the earth went around the sun. I brought all the articles I had copied for the pulmonary group, but they refused to discuss the science with me. I just listened to what they had to say and left shaking my head. At first I thought David had put them up to it, but years later Jim told me Emil had talked them into it, and Jim apologized to me. When I brought it up with Larry, he said he didn't remember any meeting in Denny's.

I knew my partners in the group, especially Madhavan, were just as concerned about the pulmonary group causing heart failure in our patients as I was. We would have open discussions about it at our practice meetings, where everyone agreed that the pulmonary group was too powerful and standing up to them would make us susceptible to retaliation. Since Larry agreed with us in private, I knew that he hadn't really believed what he had said to me at Denny's. I thought that Larry was just taking me out to the woodshed to cut me down to size in an effort to gain some control over me. It was a pattern I was getting used to in life. People who disagreed with me would use perceived personality flaws against me when they couldn't muster cogent arguments to support their positions. I just let it go, but I was not going to allow any of my patients to suffer because of what I perceived to be Emil's lack of understanding of heart failure. I told David that, from then on, our group would be the only one allowed to write fluid orders on our patients. If we were consulted on one of their patients, they could write the fluid orders and we would stay out of it. Our patients were our responsibility, but I wasn't going to interfere in the treatment of their patients. A truce and ceasefire went into effect that lasted for several years.

This problem would not have been an issue if we had had another pulmonary group at Jefferson in competition with David's group, but their group was the only medical sub-specialty group that had no real competition, so they could do anything they wanted without fear of losing business. In future years, the hospital administrators told me that the pulmonary group used every bit of political clout they could muster to prevent another pulmonary group from establishing themselves at Jefferson. In the 1980s, Dr. Money had a feud with George Heymach and asked the pulmonary group from West Penn Hospital to develop a presence at Jefferson. I think they lasted six months at Jefferson before they gave up. At Shadyside Hospital, David's group did not have much power and they had serious competition from Murray and Joel. Because I knew I would be in charge of the fluids on our patients at Shadyside, I would occasionally order a consult from David's group instead of Murray's group. Eventually I had to stop doing this because the nurses in the post op cardiac ICU begged me to. Almost every time I ordered a consult from David's group, the nurse taking care of the patient begged me not to consult them. In time I began using Joel's group exclusively.

I remember one case in particular in the coronary care unit at Shadyside. The patient was on David's service, so they had control of the patient's fluids, while we were taking care of the patient's cardiac problems. For several days the chest x-ray showed more and more fluid in the patient's lungs. I remember talking to George about it, but he refused to change the fluid orders. One day I came in to make rounds on the patient and found that the family had asked for David's group to be removed from the case. Dr. Weinberg took over. He completely changed course and began to remove fluid from the patient. Within two or three days, the patient's chest x-ray revealed clear lungs.

CHAPTER 40

LOOKING FOR LOVE

Between 1989 and 1994, Barbara and I had made only minimal progress in our sexual relationship, but we had put considerable energy into restoring the house. We hired one of the most highly-regarded interior design firms in Pittsburgh, Mark Christy Associates, to work with us on interior restoration and decoration. Bill McGrath was the designer working with us. We addressed one room at a time, and each room required about six months to complete from start to finish. Bill would give us an assortment of options to choose from for every aspect of each room and tied all the rooms together with one consistent theme. Despite the fact that the process was laborious, I enjoyed doing it.

We put the same effort into the outside of the house, hiring a top quality general contractor, Joint Builders. We hired a young architect to design and integrate a detached two car garage with an 85-foot driveway. Just finding bricks for the garage to match the hundred-year-old bricks of the house required a full month. The front, side, and rear porches were completely rebuilt, and the landscaping was redone from scratch. All the wood moldings of the exterior were completed refurbished, including some ornamentation that had to be manufactured by hand. We had finished almost everything by 1994 at a total cost of more than half a million dollars, which I was able to pay in cash.

The house was absolutely spectacular. Some real estate agents said they thought it might be the most beautiful house in Pittsburgh. People would almost gasp when they saw it for the first time. Bill McGrath had a professional photographer take pictures of the interior to put in his portfolio. I loved living in the house, as did Ben and Sarah. On some level I had hoped that by giving Barbara her dream house I could pay her back for all the pain I had caused her during my illness in 1989. In retrospect, I realize that money and material possessions do not necessarily compensate for or rectify the effects of emotional trauma. I tried to increase the amount of time Barbara and I spent alone together, and I repeatedly asked her to go on a vacation without the kids. She absolutely refused to do this, insisting that we always take the kids and their nanny. I hoped that having the nanny with us would allow Barbara and me to spend more time alone, but nothing seemed to work.

By 1993 my income had fallen to $450,000. I had deliberately planned for a reduction that year because Tauberg's and Chandra's salary were set to increase. My plan was still to sacrifice money for time with my family. The house was finished, and Ben's and Sarah's college funding was complete, with investments in municipal bonds. I was still rolling in money but was not very happy. I remember very well coming home from work one evening, standing on the driveway, looking at the house. I had just parked my new 740i BMW in the beautiful new garage, and I felt good about giving Barbara and the kids such a nice place to live. I knew I was extremely fortunate to have arrived at this point in life. But as I looked at the house I said to myself, *This is a beautiful house; too bad there's no place for me here.* At that moment I fully understood that money could not make you happy. I wanted and needed love, which money, alas, could not buy.

By 1994, my professional career was peaking and I was deriving pleasure and satisfaction from it, but my loneliness was starting to take its toll. I always tried to maintain good relations with the nurses I worked with, and I knew most of the nurses liked and respected me. On several occasions, a nurse in the ICU had said to me, "Dr. Schneider, you really care about your patients."

One of the new nurses in the ICU was a woman named Sue (her real first name). Sue was 37 and a former flight attendant for USAir. She was tall and slim, with beautiful medium-length red hair. I was certainly attracted to her. We began to spend time talking every time I saw her in the ICU, and she was clearly attracted to me as well. She never gave a single indication that she didn't like the attention I was paying to her. I developed what can only be described as a serious crush on her. Except for a one-night stand during a cardiology conference in Atlanta in 1981, I hadn't slept with any woman except Barbara during our marriage. I believed in marital fidelity. At no time did my conversations with Sue ever include any discussions about getting together socially. I never said anything to indicate that I was about to cheat on my wife. I can't say I didn't think about her, sometimes to the point of distraction. I certainly fantasized about her, and while these reveries did include some sexual thoughts, I was mostly attracted by how nice she was to me. I was lonely and felt unloved, and Sue seemed as if she might love me if given a chance. However, since I have a lot of willpower, I was able to prevent myself from taking any action.

After this "friendship" went on for a month or two, I started to feel that I wasn't being fair to Sue. She started to indicate that she wanted our relationship to progress beyond just being friends, and I knew I had to stop leading her on. One day soon after I had a conversation with her in the ICU, I went into one of the private doctor dictation rooms and called her in the ICU, where she was caring for one of my patients. I wanted to be as nice as possible. "I'm sorry, I can't do this," I told her. "I have a wife and two kids." I knew she didn't want to hear this, so I repeated my apology several times in as nice a way as possible. She didn't say much and the conversation lasted only a couple of minutes. I thought I was acting as a perfect gentleman under the circumstances, and I still wanted to be friends with her. I had no idea how upset she really was, because she didn't express any anger or disappointment on the phone.

A few days later, when I saw Sue in the ICU, she grabbed both my hands in hers and pulled me into an empty patient's room. She held my hands tightly and said, "Rich, what do you want?"

"I just want to be friends," I said. "I want to talk and joke around." This was absolutely true when I said it. What I didn't know at the time was that Sue was furious with me. She was in the process of trying to frame me for a future allegation of sexual harassment. Years later, as part of the discovery process for my lawsuit against the hospital, I read one of her letters to the hospital about me in which she claimed *I* had pulled *her* by the hands into the empty room. I came to believe that her false allegations were used as part of an elaborate ruse that Larry Adler and Terry Kostrub tried to use to destroy my career in 1997.

The week after Sue pulled me into that room, I was called by Lois, the head nurse in the ICU, a woman I had worked with for many years. Lois said she and Sue wanted to meet me in my office. Sue accused me of inappropriate behavior and demanded that I talk to her in the future only about my patients. I indicated to both of them that I had told her the previous week I did not want to get involved with her. She ignored this and threatened to report me to the hospital's Human Resources Department. I said I had no problem doing what she asked. After she left, Lois and I just sat there shaking our heads in bewilderment as to what that little performance was all about.

One evening a few days later, when I was in the hospital finishing rounds, I got an indication of her motivation. I was paged to an outside call, and a woman got on the phone. She wanted to be anonymous, but I immediately recognized her voice. It was Kim Wagner, a nurse in the ICU. I told Kim I recognized her voice. She said, "Dr. Schneider, Sue is out to get you, big time, big time. She was talking to a few of us. She bragged about how she got you to look at her and told us she was going to get you." I replied that Sue was a nice person, and I couldn't believe she would do anything like that. Nevertheless, I took the threat to heart and didn't talk to Sue about anything but patient care for more than a year. In 1996, Sue tried to make good on her threat. Those events appear in a subsequent chapter.

CHAPTER 41

MANAGED CARE BEGINS

The first time I encountered managed care, Health Maintenance Organizations or HMO's, was 1985 while I was working in MD Cardiology. Representatives of US Healthcare met with us to propose a contract for us. The reps told us that they were going to take over medical care in this country and that, if we knew what was good for us, we would sign up immediately. We were told we would be working for them in the future, and, at that point, we would have no say about it.

I couldn't believe how arrogant these guys were! It seemed to me that patients would prefer for me to work for them and not some corporation. This was the beginning of the dismantling of the doctor/patient relationship that has only gotten worse over the intervening 20 years. Prior to the onset of HMOs, the doctor/patient relationship was sacrosanct. Patients with insurance, including Medicare and Medicaid, had a direct relationship with their physicians. We provided the service and the insurance company paid us directly, no questions asked. The new business model was created by businessmen anxious to direct a large piece of the heath care money pie to themselves.

The HMO business model was for employers to contract with an HMO to provide health insurance for their employees. The HMO would then contract with providers, doctors and hospitals to provide care for these patients at a reduced fee. The idea was sold to the public as a way of reducing health care costs. As I mentioned in a previous chapter, doctors were assisting the HMOs in making this argument by devising schemes to milk the current system for as much money as possible. By killing the goose that was laying the golden eggs, Medicare and private fee for service insurance companies, we were insuring the destruction of the doctor/patient relationship as we had known it. A person's employer now had a say over which doctors and hospitals he could use. The choices were predicated on lower cost, not better care. If a patient was seeing a doctor in whom he had confidence, and his employer changed his insurance coverage to a company that did not have a contract with the patient's preferred doctors and hospitals, the patient was forced to change providers. The HMOs and employers gave lip service to the concept of quality care, but quality did not play a role in choosing an HMO. The reason for this was that actual quality was not measured. HMOs advertised the quality of their providers, but measures of true quality, i.e. outcomes, were almost never measured.

We did not want to take any chances of being driven out of business by the HMOs, so we signed contracts with all the HMOs doing business in Pittsburgh as they opened for business, when they were signing up anyone who wanted a contract. As the years went by, HMOs became highly selective, and not all doctors were allowed to join. We were not subjected to this discrimination because we already had contracts with all the HMOs. As a result, none of my patients were forced to change cardiologists if their employer changed their insurance. By the early 1990s, HMOs and other types of managed care plans were taking significant market share from traditional indemnity insurance plans. Gradually, the only patients with fee for service indemnity insurance were Medicare patients.

I was very comfortable working for Medicare, since it paid fairly promptly compared to HMOs, all doctors and hospitals were allowed to participate, and patients were not restricted in their choice of doctors and hospitals. Of course, Medicare had to address issues of cost, so Medicare instituted Diagnosis Related Groupings, or DRGs, in the mid 1980s. Under this payment scheme, hospitals were no longer paid for each day a patient stayed in the hospital. Instead, hospitals were paid a fixed amount for the entire patient stay. The amount paid was predicated on the patient's specific diagnosis. DRGs amounted to price controls for hospitals determined by the Federal Government. At first the payments were overly generous to allow hospitals to adapt to the new system gradually over a few years. Then hospitals went on a campaign to get their doctors to decrease the number of days their patients stayed in the hospital. As I mentioned before, at Jefferson all doctors were evaluated for their average length of stay for a given diagnosis. We were then given "report cards" every six to twelve months, comparing our lengths of stay (LOS) with the other doctors at Jefferson and with national averages. The hospital put pressure on doctors whose LOS was above average. A doctor with a shorter LOS was looked on more favorably by the hospitals and benefited in subtle ways from favoritism.

Asking doctors to limit LOSs voluntarily did not significantly reduce doctor costs to Medicare. I vividly remember once trying to save a day in the hospital for a patient. The patient had lung and heart problems and was being seen by the pulmonary group. Emil Deliere was seeing the patient that day, and I asked him if he could do something to help me get the patient discharged that day. He replied, "I'm not interested in doing what's convenient for the hospital; I'm going to do what's convenient for me." Medicare considered the idea of introducing doctor DRGs, but this was thought to be unwise because it would discourage primary care physicians from consulting specialists for the sicker patients. Instead, in the early 1990's, Medicare instituted a system of payments to doctors called RBRVS, Resource Based Relative Value Scale. This system, developed by Harvard University, determined the reimbursement a doctor would receive for any service rendered. The amount paid was determined by a complicated formula that took into account the cost of resources for a physician to provide a particular service in a certain geographic area. Every year Medicare published reimbursement rates for each practice. Initially, HMOs fixed their reimbursement for any given service at a certain percentage of the Medicare reimbursement. My first contracts with HMOs set payments at 105% to 110% of Medicare levels. As the years went by, many HMOs reduced payments to far below Medicare levels.

Even at this early stage, I was concerned the HMO movement could prevent my referring physicians from asking me to see their patients. I advocated the idea that the best solution to the problems in health care would be to place the whole country on Medicare. At the time doctors were afraid that a national program of health insurance would lower their incomes and usurp their prerogatives in providing care; only a small percentage of doctors favored such a system. HMOs no longer paid primary care physicians (PCPs) a fee for each patient visit. Instead, HMOs paid a fixed monthly fee for each patient signed up for a given PCP. Specialists like me were still paid "fee for service." PCPs were not even paid extra to see their patients when they were in the hospital. This created a rift between some PCPs and the sub-specialists they asked to help them care for their patients. Some PCPs felt the only way to counteract the negative effects on them was to form larger groups and hire sub-specialists to do their consulting work. A group practice could legally bill fee for service for their cardiologist's work and cut a deal in which part of the money collected could be shared with the PCPs. This was clearly fee splitting in my book and therefore unethical, but it was completely legal. The patients were the ones to suffer. A PCP in the group would no longer pick a consultant based on how good a doctor he was, but rather who would give him a kickback.

I did not suffer any of the negative effects of the managed care movement until 1993, when the Prime Medical Group was formed. Prime Medical was conceived by a group of doctors as a way of improving their financial outlook in the face of the managed care revolution and protecting members of the group financially from the damaging effects of managed care.

I clearly recall one afternoon in the mid 1990's I was attending one of my son Ben's Little League baseball games; Jeff Blum, my former attorney, was also there to see his son play. Despite our falling out a few years earlier, Jeff and I got to talking. He asked me if I would consider retaining him again to do my legal work, and I agreed. Then in 1997, when he was representing me against Larry, Jeff and I were discussing my future professional plans. I brought up the idea of joining Prime. Jeff told me that he had been involved in some capacity with Prime, and he warned me not to consider joining them. I recall that he said something like, "Stay away from them. All they are interested in is money."

I was not privy to the details about Prime's background, so in the next chapter I will relate what I know from firsthand information and qualify conclusions that I drew from this information.

CHAPTER 42

THE BEGINNING OF THE END

Abe Chauhan, an internist, and Dave Laman, the pulmonologist, were the main people behind Prime's formation. They felt that the formation of a very large group would give them more power to negotiate with the HMOs and hospitals. The group was to consist mostly of primary care physicians, with a few selected specialists who would be preferred by the PCPs. I have no idea what the financial arrangements were, but during the subsequent years I heard tales of woe from several of the players.

My three biggest referral sources in the early 1990's were Lee McCormick, Jim Brooks, and Tom Schaefer. I was involved with the initial meetings of Prime Medical Group as a representative of our group. Tom Pinto was an interventional (angioplasty) cardiologist who was a very good friend of Abe Chauhan. When the vote came to select a cardiology group to be in Prime, Pinto's group was selected over our group. Years later Tom told me that he always did what Abe told him to do, so I guess that influenced the vote. My misfortune at the time was that Jim Brooks was in Prime, Tom Schaefer joined, and finally Lee McCormick thought it was in his best interest to join as well. These three doctors accounted for a large part of my referral base. They told me that I would continue to care for the patients of theirs with whom I had already been involved. Their new patients would be referred to the cardiologists selected to be part of their group. They lived up to their promises in this regard, and we continued to be friends and work well together in caring for our mutual patients. I didn't have any hard feelings about what they had done because I knew they had to do what they considered necessary for their own financial survival. My practice did contract somewhat, but as a group we had enough work to keep us all busy.

My political clout in the group, however, did suffer, so I attempted to look for more business elsewhere. In 1994, I believe, I was approached by a cardiologist at Shadyside, Steve Heilbrunn. Steve and his partner, John George, had split off from their original group. They worked primarily at St. Margaret's Hospital, which was located on the north side of the Allegheny River, about six miles northeast of Shadyside. Steve, a very smart interventional cardiologist who was also from New York, asked me if my group would consider merging with him and John. I thought it was a good idea because it would allow us to expand our geographic base and allow us to capture new business. Besides, I liked Steve and his wife Adriana Selvaggio, who was a kidney doctor at Shadyside. I presented the idea to Larry and the other guys, and everyone thought the idea was worth exploring. We arranged for a meeting to be held with all eight cardiologists at Larry's house.

We had an excellent meeting, which lasted several hours, and after Steve and John, left we took a vote. Everyone, including Larry, voted to proceed with the merger. I was elated. The merger would make us the largest cardiology group in the Pittsburgh area. I knew there was safety in numbers, and I wanted to stabilize the group for the long term. As the head of the group, Larry said he would call Steve and begin making the arrangements. The next day I spoke to Steve to give him the good news. Everything was set, and we awaited Larry's call to Steve. I think I asked Larry a couple of times when he was going to call Steve. He said soon, but when a month passed with no word to Steve, I asked Larry again when he would call. It was then that Larry told me he had found out that Steve was "difficult to work with" and had changed his mind. I was shocked; I felt that Larry had sold me down the river. It was one thing for him to lie on his own, but now I was made to look like a liar and a fool as well. He was not even willing to call Steve with the news and take responsibility for his behavior. Larry had no business voting to bring Steve into the practice without first doing his "research" about Steve's personality. Larry also had no right to get me involved in his shenanigans.

So it was left to me to break the news to Steve. Being an honest person and wanting to preserve my reputation, I told him exactly what had occurred. Steve said Larry must have heard about him from his old partner. We were both pretty miffed. The next day I got a call from Larry. *He* was angry with *me*. Talk about the pot calling the kettle black! I couldn't believe his chutzpah. Larry said that Adriana had given him the cold shoulder when he saw her at Shadyside that morning. I told him he was the one who had put me out on a limb and then sawed it off. He was furious. "I will never confide in you or trust you again," he said. The seeds of the destruction of my relationship with Larry were sown. Larry had once mentioned to me that he didn't want to stay in New York after his year at Sinai because "they would eat me alive." He was referring to the New York Jewish cardiologists. I guess he thought Steve and I, being New York Jews, would take over control of the practice. I never had any intention of hurting Larry. I had just wanted to help the group.

Life wasn't any smoother back at home. Barbara and I were back in marriage counseling but not making much progress. That year Barbara began to say she thought I was misdiagnosed by my doctors. They had diagnosed me as depressed only, a condition called "unipolar depression." Barbara became convinced that I was "bipolar," or manic depressive. Steve Carter, my psychologist, however, was adamant that I was not bipolar. This led to several heated discussions between me and Barbara, without any resolution. By December, 1994, I was a little more depressed despite still being on the imipramine. Alexandra, my medication psychiatrist, asked me if I wanted to boost the effect of the imipramine by adding a small dose of lithium, 450 mg. Usually, lithium is prescribed for bipolar disease to prevent manic episodes, but that requires a larger dose. I may have noticed a slight degree of improvement in my depression, but it wasn't until years later that I realized the actual effect even this small dose of lithium had on me.

One evening, in January, 1995, at a medical staff meeting at Braddock, Larry said to me, "You're goofing off." I assumed his comment was about the latest computer print-out of everyone's billing. Larry never shared those with the group. I was even elected nominally to be the treasurer of the corporation, and he still refused to let me see them. I think he felt more in control of the group if he kept the information to himself.

Because I usually minimized my symptoms to myself, I didn't realize what the addition of lithium was doing to me. I was getting exhausted every afternoon. I thought I was just sleep deprived and didn't even consider that it might be the effects of my medication. My doctors didn't suggest this might be a problem either. I didn't know at the time that the side effects from the treatment of my illness were only going to get worse, and that Larry was going take advantage of the situation to get me out of the practice.

CHAPTER 43

WORSENING RELATIONSHIPS

My marriage difficulties continued as Barbara and I could not get onto the same page. I was really frustrated and started to think seriously about the nature of human sexuality, so I did some reading and began to write down my thoughts. I hand-wrote pages about what I thought was going on between men and women. I tried to draw on my personal experiences in prior relationships, in addition to what I read and talked about in my individual therapy with Steve and during sessions with the marriage counselors and Barbara. My philosophy about intimate relationships began to emerge.

I took as a given that most people have sexual fantasies, though I know for many years I did not reveal my fantasies to any woman. I just didn't feel safe enough in any relationship to show my true self. I didn't try to live out these fantasies in any way. I began to realize that, in order for a man to achieve real intimacy with a woman, both people had to reveal their inner sexual thoughts to each other. I came to believe that revealing one's deepest fantasies required total trust and commitment. It was only under these circumstances that a person could reveal him or herself without fear of rejection. I discussed this with Barbara but she was having none of it. She had told me she didn't trust me in bed and nothing had changed since she first told me this more than ten years previously.

Meanwhile, at work I was doing everything I could to get along with Larry. I knew I was in a somewhat weakened position in the group and with Larry, but I considered my relationships with Van, Gerry, Ramesh, and Stuart to be excellent. Stuart and I had originally butted heads, but by 1995 he began to express serious respect for my knowledge and clinical judgment. He told me that, when he had a tough clinical decision to make, he would ask himself: "What would Richard do?"

Madhavan and I were able to thrash out clinical disagreements in private. These discussions were based on mutual respect for each others opinions. He was very well read, and we would exchange large amounts of information with each other. He always knew things I didn't know and vice versa. Madhavan was the director of the cath lab at Jefferson. He had gotten this position in 1994 when the cath lab had opened. The hospital had originally asked me to be the director of the cath lab. I was Chief of Medicine at the time, and I told them I didn't want to take on any more administrative responsibilities. In addition, I wasn't doing many caths at that point because three other members of the group were also doing caths. Also, I didn't do angioplasty, and therefore I told them I was not qualified to do the job. I thought Madhavan was qualified for the job and pushed hard for him to get the position, which he did.

Van and I never failed to reach agreement on any clinical issue in the whole time we worked together. The only disagreements we had involved two administrative issues as to which patients could be taken to the cath lab, and both these issues were resolved by third parties in my favor.

My relationship with Ramesh was also excellent. I had a lot of respect for his clinical skills and he seemed to respect mine. We didn't have much contact, however, because he spent most of his time at Braddock and Shadyside. Gerry and I continued to get along famously in our complementary roles, but my relationship with Larry remained extremely problematic. The problems mostly concerned Larry's relationships with Ramesh and Stuart. Larry had still not made Ramesh a partner, which he was to have done in 1993. Stuart was due for partnership in July, 1995 according to the contract that he, Larry, and I had hashed out and signed in 1992. The conversations between me and Stuart and between me and Ramesh were riddled with their complaints about the situation. I told them I was doing everything I could to get Larry to live up to his contractual responsibilities.

I felt responsible since I had negotiated both their contracts, and they had joined the group with the understanding they would be made partner after three years. I tried to be diplomatic with Larry and limited the frequency with which I brought up the issue. Larry subsequently, in January, 1996, accused me of trying to take over the group by advocating partnership for Ramesh and Stuart. I never had any interest in "taking over the group"; all I wanted was stability. I knew the group would have to be democratically run if it were going to survive in the long run. This was no secret, inasmuch as I had told Larry in no uncertain terms in 1989 that I would only join the group if he guaranteed me that it would be run democratically. I felt he had lied to me as well as to Ramesh and Stuart, but he wanted me to pretend that he had done nothing wrong. His resentment of me seemed to grow.

Larry also did not want me to go to Shadyside to make rounds every Wednesday, as I had been doing for the previous five years. One incident comes to mind that probably influenced his desire to get me out of Shadyside permanently. One of his woman patients was admitted to Shadyside with increasing congestive heart failure. She was in the hospital for about a week before she was stable enough to be discharged. I had seen her twice while she was in the hospital and knew her case well. Her heart was still pretty strong and she responded well to the medication. This usually indicates that the patient will do well for quite a while after discharge. If the patient has recurrent heart failure soon after discharge, this almost always has a discernable cause. Among these causes are: a new infection somewhere in the body, a new heart attack, or the patient's inadvertent consumption of too much salt. So, when I saw her in the hospital again a week after she had gone home, I was quite surprised.

I did what I always did under these circumstances: conduct a careful history and physical exam to try to determine the precipitating factor causing such a swift decompensation of her condition. She said she had not been taking her Lasix, the water pill, which she had been on even before her first hospitalization. When I asked her why she stopped taking it, she replied, "Dr. Adler didn't prescribe it for me when he discharged me." I had never seen this happen with a heart failure patient in my career. If I had made such a harebrained mistake, I would want to be told about it immediately. I called Larry at our Jefferson office where he had office hours and told him what had happened. He seemed to be quite annoyed that I had bothered him. He and I were getting nowhere fast, and he didn't have to wait long to find a reason to bring the situation to a head.

CHAPTER 44

TRUTH, JUSTICE, AND O.J. SIMPSON

I had been brought up to believe in truth and justice. My father was a liberal Democrat with very strong beliefs, and he was especially concerned about the struggle for civil rights in the fifties and sixties. I was exposed to constant vituperative conversations between both my parents and my father's sister and her husband, who were conservative Republicans. My aunt and uncle, whom I liked a great deal but often disagreed with, believed in social Darwinism or more simply put, survival of the fittest. I remember well President Eisenhower sending the 101st Airborne Division to Little Rock in 1957 when I was ten years old. I watched the events unfold on television. The soldiers escorting the black students to the high school brought tears to my eyes, and I still react the same way when I see the newsreels from that day. The good guys were the soldiers who were protecting people who couldn't protect themselves from the rabid racists of the South. There was no question in my mind as to whose side I was on. The early sixties were a time of real change in this country. Even though my high school was lily-white and working and middle class, I never heard a racist comment from my classmates. We were all on the same page.

After the Civil Rights Laws of 1964 were signed into law, I felt relieved. This sense of calm was short lived because the Vietnam War soon replaced Civil Rights as the number one issue for me. The confluence of the two issues became apparent when a disproportionate number of casualties were incurred by minority soldiers. Also, the bussing of school children to promote racial integration of the schools became a big issue. I thoroughly supported bussing.

Ann Arbor was a hotbed of anti-war counterculture, and I identified with the far left on this issue at that point in my life. I went on an all-night drive to Washington, D.C. to join the huge anti-war demonstration on November 15, 1969. Despite my war protests, I never lost faith in my country. I believed totally in the concept of "justice for all" and still think of it as the defining concept of democracy. But without truth there can be no justice. Whether in a court of law or in the halls of science, it is the constant search for truth that allows us to apply justice.

When, in 1994, Nicole Simpson and her casual friend Ron Goldman were brutally murdered in the yard of her house in Los Angeles, suspicion centered on her ex-husband, O.J. Simpson, the famous football star. I was perplexed. It had been axiomatic on the Left that crime in minority communities had its origins in social injustice. I just couldn't understand why a person who had been treated so well in his life could be so deranged that he could murder two people in cold blood. What was the truth? Did he actually do it? If so, then why? O.J.'s attempt to escape to Mexico and the televised "slow chase" on a California highway certainly suggested that he was guilty.

His trial began in early 1995, and I followed the trial very closely. The trial hinged on two main issues. Johnny Cochran, O.J.'s lead attorney, based his defense on racial discrimination and a frame-up by the police. The prosecution based its case on DNA evidence from the scene of the crime. Because I was a physician, I was able to follow the science of the evidence. At the end of the trial, I thought that the prosecution had scientifically proven that O.J. had committed the murders, and I was convinced of his guilt. Therefore, I was totally shocked that October when he was acquitted. After the verdict was announced, the television networks reported on the reaction to the verdict by different segments of society. The image that disturbed me most was the sight of African-American teenagers in a school auditorium jumping up and down in celebration, as if this were a football game and not a murder trial. I saw this behavior as a sign of severe racism by blacks against whites. How could anyone cheer at the brutal deaths of two perfectly innocent people? I hadn't realized up to then the severity of reverse racism.

At this point in time, my illness interfaced with my career, and in

August of that year, I started to get somewhat depressed again. Barbara had noticed this, and by September she thought that I might have Seasonal Affective Disorder, SAD for short, a fairly common problem thought to be caused by diminished sunlight in the autumn. Sunlight stimulates the pineal gland in the brain to release certain neurotransmitters. A decrease in sunlight is thought to cause depression because of a decrease of these neurotransmitters.

I was trying to be a good patient because I needed all the help I could find to get along with Larry and Barbara. I told Dr. Kreps about my symptoms and suggested SAD as a possible diagnosis. I was already on medication, imipramine and lithium, for depression and didn't want to add more medications. SAD can be treated with strong light from a box called a "light box," so I asked Alexandra what she thought of this. She thought it was a good idea and wrote me a prescription for such a box. I started the light box therapy in mid September. Unfortunately, my reaction to the verdict reached at the O.J. trial was greatly exaggerated by a state of "hypomania" induced by the light box.

The day after the trial I thought it was going to be a lively topic of discussion in the hospital. I had no idea that Shadyside Hospital had recently put into place a regulation prohibiting discussion of any racial issues. As the day after the verdict was a Wednesday, I was scheduled to make rounds at Shadyside, and I arrived around 8 a.m. The first person I saw was Cathy, an African-American, who was the unit secretary at the nursing station on one of the cardiac floors. I had known her for some time and thought of her as a friend, or at least a friendly acquaintance. We had had quite a few nice conversations, and she seemed to have a good sense of humor. The trial was on my mind and I thought nothing of discussing it with her. I said the trial was an injustice and felt people should speak out. I said something to the effect that justice is only justice if it applies to everyone white or black, including Ron and Nicole. She said, "There's a price to pay for saying that." As soon as she said that, I ended the conversation. This conversation was witnessed by the unit supervisor, Linda Altenbaugh. I assumed that Cathy wanted to sue me if I made any comments, so I said something nice and then shut up. She seemed okay and I went about my business.

Four hours later, I was at a different nursing station when Helen and Marcia, two African-American nurses I had known for many years, approached me and pulled me into the nurses' lounge. They said, "Dr. Schneider, we heard you were a racist. Tell us it's not true." I reassured them that I was not a racist and they expressed relief. They said they knew I wasn't a racist. In fact, I knew I was the exact opposite of a racist. They had worked with me for more than ten years and we had a friendship that included many discussions about our personal lives, so they knew me quite well. They told me that Cathy was running around the hospital telling everyone I was a racist.

As it turned out, Cathy had sat at her desk from 8 a.m. until 12 noon concocting a story that she hoped would yield her a lot of money. She not only accused me of being a racist, but also told people that her supervisor, Linda Altenbaugh, was also a racist. I guess she included Linda so she could also sue the hospital and have an even bigger payday. Cathy already had picked out a lawyer, as I was told she and her lawyer came to the hospital shortly thereafter. I had no idea what she was accusing me of saying as no one in the hospital administration called me to tell me about the problem. Hospital bylaws mandate that any accusations made against a doctor must be kept secret, except for the President of the Medical Staff and the Chief of Medicine. One of these two people should have been designated to speak to me about the incident.

The Vice President of Nursing at Shadyside was Gail Wolf. She had been at Shadyside for many years and knew Larry well. The bylaws specifically forbade her from notifying Larry about what had occurred. Despite this, Larry must have been among the first people she called because apparently she had some archaic notion that he was my boss and had to be informed. She was wrong, but that didn't help me after the fact. This was the perfect opportunity for Larry to get some dirt to use against me. At that point he did everything he could to inject himself into the situation and prevent me from defending myself with the truth. If Gail Wolf had used the proper channels, she would have asked George Arnold, the Medical Staff President, or Fred Rubin, the Chief of Medicine, to discuss the issue with me. I had known both of them for years and I know they would have believed me. George and I had even been neighbors for several years in the 1980's. As it turned out, both of them were very supportive of me throughout the episode. I called the Chief Counsel for Shadyside Hospital, James Roberts, two days after the incident, and told him exactly what I had said to Cathy. He replied, "It sounds as if it's just a misunderstanding." George Arnold told me he was trying to persuade Cathy to accept a letter of apology from me, which I certainly would have written, but Cathy refused to talk to him. She was interested in money, not an apology.

So it was Larry who called me at the hospital, saying, "Richard, you're starting a race riot. Get out of there." He knew that by getting me out of the hospital I would not be able to address the issue and defend myself properly. In retrospect, I think he interjected himself into the process with the express intention of making me look as bad as possible, and he was pretty successful in achieving this. I found out a couple of years later that he had even spoken to Cathy directly to get her lies about me and present them as truth to everyone in the group. I ended up, a few years later, getting Cathy to make a deposition and testify under oath. She volunteered that she had spoken directly with Larry. I guess Larry thought I would never find out about it.

Some people at the hospital wanted to throw me off the staff. I attended a hearing with a large hospital committee, at which time I was presented with a typed statement from Cathy accusing me a saying several vicious racial comments. I told them I never said anything she accused me of saying. The statement was so coherent that I thought her lawyer must have written it for her. I told the committee about the light box and how it had put me into an altered mental state that adversely affected my judgment. I explained my belief in justice for all and why the trial had upset me. George Arnold and Fred Rubin were there and felt they needed to hold me by the arms as they led me out of the room. They knew Cathy was lying about me and expressed their sympathy and support. After the committee meeting, I was sent the minutes of the meeting and asked to sign off on them as accurate. They weren't, and I made numerous corrections. I also sent a long letter in which I defended myself and espoused my feelings about truth and justice. I also found out subsequently that Linda Altenbaugh had testified that my conversation with

Cathy was just a normal conversation. Since Linda was also accused of being a racist, I guess some on the committee thought both Linda and I were lying about what had occurred.

When I found out the extent to which Larry had injected himself into the situation, I wrote the hospital a letter telling them they were violating my right to privacy and specifically telling them not to communicate with anyone except me and especially not Larry. Larry was out of town when I sent the letter. When he returned he told me: "They shut me out completely." The hospital ended up suspending me for two weeks. This was not a real punishment because it didn't inconvenience me and was not reported to the National Practitioner Data Bank. Only suspensions of 30 days or longer had to be reported. I took it as a slap on the wrist, but since I hadn't done what I was accused of doing, it was difficult to be contrite. In addition, I spent a lot of time on the phone with the hospital attorney, Stanley Milavec, assigned to handle the situation. We talked extensively about justice and constitutional law. Stanley was the one who called me to tell me of the committee's decision and the reasons for it. At the end of the conversation, he said something I will never forget: "You are the finest human being I have ever had the privilege of knowing." I couldn't believe it and asked him if I had heard him correctly; he said I did. In my opinion, the evidence will show that this was not the last time Larry tried to use his connections to hijack the medical staff apparatus to try to destroy me.

CHAPTER 45

LARRY AND BARBARA

The evening of the Cathy episode Larry called me to say he wanted Barbara and me to come over to his house. We sat in his den while he accused me of making racist comments to Cathy. I told him I did no such thing. I didn't know at the time that he had spoken directly to Cathy and that he was using her lies to attack me in front of my wife. His diatribe further enhanced Barbara's impression that I was the problem. She was beside herself. Her idea that I was bipolar and not unipolar was reinforced. She wanted me to see another psychiatrist for a second opinion about my diagnosis and selected Michael Thase, a professor at WPIC (Western Psychiatric Institute and Clinic) and a nationally renowned expert on bipolar disorder. Barbara came with me for the appointment, which was in the latter half of October.

Dr. Thase interviewed me for two or three hours and concluded that I was in fact bipolar. Shortly thereafter, Alexandra increased my lithium to a full therapeutic dose. I didn't notice the increase in fatigue from the drug enough to report it to my doctors, but around that time I increased my caffeine intake to about twelve cups of coffee daily. I also began to feel like a pariah in my own home. I'm sure Barbara saw me even more as a patient and a child in the family. For my part, I was trying to hold my life together and accepted what my doctors said. I followed all their instructions and took my medicines as prescribed, as any good patient would.

I received a letter from Cathy's lawyer shortly after the episode, asking me to tell her the name of my insurance company. She included a long statement from a psychologist indicating the emotional damage I supposedly inflicted on her client. I had homeowners' insurance, with a large umbrella policy for liability, with a large insurer. By now Cathy had embellished her story, including a charge of assault and battery. I spoke with the insurance representative and explained that the allegations against me were false and that Cathy and her lawyer were committing insurance fraud. I was told my insurance did not cover criminal behavior and I wasn't covered. The practice also had a liability policy, which I needed to check out. I ended up hiring a lawyer specializing in dealing with insurance companies. Over time Cathy's lawyer wasn't satisfied and filed a lawsuit against me demanding $250,000. I offered her $5,000, which she did not accept.

My personal insurance company said they might cover me if I were being sued for negligence for not taking my medications. My lawyer notified Cathy's lawyer and suggested she amend the lawsuit to include a count of negligence. She did this, but my insurance company still refused to cover me. I knew I hadn't done anything I was being accused of, so I wasn't about to offer her more than the $5,000 to pay her off. At my request, Linda Altenbaugh wrote a letter to my lawyer on October, 11, 1997, confirming my version of events.

A couple of years later, Cathy said she saw me in an elevator at Shadyside and now claimed to have some sort of breakdown from the stress of seeing me. Her lawyer sent my lawyer documents indicating that she was admitted to WPIC for several days. I also received a copy of some of her hospital records as part of the discovery process. This included a statement from her doctor at WPIC with a description of her problems. By now the incident was about three years in the past, but she still blamed me for all her problems. The hospital records seemed to indicate that her doctors did not think this was the case. Nevertheless, I received another letter from Cathy's lawyer, increasing her demand to $350,000.

At this point I insisted we take her deposition. I deliberately did not attend because I thought she might fake something if I were there. Prior to the deposition, my attorney asked to see a copy of the accusations that was read to me during the committee meeting. Her lawyer said she couldn't find it. During the deposition, on February 16, 1998, Cathy refused to repeat her accusations. My lawyer at this point was Joel Dresbold. He said Cathy's demeanor during the deposition was bizarre and that she was just "crazy." All Cathy seemed capable of saying was that I had called the Simpson trial an "unjust" (sic), which she repeated over and over.

After the deposition, we knew Cathy didn't have a case. I told Joel to tell her lawyer that Cathy lied about me, and I delineated the damage I had suffered because of her lies. I was tempted to sue her for defamation, a course which her lawyer seemed to understand: I never heard from them again. Her lawyer never even took my deposition. An interesting postscript occurred in 2001. One of the insurance companies paid me $12,000 for agreeing to relieve them of any liability in the case. I bought a 65" wide screen Sony high definition television with part of settlement. Cathy didn't get a penny. I heard that she didn't work at Shadyside for very long after the episode. The experience taught me a lesson, and my belief that "honesty is the best policy" was reinforced. Telling the truth means you never have to make things up to defend yourself.

The episode with Cathy put even more stress on my marriage. In fact, the episode was the straw that broke the camel's back. A month or so after the episode, in November, 1995, I became completely disillusioned with my marriage. I knew I was a victim of Larry and Cathy, but Barbara didn't see it that way. It is at times of trouble that people sometimes reveal their true colors, and Barbara simply did not believe my version of events. I remember exactly where I was standing in our bedroom one morning when I thought to myself, *She doesn't love me anymore.* I think at that moment I emotionally withdrew from the marriage. I wondered what to do next. I didn't want to get divorced, but I didn't want to spend the rest of my life without love either. I thought this must be why people had affairs. I resolved to have an affair, thought of the women I knew, and tried to decide whom I liked the most.

Strange as it may sound, I chose one of the women who worked at my answering service; her name was Jennifer. I had had many brief conversations with her and found her to be very bright, articulate and engaging. As it turned out, I never did have an affair. Jennifer and I simply developed a very close telephone relationship, which only rarely became sexual. Two years later Jennifer told me that I had been a social experiment of hers. In reality, she told me, she was morbidly obese, weighing almost 400 pounds. She originally told me she was 5'4" tall and weighed 107 pounds. When she finally came clean, she told me she had been describing an acquaintance of hers named Wendy. Nevertheless, Jennifer ended up being my "transitional relationship." She was my best friend during times of terrible upheaval in my life. We both used the word "love" all the time. To this day we have never met in person. She has, however, called me on occasion to ask for a letter of recommendation or discuss her health problems.

When I told Steve Carter about Jennifer he freaked out. Jennifer told me she was only 20 years old, and Steve thought I was going to destroy my life if I formed a physical relationship with her. He immediately called Alexandra and asked her to put me on Trilafon, a powerful anti-psychotic medication used to treat serious mental illness. Steve and Alexandra had experience using it to treat patients with bipolar disorder to prevent manic episodes. One of the side effects is fatigue and drowsiness, so I was to take it at bedtime. I started on a small dose and it was increased after a brief period of time. I became a little more fatigued during the day, but I didn't want to complain because I thought my doctors and Barbara knew best. After all, she did have a doctorate in clinical psychology. My ability to get work done, however, continued to decrease. I fought through the side effects and the quality of care I delivered did not suffer, even though the quantity diminished.

Larry did not fail to use my problems against me as best he could. In response to Cathy's allegations, in January, 1996, Larry demanded that I sign an agreement that I would treat people with respect. He also used the opportunity to force the whole group to acquiesce to his demand to have 51% of the voting shares of the corporation in perpetuity. I remember sitting at my kitchen table, talking to him on the phone. "I know what you tried to do with Chandra and Tauberg," he said, meaning that he thought I was using them to try to take over the practice. I responded that I was proud of standing up for them. He continued, "If you don't sign the paper, I am going to break up the group." In addition to signing, I was also permanently barred from going to Shadyside to make rounds. The other members of the group supported me privately, but said they felt helpless to stand up to Larry because of his threat to break up the group. I knew this type of agreement was used to eventually fire someone by claiming he violated some provision of it, and I was determined not to violate any of its provisions. I never did. Later, I will present evidence to show that Larry eventually had to resort to a different subterfuge more than a year later.

CHAPTER 46

THE MARRIAGE FAILS

I tried to muddle through 1996 as best I could. I had not given up completely on my marriage and I was trying desperately to get along with Larry. Early that year Barbara suggested that we enter a third course of marriage counseling, but, as the first two had not yielded any results, I told her I saw no point in trying again. I fruitlessly hoped that Barbara would have an epiphany and we could make some progress with our sex life. I continued to turn to Jennifer for positive reinforcement in our phone conversations but had no intention of having an actual affair with anyone else. Barbara and I took the kids to Colorado to ski in March. I did not ask Barbara to have sex during the vacation; I deliberately waited for her to initiate it, because I was tired of begging and being rejected. The week went by without us getting together. When we got home I still didn't ask. As I mentioned earlier, the spouse with the lower sex drive controls the couple's sex life. I waited and waited, but more than three months went by and nothing happened. I thought that Barbara was starting to prepare herself to ask me for a divorce, since I noticed her reading books on that subject. Sure enough, on August 2, 1996, she asked me for a divorce. She sat the four of us down at the kitchen table and told the kids that we were getting a divorce and that the reason was "sex." I was startled by her candor with the children and remember the scene vividly.

Ben was unhappy, of course, but Sarah's reaction was heartbreaking. She was seven at the time, and she cried nonstop for a week. She was inconsolable. For years afterwards she blamed me for the divorce. Ben never did, and sometimes he would defend me and tell Sarah in my presence that the divorce was not just my fault. Of course, he was correct; it takes two people to screw up a marriage.

I didn't want to move out of the house. Barbara's lawyer told her she couldn't force me to leave unless I had ever physically attacked her, which I never had. In fact, I did not want to get divorced, and I constantly asked her to reconcile. I didn't want to break up the family, but I knew she was right. Every time she said she might consider reconciliation I panicked inside. In reality, I didn't want to give up the chance to find true love and sexual intimacy with a woman. I was afraid of being alone for the rest of my life. Barbara was still my best friend, even if we weren't lovers anymore.

Since the house was so big, we both stayed there. Barbara moved up to the third floor bedroom, which had its own full bathroom. I knew I wouldn't be able to afford to keep the house and finance two separate abodes, so I put the house on the market. Our real estate agent told us to ask far too much, so we got no offers. By now my income was "down to" $350,000, and somehow Barbara managed to make sure we spent every penny. I guess she felt entitled to it as compensation for having to live with me. Both kids were in the best private schools, and maintaining the house was very expensive. We were both in therapy as well as "divorce counseling." The lawyers we hired were very high-end and extremely expensive. We managed to coexist pretty cordially under the same roof. Outside the bedroom we always got along well, so not much changed.

While this was going on, my doctors kept me heavily medicated, and I was having more and more trouble staying awake at work. In September, 1996, I took Barbara's advice and changed therapists. Since she was in the therapeutic community, she knew who had the best reputation. I felt a change was a good idea and started seeing Paul Scott, MD. Paul was a few years older than me and had an appointment as a full professor of clinical psychiatry at the medical school. Paul was not an expert in medications, so I continued to see Alexandra to manage my meds. As I write this, I am still seeing Paul and, as of August, 2007, I have been with him for eleven years. He has been a life-saver for me, and I will always thank Barbara for picking him.

Once Barbara set me free, I had to start life as a single man all over again. I wanted to find companionship. I had no interest in zipless sex or the promiscuity that I had indulged in during my twenties. I began to ask my female friends at the hospital how I should go about meeting someone. I was not into bars. One evening I did go to a night spot where there was dancing, and I was approached by an attractive woman a few years younger than me. We dated for a few months but it didn't work out. I also became platonic friends with a woman named Michelle, whose brother ultimately replaced Jeff Blum as my lawyer. Michelle was very attractive but wasn't interested in me romantically. The fact that I had a severe tremor from the lithium didn't help matters any.

Around February, 1997, I had a fateful conversation with two women friends of mine at Jefferson. I had known Bonnie Andrews and her friend Joan Jenkins for more than ten years; both worked in the cardiology department at Jefferson. We had been working together doing treadmill tests and other cardiology tests for all that time and always got along very well. I had no reason to think they were not my friends. Both were married, in their forties, and I wasn't physically attracted to either of them. One day we were in the department in a room with no one else present. They had lived in Southwestern Pennsylvania their entire lives, and I thought they would be a good source of information about the social norms of the area. I knew I could expect the social mores to be quite different and much more conservative than they had been in Manhattan. As mature women, I thought they would be able to discuss the sexual mores of single people, so I began to engage them in talk about relationships. From my perspective, we just had a normal conversation. I had had similar conversations with many other women at the hospital and no one seemed to be uncomfortable discussing the issue with me. From my perspective, I was just a guy asking for advice from my friends.

At one point, Bonnie said something to indicate that Larry Adler did not treat them with the respect they deserved. I replied: "He treats you like @#$% peons." I meant this to mean I supported them. I always tried to treat the hospital personnel with respect and dignity. I knew Larry could be disrespectful at times, and I wasn't surprised to hear their complaints. When we left, I didn't give our conversation a second thought. What I didn't realize was that Bonnie had a strong bond with Larry. They had worked together since before I came to Pittsburgh in 1984. Larry had been the titular chief of cardiology at Jefferson since it opened in 1977, but he didn't play any real role in the department as far as I knew.

A week or so later I got a cryptic phone call from Larry admonishing me for being disrespectful to the nurses. He didn't say whom I had disrespected or at which hospital. I was still going to Braddock at that point, so I thought he could be referring to something there or at Jefferson. He told me, "Just get their phone number and then ask them out." I had no idea what he was talking about. No one in the hospital had mentioned anything about any complaint about my behavior, and I didn't find out until 2003 what he was talking about. I did know he was the only one who knew what he was referring to. As it turned out, I ultimately found written evidence that strongly suggested that Larry had used my conversation with Bonnie to try to destroy me.

CHAPTER 47

LARRY SUCCEEDS

I planned a vacation for March, 1997. Gerry Myers owned a house near the Beaver Creek ski resort in Colorado, and he had let me use it for a week every year since I joined the group in 1990. I obviously could not take Barbara and the kids with me, so I asked Michelle to accompany me. I hoped she might want to get involved with me. (She didn't, but we did have a good time skiing.) A week before the trip, I saw Alexandra to discuss my medication. My stamina on the slopes had been very limited the previous year, and I thought this might be due to my meds. I asked her if I could reduce the doses for my trip. She told me which meds to decrease and what dose to take. To prevent me from having an adverse reaction to the decrease in dosage, she prescribed a new medicine, Klonopin. Klonipin is in the same class of drugs as Valium and Xanax, but much more powerful. It is used in people with bipolar disease to prevent or treat manic episodes. As instructed, I started the Klonopin five days before my vacation. The amount of Klonopin in the blood builds up slowly until it reaches a peak after five days; that's why Alexandra instructed me to start it five days early. Before I changed the meds, I reviewed her instructions with Paul Scott. I wanted to make sure I was doing the right thing. Paul approved the changes. My plane was to leave for Colorado on Friday March 17 in the afternoon.

Stuart and I were both making rounds the morning of the 17th at Jefferson, and around 9 o'clock I got a call from Stuart. He had a cath to do on one of Seymour's patients scheduled for 11 o'clock. We had all taken some of Seymour's Jefferson patients into our Jefferson office after Seymour stopped coming to Jefferson a few years earlier, so I assumed this was now Stuart's office patient. He said he was bogged down on rounds and asked me if I could do the cath before I left for the airport. I was feeling a little sleepy, but I didn't think I would have any problems with a simple cath, so I agreed to help him out. He knew I would have to leave right after the procedure, so I expected him to take over the patient's care after the cath.

I didn't have any trouble doing the cath, but after a few dye injections the patient developed chest pain. The head nurse in the cath lab, Bob Werkin, was in the lab assisting. He asked me what I wanted to do about the patient's pain. I thought the pain was a dye reaction and would abate spontaneously in a few minutes. Bob asked me if I wanted to put up intravenous nitroglycerine, but I didn't want to at that time. I was so focused on what I was doing that I didn't answer him immediately. I was just going to wait a few minutes before the next dye injection to let the heart recover spontaneously. Bob became concerned when I didn't tell him to hang the nitro, so he put up the nitroglycerine on his own. The patient's pain went away promptly in any case. At that point Stuart arrived in the lab and was standing behind me. I asked him what he was doing there. He said Bob had called him to come because he didn't think I was responding promptly enough to his questions. Stuart stood there for a few minutes until I finished.

I went to do the report and Stuart stayed with the patient. I thought the patient was Stuart's, so I didn't think anything of leaving the patient with him. After I finished the report, I decided the patient needed to have an urgent angioplasty. Since we didn't have cardiac surgery at Jefferson, we could not do angioplasty there. This was a fairly routine situation, and Madhavan and I had coordinated patient care in this manner many times before. Madhavan was at Shadyside, so he and I decided to send the patient immediately to the cath lab at Shadyside by ambulance. I had taken care of all the details and felt free to leave the patient in Stuart's care. When I left to go to the airport, Stuart was with the patient in the holding area outside the cath lab. Shortly thereafter, the patient was taken to Shadyside and Madhavan did a successful angioplasty without complications. I knew I had done my job correctly and the patient was fine, so I didn't give the situation another thought.

I was going to take a cab to the airport, so I had to go home to pick up my luggage and put my car in thc garage. Earlier that week, I was driving to Braddock from Jefferson and became so drowsy that I scraped the right front fender against the guard rail on the side of the road. That Friday, a few blocks from home, I fell asleep at the wheel and bumped the car in front of me at a red light. I was going less than ten miles per hour, so the damage was minor, and I arranged with the other driver to pay for the repairs on his car. I drove home and called my car dealer and asked him to pick up my car at my house while I was away and fix it. It was no big deal. I attributed my sleepiness primarily to sleep deprivation, but I knew the Klonopin in combination with the other meds was certainly a contributing factor. The next day I decreased the Klonopin dose from twice daily to once daily. As I was on vacation, I didn't feel the need to notify Alexandra at that time and planned to discuss it with her when I got back. I was scheduled to stop the Klonopin after vacation in any case.

I was planning to relax and have a good time skiing and spending some time with Michelle, but the second day on the slopes I did something stupid. I was not a good skier and usually stuck to the beginner slopes. I had hoped to advance to the intermediate slopes that week. Michelle had told me she would be able to teach me how to do it. She was quite an athlete, as she had been on the swimming team at the University of Michigan as an undergraduate. I was anxious to advance, and considering all the trouble I was having with my personal life, I wanted to compensate a little. I went to the top of the nearest intermediate slope with Michelle there to guide me. It looked steep, but I was determined and did not exercise good judgment. I started to traverse slowly down the hill, but it wasn't long until I fell down. Falling down is a normal part of learning how to ski. Unfortunately, my binding didn't release as I rolled down the hill with my skies rotating like an airplane propeller. The end of my left ski caught on the snow while I continued to rotate. I knew before it happened that this is how the anterior cruciate ligament in the knee can rupture. A second later I heard a popping sound and felt a slight twinge in my left knee.

The ski patrol took me down the hill on a sled to a local emergency room, where I was soon diagnosed with a ruptured ligament. That was the end of my skiing for the week. I was able to walk without much pain, so I knew I would be able to go to work when I got home. Having a doctor out sick in a cardiology group can place extra stress on the whole group. I called the office to tell them what happened and reassure them I wouldn't miss any work. I was more than a little surprised when our office manager said I wasn't supposed to come back and that Dr. Adler wanted to talk to me. Larry told me I had abandoned the patient and he had serious concerns about my actions in the cath lab. I didn't know what he was talking about. I reviewed the case in my mind and prepared to explain what occurred when I got back. What I didn't find out until 2000 was significant evidence that Larry had concocted a devious plot to destroy my career and steal my practice.

CHAPTER 48

SUE (PART II)

In a previous chapter I described how a nurse name Sue hatched a scheme to retaliate against me because she was angry with me for not wanting to get involved with her. After the events with Sue in 1994, I had limited my conversations with her to discussions about the care of our mutual patients in the ICU. When Barbara and I separated in August, 1996, I thought enough time had passed for her to get over her grudge against me. Now that I was single again, I thought she might still be interested in a relationship with me. I dipped my toe in the waters by gradually expanding our topics of conversation to non-medical matters. She was very responsive, and we gradually increased the amount of time we spoke. She was definitely giving me the message that she no longer wanted to limit our conversations to business matters.

One morning I had a patient in room 19 of the ICU for whom Sue was caring. While we were in the room, she was very engaging and smiled at me repeatedly. I took this as a sign she might be willing to let bygones be bygones. When we walked out of the room, she continued her ingratiating behavior, and then sat down at the table to write her notes. The table was about four feet wide and out in the open in the ICU. I sat down across from her at the table. I just sat there for a few minutes, looking at her and thinking how beautiful she was. She obviously knew I was looking at her but continued doing her work. She gave absolutely no indication that she was uncomfortable about the situation. In fact, the small smile on her face seemed to indicate she liked the attention. I sat there for awhile, not saying a word, and then left the ICU to do other work.

When I got back to the office, she called me to ask a question about the patient. I was trying to think of something nice to say to her to break the ice. After we finished talking about the patient, I took a small risk and said to her, "When you smile at me it takes my breath away."

"You're not supposed to say things like that to me," she said angrily. I realized immediately that she had suckered me in with her flirtatiousness. I certainly didn't think I had said anything wrong or that could remotely be considered to be sexual harassment. She was just completing her plan to get me "big time," as she had told Kim Wagner more than a year earlier.

The next thing I knew, she had written a letter to the director of human resources; it was a diatribe against me that distorted everything that had actually occurred. Howard Lang was President of the Medical Staff at that time, the only person, as designated in the bylaws, allowed to be privy to Sue's letter. Howard approached me in the hospital cafeteria and told me she had complained. I tried to explain to Howard what had occurred and why, but he said he wasn't interested in any details. All he wanted me to do was for me to stay away from Sue. If Howard had thought I had done something serious, he was obliged by the bylaws to order a formal investigation. This didn't happen. I was never given a chance to give my side of the story. I went to see the director of Human Services myself to complain about what she had done and tried to give my side of the story. He showed me the handwritten letter Sue had given him and read it to me. I told him what Sue said was defamatory and untrue. I said that if this were repeated or any action taken against me, I would defend myself with a lawsuit against the hospital and Sue.

The story seemed to spread quickly to a few people around the hospital. Some of the female employees came up to me and said, "Dr. Schneider, what you said to Sue was a very nice compliment. The idea that you were harassing her is ridiculous." I let the whole thing drop, but I did take a few precautions. I spoke to Kim Wagner and asked her if she would be willing to testify about what Sue had threatened to do to me, and she said that she would. I also asked one of the senior nurses in the ICU, Sandy Harrod, if she would testify in my behalf if necessary. Sandy said she would be happy to testify that Sue was extremely flirtatious in her relations with males working in the ICU, especially doctors. Their testimony was not necessary because no one in the hospital ever brought up the issue again. I thought the allegations were dead and buried, so I didn't discuss the matter with Larry. I knew that if Larry found out about it, he would try to use it against me immediately. The fact that he never brought it up with me indicated he didn't know. The only people at the hospital who had access to my file in the medical staff office were Terry Kostrub and the President of the Medical Staff. These files were secret; the doctors were not even allowed to see their own file. I didn't find out until 2000 that Terry had probably informed her friend Larry about the contents of my file to help him get rid of me in 1997.

CHAPTER 49

THROUGH THE LOOKING GLASS

When I returned from my vacation in Colorado, Larry told me that he was considering firing me. He was to have a practice meeting without me to decide my fate. I knew Larry was violating the corporate bylaws that specified exactly how much notice to give the other partners for a corporate board meeting. The bylaws called for a two-thirds majority to fire a partner. Larry needed to get a unanimous vote from the other partners in the group to get me out because I still had 20 percent of the voting shares. At that point five people were partners: Gerry, Madhavan, Larry, Ramesh, and myself; only one other person had to support me for me to retain my job, but Larry got all the votes because he again threatened to break up the group. Legally he couldn't actually break up the group because he had the same restrictive covenant that prevented anyone from quitting the group and going into competition with the group. I could have fought the decision if I had wanted to, but I decided not to because I felt I didn't want to work with Larry anymore. I had had enough of him. I just planned to go back into solo practice. I did persuade Larry to speak to Alexandra, who told me she tried to get him to just let me take off two weeks to get my meds adjusted. She told me she thought she had won him over, but of course, he never meant anything he said to her. A few days later Larry told me I was out. Subsequently, all the other members of the group called me individually at home to tell me they didn't want this to happen but felt they had no choice because they needed their jobs. They essentially told me that Larry coerced their votes. I was still due three months' continued salary, so I felt I had plenty of time to get my individual practice up and running. I didn't know at the time that Larry was trying to use his connections to get me thrown off the hospital staff.

The story I am about to relate contains information from hundreds of documents in my medical staff file (which turned out to be not so "secret"), my medical records, and an extensive investigation I carried out starting in 2000, which included many interviews and discussions with numerous witnesses.

As I mentioned before, Larry had a longstanding friendship with Terry Kostrub, the person in charge of all administrative processes for the medical staff in the hospital. His behavior was reminiscent of how he behaved during the situation at Shadyside in 1995. Just as I thought he tried to use his relationship with a hospital official, Gail Wolf, at Shadyside, my investigation suggested that he was now using his relationship with Terry Kostrub at Jefferson. I would have assumed that any hospital investigating an incident in the cath lab would talk to the physician witnesses and then discuss the issue with me to get my side of the story. During my investigation both Madhavan and Tauberg told me that no one at Jefferson had ever spoken to them about what had occurred. Madhavan told me that Adler had "taken care of all that." So I know that the only person from the group with whom anyone at the hospital spoke was Larry. At Shadyside, I was in town and Larry was out of town when I wrote to the hospital that they had no right to talk to Larry under the bylaws of the hospital. They knew that I was correct and excluded Larry from any further participation in the process. I knew the bylaws at Jefferson also required strict confidentiality about all the medical staff disciplinary processes. Since Larry was not a witness to the events, the hospital was prohibited from talking with him.

I surmised that Larry's first course of action was to get the dirt on me from the cath lab and then use that against me with the group. Bob Werkin, the head nurse in the Jefferson cath lab, was asked to write a letter about the March 17th cath lab incident. Bob told me he was told to address the letter to Dr. Adler and that's what he did. The only letter I subsequently discovered was sent to Terry Riffer, the administrator of the cath lab, suggesting they had falsified Bob's actual letter to Adler in order to hide the fact that Werkin had violated the bylaws by sending the letter to Adler. (It was Terry who had tried to persuade me to be the director of the Jefferson cath lab in 1994). Bob's letter to Terry was dated April 2, 1997, more than two weeks after the event, which occurred on March 17. By the time he wrote the letter, I'm sure his memory of the event was less accurate than if he had written the letter spontaneously and in a more timely fashion, so it made sense to assume that his letter had been solicited. Bob described his version of events, but he was mistaken in saying that Dr. Tauberg sent the patient to Shadyside for an angioplasty. Madhavan later confirmed to me that I was the one who sent the patient to him at Shadyside. I also disagreed with some other aspects of Bob's account of events. Nevertheless, I was never asked for my version of events. Bob indicated in his letter that he had spoken to Adler and Madhavan. (The bylaws' mandate for confidentiality was violated by his talking to Adler.) Because Tauberg and Madhavan told me that no one in the hospital administration or the Medical Staff leadership spoke to either of them, and because I was never asked for my version of events, it proved to me, *a priori*, that the hospital was not acting in good faith as required by the Peer Review law. This pattern of not dealing in good faith persisted even as I was forced to resign from the Medical Staff in 2001.

Larry must have known that the incident in the cath lab was not enough to get me removed from the staff. He knew about the "Cathy event" at Shadyside; he also knew of my conversation with Bonnie, as Bonnie, years later, told me she had complained to Adler about it. No one in the hospital staff administration or Medical Staff leadership knew about Bonnie's complaints. If they had, they would have been required to talk to me about it. By conspiring with Terry Kostrub, Larry would have been able to give his version of those events to her without my knowledge.

On April 7, 1997 Bonnie and Joan were interviewed by an unknown person. I reviewed the written statement of their interview and the typed notes in my file. Bonnie signed the statement, but Joan Jenkins did not. Bonnie did not say when the event occurred and most of what she said wasn't true. I guess they didn't want to indicate that the event she was discussing occurred weeks or months prior to her interview. Her statement was obviously solicited, which would have been even more obvious had they indicated the actual date of the incident in her statement, which they did not. Most people would probably agree with me that a statement solicited by an employer from an employee is subject to pressure to say what the employer wants to hear. Larry and Terry must have felt they needed to generate another fallacious written complaint about me to justify having the hospital take action against me.

As the administrator in charge of Medical Staff Services, Terry Kostrub would have been the one to arrange for a meeting of the Physician's Health Committee. A meeting of this committee occurred on April 10, 1997, only three days after Bonnie gave her "statement." Present at the meeting at 7:30 that morning were: Arnold E. Fingeret, MD, President of the Medical Staff, Howard N. Lang, MD, the president's appointee, Stephen T. Patternac, MD, substituting for the medical director of the Chemical Abuse Services, Guillermo Borrero, MD, Chief of Psychiatry, William R. Jennings, CEO, Terry S. Kostrub, Vice President, Medical Staff Affairs, and Frederick A. Boehm, Esquire, the hospital's legal counsel.

At that meeting they discussed several issues concerning me. Fingeret said he had spoken to George Arnold about the Shadyside incident. In the letter from Stanley Milavec, the Shadyside lawyer, to me, dated October 11, 1995, he wrote: "All information provided...shall be kept strictly confidential and shall only be used for properly authorized purposes pursuant to the Medical Staff Bylaws." This meant that, without a court order, Shadyside could not release any information about me, even to another hospital, without my prior written consent. I had known George Arnold for more than a decade and he is a fine, honest person, so I doubt he gave Fingeret much information. Because no one on the committee could have known about the Shadyside episode, I concluded that the original source of this information to the committee had to have been Adler, probably relayed through Kostrub.

The committee addressed the "Report of sexual harassment which took place in the Jefferson ICU." This was despite the fact that Sue had lied and I had never had a chance to give my side of the story or defend myself in any way. They also used reports of my minor car accidents, despite the fact that they had no way of knowing what had occurred because they never asked me and they had no witnesses. (I had, however, mentioned my "fender benders" to Larry.) Fingeret told the committee that he had "Information relayed to him that Dr. Schneider has been diagnosed as bi-polar and has been seeing two psychiatrists, one for discussions and the other one for medication." (I'm sure that Larry was the only one at the hospital who could have known this information at that time.) Fingeret also relayed to the committee that "Dr. Schneider has in the recent past experienced a divorce proceeding with attendant psychological consequences." Fingeret "also mentioned that he has learned that Dr. Schneider has been terminated from his cardiology practice with the Adler group." Fingeret then "appointed himself and Dr. Patternac to serve as members of an intervention team." This team was to contact me "so that (1) assistance could be offered him, and (2) any action deemed necessary could be taken to protect the health and safety of the Hospital (sic) patients."

Terry Kostrub called me later that day to tell me that Dr. Fingeret wanted to meet with me the next morning, April 11, 1997. I thought he wanted to talk to me about the cath lab incident. The bylaws of the Medical Staff mandated that, when an intervention team meets with a doctor to suggest a "medical leave of absence," all the reasons for this leave have to be explained to the doctor and that the doctor has to agree there is a problem. At my meeting with Fingeret and Paternac, I was asked to take a medical leave of absence because of the cath lab incident. I was never asked what had happened. At no time did they mention anything about sexual harassment or the Shadyside incident. This was confirmed in the minutes of the meeting. The minutes also confirmed that Fingeret threatened to immediately suspend me and report me to the National Practitioner Data Bank if I did not agree to take a medical leave. I didn't know at the time that this form of coercion was being used routinely to avoid giving doctors due process and a chance to defend themselves against false accusations. I knew the medicines I was taking for my illness were causing me a lot of problems. I felt that Alexandra had not been treating me wisely and I welcomed the opportunity to get a second opinion. Since I knew the problems were with my meds, I thought I'd be off work for a few weeks at most. I told them that I needed to get back to work as soon as possible because I had to set up my own practice again, and I didn't want to be away from my patients for any extended period of time. I was surprised when Fingeret said that he felt sorry that he "had to do this" because he said he felt that I was one of the best doctors he knew, and that he had seen some people get back to work after a medical leave in "four or five months."

As part of my leave I was referred to the Physician's Health Program (PHP) of the Pennsylvania Medical Society. The director of this organization was Dr. Thomas Hobbs, who later told me personally that he was an alcoholic in recovery. What I didn't know was that the unsubstantiated allegations of sexual harassment were being reported as fact to the PHP or their associated organizations by Adler and Kostrub (and possibly Fingeret) and that they fabricated other very serious allegations in their desire to get me out of the hospital. Interestingly, Arnold (Buzz) Fingeret told me at lunch one day in 1999 that the sexual allegations against me were "bullshit." I guess that's why he didn't mention them to me at our meeting, despite a contractual requirement (the bylaws) to do so.

CHAPTER 50

THE WILLIAM J. FARLEY CENTER

The Director of the Physicians Health Program (PHP), Dr. Hobbs, wanted me to go to the Farley Center in Williamsburg, Virginia. The medical directors of the Farley Center were Dr. Eric Hedberg and Dr. Penelope Zeigler. Dr. Hedberg was an internist with and interest in addiction medicine who told me he had once lost his medical license because of his problems. Dr. Zeigler was a psychiatrist who had preceded Tom Hobbs as medical director of the Pennsylvania PHP. I had been referred to her in 1995 about the Shadyside incident. We had spoken briefly at that time, and she told me she was satisfied that I was under treatment with Steve and Alexandra.

I drove to Williamsburg for a four-day evaluation to begin on April 22, 1997. I thought I was going there to get some help adjusting my medication. As a physician, I thought all physicians placed the welfare of their patients first, so I was very open about my medical history. As usual I related the truth as I understood it. What I didn't know at the time was that many of these so-called "therapeutic institutions" were more concerned with maintaining their business than with helping their patients. I had gone "through the looking glass" into a world where as Alice, the Lewis Carroll character, said: "Everything that is, isn't, and everything that isn't, is." I was no longer a patient; rather I had become a commodity that was to be used to bring in fees. The last thing these institutions would do was contradict a referring institution, because then they might risk losing referrals from that source. I was a victim of this unethical behavior at four separate institutions over the next four years.

To use another literary allusion, I felt that I had been thrust into a surrealistic world created by the German writer Franz Kafka. In his novel *The Trial*, the main character is forced to stand trial for the same "crime" ad infinitum, without ever understanding just what he is being accused of. In my case, the Farley Center had been informed that multiple accusations of sexual harassment had been made against me. They never told me this. I only knew, at the time, about what Sue had done, and this episode was never mentioned to me in the entire week in Williamsburg. Not only was I not told of what I had been accused of doing, no attempt was made to find out if any of he information Farley was given was true or not. The result, as in Kafka's novel, was the same: a horrifying, mentally crushing experience that appeared to have no end.

To explain the thought processes of the people responsible for my ordeal, I'd like to use an example from my own specialty, cardiology. In September or October of 2004, I attended a conference at the Cardiology Division of the University of Pittsburgh School of Medicine. A case was presented of a woman in her sixties who had had coronary bypass surgery a few years previously. Now her private physician had discovered a small to moderate leak of her mitral valve, the valve between her left atrium and left ventricle, on physical exam and echocardiography, and referred her to an invasive cardiologist at the medical school for cardiac catheterization. The patient was not having any chest pain that would suggest one of her bypass grafts might be closing off. In addition, she had not had a treadmill test to determine if she had a new blockage. So, I thought she didn't need to have pictures taken of her coronary arteries or bypass grafts. She had no signs or symptoms of new or worsening congestive heart failure that suggested she needed to have her mitral valve surgically repaired. The decision for valve surgery of this type is dependent upon clinical and non-invasive evaluation. Cardiac cath is usually performed prior to surgery to rule out any other unsuspected problems that might need to be addressed during the surgery.

During her catheterization, the patient had a stroke, and the case was presented to the cardiology fellows to discuss why this complication had occurred and how to avoid such complications in the future. During the discussion of the case, I asked why this catheterization had been done in the first place. I told the fellows that the decision for valve surgery needed to be made prior to catheterization. I didn't realize that the professor who had done the cath was sitting next to me. He immediately said he had done the cath and that the patient definitely did not need her valve replaced and had not been referred to him for that. I pointed out that, had the cath not been done, she would not have had the stroke. This was why I would never do a cath unless it was really needed. He became excited and exclaimed, "If I didn't do the cath, I would never get another referral from her doctor." I replied that, if a patient were referred to me by any of my referring physicians for a cath that wasn't necessary, I would speak to them about it and explain why it wasn't needed. Of course, I had done this on numerous occasions. He was not happy with me, and I apologized to him for my bluntness. The conference continued. About 15 minutes later, he said to me: "You're right. In retrospect, I cannot justify doing this catheterization." We chatted for awhile after the conference, and I explained to him that I understood his difficulties.

This professor was a full-time salaried employee of the medical school and hospital. I knew these doctors were under a lot of pressure from their employer to generate business for the institution and their compensation depended in part on their "productivity." He needed to maintain his volume of cases to keep his job and support his family. The pressure on these guys was enormous. I knew this from first-hand experience, but I also knew these pressures had shifted his primary responsibility from the patient to the institution for which he worked.

This type of behavior is what I experienced as a patient at the institutions I was involved with between 1997 and 2001.

I underwent the four-day evaluation at the Farley Center. This included a physical exam done by a nurse, a chemical dependency evaluation by Dr. Hedberg, a psychological evaluation by Terry Tierney, a psychologist, a psychiatric evaluation by Penny Ziegler, and an evaluation done by Deanna Mears Pandya, a family therapist without a doctorate or an MD. My intake interview was witnessed by at least ten people. I guess I was an unusual case that would be a teaching experience for multiple staff members. I didn't think I had anything to hide so I didn't mind. I spoke with Hedberg on April 22 and told him I didn't use drugs. I told him that, until 1989, I had occasionally used Xanax to help me get to sleep. I told him I still had a small bottle of Xanax in my medicine cabinet, which was virtually untouched since 1989. I met with Penny Ziegler on one occasion the afternoon of April 22. I believe I met with Pandya on the 24th. I was tested for psychological problems on April 23rd and 24th by Dr. Tierney. At the time these evaluations were performed, I was taking therapeutic doses of lithium, Depakote, Trilafon, and imipramine.

No one during the week ever mentioned to me that I was being evaluated for my sexual behavior. In fact, in my discussion with Pandya, I had brought up the issue of my marriage and the difficulties that Barbara and I had. I told her my thoughts about the role of fantasy in intimate sexual relationships. I thought she was supposed to be an expert and told her I wanted to take the opportunity to add to the knowledge I had acquired over the previous seven years from my therapy, marriage counseling, and readings. During this relatively brief meeting, she decided she had enough information about me to make the diagnosis of "sexual addiction." She said I needed to be hospitalized as soon as possible at the Menninger Clinic for treatment of my addiction. I didn't understand why she had reached this conclusion and she didn't tell me, nor did she ask me if any of the information she received about me was true or not. I know enough about medical malpractice to know that she was negligent and did not do her job properly. I think she did this because her primary responsibility was to her employer and not to me.

Hedberg and Ziegler also exhibited this negligent behavior. Dr. Tierney did do his job to the extent that he reported my testing "did not indicate the presence of a major affective disorder at this time," and "did not suggest the presence of a thought disorder." My discharge summary said my evaluation included information from "collateral sources," which included only those people for whom I had signed consent forms. These allowed the Farley Center to speak with the following people only: Barbara, Dr. Kreps, Dr. Scott, Buzz Fingeret, Terry Kostrub, Tauberg, and Adler.

The records from the Farley Center indicated the following: Barbara refused to talk to them except to say that I had a strong sex drive and that was one of the reasons for the divorce. Tauberg was asked about the cath lab incident and is reported to have said that he had never seen me like that before. Stuart later told me that I had done nothing wrong in the cath lab and that the only unusual thing about me in the cath lab was that I was moving slowly. Dr. Kreps confirmed my medications. The Farley Center listed Dr. Scott as a source of collateral information, even though Paul has a strict policy of not discussing his patients verbally. Dr. Scott always insists on only given written replies to questions and always has provided me with copies of any written replies. So, I think Hedberg and Ziegler may have deliberately lied about talking to Dr. Scott. The only other people who gave them information were Kostrub, Adler, and Fingeret. Kostrub and Fingeret were named in my legal complaint in 2004. On April 25 I had a "wrap-up session" with the staff at Farley, during which I received some big surprises, not unlike a character in a Kafka novel.

CHAPTER 51

"MY DIAGNOSES"

In his subsequent letter to Dr. Hobbs at the PHP, Hedberg wrote: "There have been multiple complaints concerning his inappropriate and bizarre behaviors. Dr. Schneider has some difficulty perceiving reality in the same light that others around him perceive reality. For this reason, we came to the conclusion of 'Schizo-affective Disorder, secondary to some of his delusional beliefs.'" Dr. Hedberg never told me what those "delusional beliefs" were, nor asked me if the events related to him were true. Had he done his job and received information from my treating psychiatrist, Dr. Scott, he would have known I was not delusional in any way. Instead he and Dr. Ziegler were motivated by the desire to please their referral source, Dr. Hobbs. Dr. Hedberg took it upon himself to make the following additional diagnoses, all of which were found to be completely erroneous by other doctors over the next six months: sexual compulsivity, personality disorder, possible Xanax dependence, and cognitive disorder. Just as Dr. Money would ask me if I "found good pathology" in his patients, Dr. Hedberg seemed to want to find as much pathology in me as possible to please his referring doctor. The fact that Dr. Ziegler had recently been the director of the PHP probably also fed into this desire.

I was apprised of their diagnoses at the wrap-up session. Dr. Hedberg told me I was out of touch with reality and that, because of this, I was not just bipolar, I was also schizo-affective. He told me I would never be able to practice medicine again. I expressed my amazement, to which he replied: "What are you complaining about? I lost my medical license." I asked him if they would help me get my disability insurance.

He replied affirmatively and that was it. I was off to the Menninger Clinic in Topeka Kansas.

My discharge summary from the Farley Center had the following disclaimer: “Additional information not disclosed to us by the patient or provided by collateral sources could significantly alter the assessment results, and the team reserves the right to amend its opinions and conclusions in such situations. Natural limitations in the assessment process and our state of knowledge are acknowledged....” Of course, Dr. Hedberg did not mention this disclaimer in his letter to Tom Hobbs. The letter was written as if it were true. Hedberg was not even a psychiatrist; he was a self-described miscreant who told me he had temporarily lost his medical license. I think this letter and its erroneous allegations demonstrated a reckless disregard for the truth and clearly violated civil laws against defamation and therefore represented malpractice. I did not know this for sure until I got a copy of my discharge summary in October, 1997.

My discharge summary included the following statement: “Dr. Schneider has demonstrated compulsive behaviors, including a longstanding history of sexual harassment of female staff. His sexual behavior has been inappropriate with his staff, colleagues and patients. Multiple complaints have been made against him by females at the office and the hospital.” I knew this was a lie designed to get me out of the practice of medicine. Only three people could have told them this confabulation: Fingeret, Adler, and Kostrub. Fingeret most likely did not say this because he thought the allegations were “bullshit,” and as a general surgeon he had no reason to want to get rid of me. While we weren’t friends, we had always been on cordial terms and moved in different professional circles. That left only Adler and Kostrub. Adler clearly had a desire to get rid of me, and I felt that he was a documented liar. I knew Kostrub ran the show at Jefferson and that she and Adler were very close. I also knew for certain that she had lied to Bill Jennings, the hospital CEO, about her instructing me to report the female doctor to the PHP, when I was Chief of Medicine. So, I figured she had instructed Fingeret to report me to the PHP in the same offhand manner. Since Adler was the only person at Jefferson who knew much about the Shadyside event (he had spoken to Cathy himself) and the conversation with Bonnie Andrews, Kostrub could only have gotten the information from him.

I didn't get enough information to complain about what they had done until early 2000, when I completed the first phase of my investigation. I was invited to speak at the Jefferson Hospital Physician's Health Committee meeting on March 10, 2000 by Dr. Richard Collins, then President of the Medical Staff. I spoke for about 45 minutes about how Larry and Terry had conspired against me. Dr. Collins complimented me at the end of the meeting, saying, "Very eloquent, as usual."

The CEO, Bill Jennings, was also at the meeting. When I finished, he said emphatically in a stern tone of voice, "The hospital does not take sides in disputes between doctors." I guess he meant not unless one of the doctors was a friend of Terry Kostrub. As far as I know, nothing was done about my situation. Since Bill had been at the April 10, 1997 meeting and knew what occurred, I guess he might have been covering up for himself as well.

I drove back to Pittsburgh from Virginia thinking I would possibly not practice medicine again. I sent off the applications for my disability benefits and made arrangements to go to the Menninger Clinic. In total, I would be out of work for six months. Larry's group was caring for my patients in my absence. While I was off work, in July, 1997, Jim Brooks called me and said some of my patients had received a letter from Adler asking them to permanently switch their care from me to their group. One of my patients subsequently showed me his copy of the letter sent to him. The hospital had acted to remove me from practice without giving a second thought to the welfare of my patients. Tauberg told me that many of my patients were very angry with me for going off without notifying them. Since I didn't have access to my office records because Larry had banned me from the office and I didn't know if I would be able to return to practice, I couldn't write to my patients to explain my circumstances. Because of this I lost about two thirds of my practice.

I am convinced by the written evidence that at least one of my patients died because of what Larry did to me and to her. Mr. and Mrs. B. had been my patients for many years. During my absence, Mrs. B. told me she had switched her care to Larry while Mr. B. stayed with me. I returned to practice in September, 1997. A few months later, in December, I saw Mrs. B. in the ICU at Jefferson, said hello and asked who her new doctor was. She replied, "Dr. Adler." I said she was in good hands and wished her luck. A couple of months later, Mr. B. came to my office in abject despair. He told me his wife had had bypass surgery at Shadyside in December, 1997. About a month after she was discharged, she was admitted to Jefferson, where she died. He was practically crying when he asked me to find out what had happened to her because her surgery had been a success. He said his life was over because his wife had died. He was my patient and I had no right to deny his request, so I told him to sign a release to allow me to review her hospital records.

I reviewed his wife's medical records and was appalled to find out what had happened to her. During her hospitalization at Shadyside, she had developed atrial fibrillation post operatively. Atrial fibrillation is a disorganized, irregular heart rhythm, which is not serious in and of itself in most instances. I had my own cocktail of medications that I would use immediately in these circumstances that would almost always terminate this arrhythmia within 24 hours. Then I would put the patient on oral medications to prevent a recurrence. In the rare event that a patient stayed in atrial fibrillation, blood thinners would have to be prescribed to prevent blood clots from forming in the left atrium. A blood clot in the left atrium could break off and travel to the brain, causing a stroke.

Mrs. B. had been discharged from Shadyside on coumadin, an oral blood thinner. Coumadin is used as rat poison because rats will bleed to death if they eat it. In patients, the drug must be used very carefully, and frequent blood tests must be done to make sure the patient's blood does not become too thick or too thin. Too thin, and the patient could bleed; too thick, and she could have a stroke. As I mentioned before, I was trained to be very meticulous regulating a patient's coumadin dose. I believe, because of this, to the best of my knowledge, none of my anticoagulated patients had ever had a major blood clot or serious bleeding.

Before I continue with Mrs. B.'s story, I want to relate a phone call I received in 2002 from a Mrs. P. about how Larry's group was managing her coumadin therapy. Mrs. P. was an 86-year-old, mentally alert patient with chronic atrial fibrillation. After I retired, Larry's group assumed her care. She had my cell phone number, as did most of my patients, and called me one day, panic stricken. I would always call my patients within 24 hours of their blood thickness test (INR, or international normalized ratio) to give them the result and tell them what dose to take and when to get their next blood test. Mrs. P. told me she had had her blood test ten days ago. She had called Larry's office every day but no one had called her back, and she was afraid of getting a stroke or bleeding to death. I told her how to get her results and new orders, then called Larry's office to tell them of Mrs. P.'s situation. I don't know if she had any further problems.

What I found in Mrs. B's records was that she had been sent home from Shadyside on coumadin for her atrial fibrillation. She came back to Jefferson with a massive bleed into her brain (subarachnoid hemorrhage), which is almost always fatal. The INR (international normalized ratio) in a normal person on no anticoagulation is 1.0. This increases when the patient is put on coumadin. Patients with atrial fibrillation should have their coumadin dose adjusted to keep the INR no higher than between 2.0 and 3.0. For patients with artificial heart valves, the INR should be maintained between 3.0 and 4.0. When the INR goes above the proper range, the dose of coumadin must be decreased. What I found was that, when Mrs. B. was admitted to Jefferson with bleeding into her brain, her INR was 15.0! (I think this is the highest INR I have ever seen.) At the time, I was convinced that the reason she bled was grossly negligent care of her coumadin dose.

I knew I couldn't tell Mr. B. what had happened to his wife because he would sue Larry for malpractice. No doctor would risk a malpractice suit, even for someone who had behaved as cruelly as Larry had behaved toward me. I knew the only proper way to handle the situation was to notify Larry and Stuart about what was going on and ask them to call Mr. B. and arrange a meeting with them to explain what had happened. Shortly after that meeting, Mr. B. came to my office and told me that the meeting with Larry and Stuart had lasted about 15 minutes. He said that when he left the meeting he had no more idea about what had happened to his wife than he had before the meeting. He reiterated that his life had been completely ruined by his wife's death. He said he was so disgusted with Jefferson Hospital that he could no longer get his medical care there and would be going elsewhere in the future.

I was deeply saddened for Mr. B. and extremely embarrassed for the medical profession for what had occurred. I knew I couldn't tell him myself why his wife had died. I told him I understood and gave him as much moral support as I could under the circumstances. No one will ever persuade me that, had I not been forced out of my practice for six months by Larry's and Terry's lies about me, Mrs. B. would not have died and Mr. B's life would not have been ruined. This is just one example of why I strongly believe that medical care in this country must reestablish the doctor/patient relationship as primary and sacrosanct. I believe most of the problems with poor-quality care in this country are due to a breakdown in this relationship. (I will describe my solution to this fundamental problem in later chapters).

CHAPTER 52

THE MENNINGER CLINIC

The Menninger Clinic was founded in the early part of the last century by C.F. Menninger as a facility to treat mental illness. The clinic was located on a large campus in Topeka, Kansas and had multiple buildings. In 2003, the place went out of business and moved its facility to Houston, Texas, reportedly as a result of a malpractice suit. I was referred primarily to Dr. Richard Irons, an internist with a special interest in sexual addiction. Dr. Irons was a self-described sex addict. My experience with these addiction doctors seemed to indicate that many of them, including Hobbs and Hedberg, entered the business of treating other doctors who had the same problems they had. Unfortunately, they also seemed to project their problems onto their patients, whether or not the patient had the problem. This phenomenon is referred to as "counter transference," or in simpler terms, "If you're a hammer, everything looks like a nail."

I arrived in Topeka on May 2, 1997 and entered what was called the "Professionals in Crisis" program. I lived in a double room with a roommate by the name of Bob, a Texan who was being treated for an inability to sleep. My program of treatment included care from a medication psychiatrist, a sex counselor, and a clinical psychologist, although I don't remember the exact chronology of these different treatments. Dr. Irons began me on a 12-step program for treatment of my "sexual addiction." At this point I think it's important to tell the reader that most of the clinical psychiatrists with whom I have discussed this condition do not believe it exists. In particular, Dr. Borrero, the Chief of Psychiatry at Jefferson Hospital, told me he thought the idea of sexual addiction was ridiculous. Nevertheless, I was sent by Jefferson to be treated for a disease which was not recognized as a disease by their own chief psychiatrist.

My treatment included daily morning meetings with about 15 other patients, none of whom were sex addicts. As part of the 12-step program, I had to accept the "fact" that my life had been controlled by my "addiction," and that I had to accept a "Higher Power." I had to get up in front of the group every day and declare: "My name is Richard and I am a sex addict." After a while I came to believe it. I met with Ron Cobb, the sex counselor, to discuss my sexuality. I went to classes in which I participated in learning how to put a condom on a banana. I went to the Chapel, as they suggested, asking God to help me with my "problem."

The first thing Dr. Irons did was to abruptly discontinue my imipramine, which I had been on for the past eight years. (The psychiatrist was out of town). I had once gone through imipramine withdrawal inadvertently, when the generic brand was changed in 1990, and I knew quite well that the dosage had to be decreased very slowly to avoid the severe flu-like symptoms caused by abrupt discontinuation. I pleaded with Dr. Irons not to do it and explained to him why. Although he resisted, he finally got the message, but I thought that he had no business fooling around with medicines about which he seemed to know very little.

I saw the psychologist and told him I had my own therapist, Dr. Scott, in Pittsburgh. I told him I couldn't understand how he could possibly understand me in only a few sessions. He agreed, and I didn't see him again. I couldn't think of any reason he would want to treat me under these circumstances except for wanting to collect his fee from my insurance company. Richard Irons told me, shortly after I arrived, that he would only keep me as an inpatient for three weeks because I only had insurance for 30 days and he didn't want to use it all up. So, for my fourth week, I had to stay at a hotel across the street and be treated as an outpatient.

As part of my "treatment" I had to watch video of twelve hours of lectures by Patrick Carnes, Ph.D., a guru of sexual addiction. I thought he made some good points and the cases he spoke of did seem to support the contention that some people might truly be addicted to sex. His lectures also made it quite clear that I was definitely *not* a sex addict. Despite this, Dr. Irons tried his best to pin this diagnosis on me to justify my hospitalization to my health insurance company. I think that he was also trying to protect his referral sources, Dr. Hobbs and Dr. Hedberg.

I tried to talk sense to him, but he was quite resistant; he didn't want to face reality because that would be inconvenient. I kept asking him why he thought I was a sex addict even though I had not had sex with anyone but Barbara since 1981, but he was not impressed. He acted as if he had to confirm his diagnosis to show that he actually had a patient who needed his care. I didn't meet anyone else in the month I was there who had that diagnosis, and I knew I hadn't done anything wrong. At one point, I asked him to call Terry Kostrub to vouch for me. At the time, I was still under the impression that she liked me and thought she would tell the truth, that I was one of the good doctors at Jefferson and they would want me to return to practice. After Richard Irons spoke to Terry, he told me, "They don't want you back." I thought there must be some mistake.

I kept telling him I had to get back to work as soon as possible in order to save my practice. He didn't think I could ever go back to practicing because, as he said, "You wouldn't be able to handle the stress of making a payroll." When I insisted on going back to work he said, "I can't let you go back too soon because it wouldn't look good." To whom, I wondered. It was obvious to me that his first responsibility was not to me as his patient; rather it was to protect his referral sources from the embarrassment of a false referral.

When it came time for me to go home, we had a final conference. I saw no reason why I couldn't go back to work right away, but he said that I would have to wait until August 1st. I asked him one more time, "What did I do wrong?"

"I don't know. What did you do wrong?" he asked. I replied that maybe I flirted with some of the women at the hospital. "Well then, don't flirt," was his advice. When I asked how he could still maintain the diagnosis of sexual addiction, he said, "Okay, let's see if you can do this. Don't have any sexual contacts or masturbate for 90 days." I guess this was his gold standard for the diagnosis. *This is ridiculous*, I thought.

I had to go back to Topeka at the end of July before he would let me go back to work. Back in Pittsburgh, I engaged in no sexual activity for

73 consecutive days, including my time in Topeka, and then got bored with it. He did finally accept this as adequate evidence that I was not a sex addict and recanted his diagnosis.

Dr. Irons dictated my discharge summary. In it he repeated the lie that "the patient had a longstanding history of sexual harassment of female staff, including inappropriate behavior with staff, colleagues, and patients. There were multiple complaints at the hospital and office alleged." He tried to cover for the incompetence of the Farley Center by writing: "We understand and appreciate why the assessment team at Farley Center came to the conclusion that the patient could have a schizoaffective disorder, and we certainly considered this a very reasonable and logical prospect. Yet, with our clinical experience, we came to the conclusion that we should focus on the patient's signs and symptoms as most consistent with a bipolar affective disorder." Irons also indicated that I did not have a personality disorder, a cognitive disorder, or a Xanax addiction. He did say I had some problem with impulse control, but this was later discounted by my other doctors.

In summary, the only diagnosis that was confirmed was bipolar disorder. The end result was to continue to see Dr. Scott and adjust my medications, which was exactly what Drs. Scott and Kreps had said originally. It seemed to me that, by lying about me, Larry had managed to keep me out of the hospital for six months and give himself the opportunity to steal as many patients of mine as he could. The other members of the group later confirmed to me that Larry had told them that they could pay me off and recoup the money by taking over the care of my patients. I guess Larry and Terry thought they could do what they did, that I would never find out, and they would get off scot free. I subsequently became increasingly determined to reveal the truth and fight for my honor.

CHAPTER 53

THE RETURN TO PITTSBURGH

While I was in Kansas I was in almost daily contact with Barbara and Michelle Dresbold, the friend who accompanied me to Colorado; they both offered moral support. I also continued to try to sell our house. The first thing I had to do was find an apartment for myself and help Barbara do the same for her and the kids. Barbara found a nice three-bedroom place, and I moved into a small two-bedroom in a complex populated mostly by college students.

I had to sign an agreement with the PHP that included two SLAA (sex addicts anonymous) meetings a week. Despite the fact that no diagnosis of drug abuse had been made, I had to have random urine samples twice a week. I was not allowed to drink beer or wine. I was even told I couldn't drink non-alcoholic beer. Hobbs said alcohol would affect my mood, even though there was no evidence of this. Irons said I should get the urine tests so that if someone was "out to get you, you will be able to defend yourself." Once I had proven to Irons that I was not a sex addict, I was allowed to have sex again.

I started to go to temple on Friday evenings because of the religious emphasis of my stay in Kansas. My main concern was getting back to work. Richard Irons was late with his discharge summary, and I needed it to get Hobbs to advocate for my return to work. I even had to page Irons and plead with him to provide the summary. I told him I had to get back to work, and he finally acquiesced. I still needed to get reappointed to the Blue Cross/Blue Shield program, which required first that I return from my medical leave of absence from Jefferson. I asked Lee McCormick if he could help me, and, on his advice, I called the medical director of BC/BS. His main concern was that I was a low-cost provider. After they confirmed this, I was put back on the panel by mid August.

Larry met with me in June at his house and asked me what I wanted, adding that he was prepared to give me $50,000. I told him I wanted his group to cover for me so I could get some time off. He responded that he would never agree to help me get back to work by offering to cover for me. I assumed that he didn't want to upset his plan to steal my practice; he wanted me out of town. Other members of the group told me that he had informed the group that I would not be coming back. I'm sure Terry had promised him I would not come back after she arranged for Fingeret to put me on leave. As you may recall, he had said to me that he had seen some doctors come back after four or five months. Larry probably thought he had sealed my fate by arranging to fire me and force me to go on leave at the same time, but he underestimated me in the same way Dr. Money had done in 1985. I knew I was just as tough as they were. The only difference was that I was honest and played by the rules, while they had to lie and cheat to win. I was at a disadvantage, but I stuck to my guns and wouldn't give up.

Larry and I didn't reach an agreement. He told me he didn't want to have lawyers involved in our negotiations. Jeff was still representing me at that time, and I told him that I thought I would be covered by the Americans with Disabilities Act (ADA) because of my recognized disability of Bipolar Disorder. I wanted him to threaten a lawsuit against Larry under this statute, but he was opposed to this. I thought this was another example of his incompetence, so I fought hard for a lawsuit for more than a month. Jeff finally relented and sent me to see Sam Cordes, a lawyer specializing in employment law, whom I met with for an hour. He said I had a case under the ADA, but that he wouldn't take the case on contingency because of the complicating factor of the accusations of sexual harassment. I told him there was only one allegation (Sue) and it was false, but he did not relent. (I didn't learn of Bonnie's statement until 2003.) Nevertheless, Jeff thought he could bluff Larry by saying he had sent me to a specialist and was told I had a case. I told Larry that I wanted Jeff to handle my end of the negotiations, and at that point, he had no choice but to accept.

We met at the beginning of August in Jeff's office. Larry's lawyer was Mark Stadler. Mark had been an associate of Paul Titus, the head of a medium-sized law firm, who had been Larry's lawyer for many years. I had gotten to know Paul pretty well during our collaboration on Seymour's agreement with Larry. I had told Paul that Larry had hurt me severely and deliberately during the Shadyside affair. I assumed that he liked me and didn't want to be involved in Larry's attempt to screw me. I thought Mark Stadler would identify with me because he was young and a junior lawyer. We negotiated for a few hours, and I stayed in Jeff's office while he carried on the negotiations in another room with Larry and Mark. I can't reveal the final agreement, but it is public knowledge that Larry's group did subsequently cover for me one weekend per month.

Once these legal matters were out of the way I was able to go to work setting up my office. I had everything ready to go and was open for business by mid September. But Larry was still up to his old tricks. I was to get the charts on my patients from Larry's office on the Monday my office was to open. The previous Thursday I was notified that Jeff had not written up the agreement we had reached six weeks previously. I had to have those charts on time. Larry said he wouldn't give them to me because the agreement wasn't signed. He was incorrigible.

I called Jeff that Thursday morning but he wasn't in, so I left a message for him to call me back. By 1:30 he had still not called me and was not back in his office. This was the second time that Jeff's lack of responsibility had put me at risk. I decided the only way I was going to get those charts was to take matters into my own hands, so I called Mark Stadler and told him I wanted those charts on Monday or else. He then called Larry. He called me back right away and told me that Larry was worried that I would get the charts and then sue him immediately because he didn't have a signed agreement. Mark told me he told Larry that that was extremely unlikely.

The upshot was, I got the charts. Jeff called me back at 5:30 that afternoon. When I told him what I had done, he went nuts, yelling at me that I was exhibiting bizarre behavior and he couldn't represent me anymore. Funny, he acts negligently, and I'm the one who gets yelled at. I tried to be nice but he hung up on me. At this point I took Michelle's advice and called her brother to represent me.

I knew it would take some time for any money to come into my new practice, so I took $30,000 and used it to support my practice until I could turn a profit. Once I got the charts, I sent out letters to my patients telling them I was back in practice. My doctors felt that, given my medical condition, I should only work part time. All my disability policies allowed for partial benefits for partial disability. My insurance was only a small fraction of my pre-disability income. Ben and Sarah were in expensive private schools, and I also had to support two separate residences. Since I had some cash, I thought I could get by working half time, but going back into practice was not that easy. This is called "re-entry." One of my disability case managers expressed surprise that I was going back to the same hospital and said she had not seen that before. "That's very courageous," she told me. Perhaps none of her previous clients had worked for themselves. This just confirmed in my mind why Larry and Terry were so sure I wouldn't come back. I didn't think I had a choice. I couldn't leave Pittsburgh because the kids had to stay with Barbara, and I was not going to leave them without a father. In addition, I wasn't going to lie about my medical condition, and didn't think I would be offered a job in another practice. Who would hire a bipolar cardiologist?

CHAPTER 54

RE-ENTRY

My re-entry into the practice of medicine was mostly uneventful. Some of my patients returned to see me, but I was much less busy than I had been. I rarely had more than five patients in the hospital at any one time, compared to ten or fifteen before I joined CMA in 1990. I had no more than ten office visits per day. I was able to take care of my patients and run my business working 25-30 hours per week. Larry's group covered for me one weekend a month. I knew Dr. Money would agree to cover for me because it would mean more business for him. I returned the favor of both groups by referring my patients to them for procedures I didn't do personally. These included angioplasty, nuclear cardiology, and surgically placing permanent pacemakers. I worked closely with both groups. We had no interpersonal disagreements because we had no conflicts of interest, and I enjoyed being treated as a revered referring physician. I was quite happy with the situation. I had no financial responsibilities to another doctor and had complete control of my patients' care. Madhavan even commented to me that I was still functioning as part of the group. The big difference for me was that I didn't have to deal with Larry.

I didn't carry a grudge against Larry because he was covering for me and I didn't want to rock the boat. I didn't let on to him that I knew what he had done to me, so we continued on friendly terms. He even started to confide in me about his frustrations with other members of the group. For example, he told me on several occasions that he didn't agree with Stuart's clinical decisions. Once he told me, almost nostalgically, that he never had any problems with my clinical care. I think he never gave

Stuart partnership, in part because of concerns about Stuart's quality of care. Gerry Myers told me once that Larry thought his problems were over once he got rid of me, but now the other members of the group were feuding with each other over various issues.

Because I was a little rusty clinically, Madhavan was assigned by the hospital to monitor my first three catheterizations. I was a little slow at first, but doing cath is a little like riding a bicycle; it comes back quickly. I had a problem with an old lady having a treadmill test, but with no permanent side effects. A few of my referring doctors continued to send me patients because they could not get the type of service they wanted from the other groups. Although I wasn't able to take a salary from the practice in 1997 or 1998, I continued to make ends meet with my disability insurance and other financial resources. Throughout 1998, the practice gradually paid off the $30,000 I had lent it to get going.

Once I got settled, I started to investigate what had happened to me that would have caused me to have almost been driven out of practice. I knew my only problem had been side effects from my medicine. Why was I kept out of my practice for six months? I was under the false assumption that the hospital and Larry had acted separately from each other. When I called The Farley Center in October 1997 to get a copy of my discharge summary, I was told the records would only be released to a lawyer, so I had Joel Dresbold send in a written request. When I got the records, I was stupefied to discover that the Farley Center had been under the impression that I was guilty of multiple recurrent incidents of sexual harassment. Not only was this untrue, but I had never even been accused more than once, and that involved the lies perpetrated by Sue. At that time, I didn't even know that Bonnie had ever complained to anyone about our conversation. I asked Buzz Fingeret about these supposed episodes of sexual harassment, and he told me there were only two complaints. I obviously knew about Sue, but I had no idea what the other one was, and he absolutely refused to tell me. My practice had almost been destroyed because of these accusations, yet no one would tell me what my "crimes" had been. The hospital had acted like the Queen of Hearts in Alice in Wonderland when she said, "Sentence first, trial later." And the trial went on and on, repeating itself, while I, like the hero in the Kafka novel, didn't even know the details of the accusations against me. No wonder Buzz subsequently told me the accusations were "bullshit."

At the time I resumed my practice I was in therapy with Dr. Scott and had been required by Dr. Hobbs to see Eric Gildersleeve, a sex therapist. I was also still required to go to the sex addicts meetings twice a week and have weekly urine tests. Once I had the opportunity to review what had been said about me, I was able to discuss it with both my doctors. I knew I wasn't a sex addict and that I hadn't harassed anybody. I wanted them to write letters to Tom Hobbs saying I was not a sex addict. (Somehow, Richard Irons had neglected to tell Hobbs this.) When I told Gildersleeve that the only allegation against me was from Sue, and that I had never been given due process or any other way to defend myself, he was aghast. "You never had due process! Of course, you shouldn't be here," he said.

I asked Gildersleeve and Paul to discuss my case. Both then wrote to Hobbs, telling him I was not an addict of any kind and I did not need to be in a 12-step program. I called Richard Irons, and he told me I shouldn't go to the sex addict meetings anymore. Irons did not put this in writing to Hobbs until his letter to Hobbs on November 4, 1997. In the letter he summed up my case as just bipolar disease that should be treated by Dr. Scott. The three letters confirmed that my problems were strictly due to side effects from my medications. This was exactly what Dr. Kreps and Dr. Scott had said before I was forced to take the medical leave of absence. My six months off had accomplished nothing of medical importance but had almost destroyed my career. I was convinced that Larry and Terry had almost accomplished their goal with their defamatory statements about me.

I felt that I was enlisted into the PHP under false pretenses and should not be required to continue. I hand wrote a letter to the Physicians Health Committee on October 7, 1997 requesting I be allowed to stop my urine testing because I had no history of drug abuse. I also stated in no uncertain terms that I had never sexually harassed anyone in my life. I said that Fingeret had told me there were two complaints and wouldn't tell me what the second one was. I told them at least two nurses in the ICU would testify that Sue's allegations were untrue, but no one ever followed up to find out who the two witnesses were.

The committee met on October 9. What I didn't understand at the time was that Hobbs was primarily concerned with keeping as many doctors in his program as possible to encourage donations and funding. He was running a business, and his source of revenues seemed to me to be more important than his patients. He told the hospital I needed to stay in the program, and said the same thing again in March, 2000. I believe that Drs. Scott and Gildersleeve told the truth about me because they were functioning as my physicians and their first responsibility was to my health and welfare. Hobbs, Irons, and Hedberg, on the other hand, felt they had no obligation to me. Their main concerns were their organizations and their referral sources. To them I was a commodity. This was confirmed to me in no uncertain terms during a phone conversation with Tom Hobbs. Richard Irons had agreed with me when I said that Hobbs' organization did not know how to deal appropriately with doctors with mental illness as opposed to addiction. In fact, at the time, Hobbs did not even have a psychiatrist on his staff. When I repeated what Irons had said to me, Hobbs said: "He said that! I'll never send him another referral again."

Once or twice a year I get requests from the PHP asking for a contribution, and the pamphlet always brags about the exact number of patients in the program. I guess the more patients they can claim to have, the more they think their contributions will be. They also claim to have doctors with mental illness in the program, even though the figure they give indicates that they represent only 5% of the total. Hobbs, Hedberg, and Irons all had one thing in common: They were self-described addicts of one form or another. Addictions are not just about the addiction; addictions are associated with narcissistic personality problems. In other words, these guys were demonstrably more concerned about their own welfare as providers than they were for my welfare as their patient.

CHAPTER 55

DATING IN MIDDLE AGE

A recent (2006) *Time* magazine article about single people over the age of 50 stated that fewer than one in five women want to marry or cohabitate. Fewer than one in four men that age are similarly interested in living with a woman. I turned 50 a few months after Barbara and I separated, and I dated one woman for a couple of months later that year.

I did ask out one other woman prior to my hospitalization. Her name was Donna, she was 46, she worked in the transcription department at the hospital, and she was very pretty. She declined, saying she had a boyfriend. At least six months later, Donna sent me a letter, which was waiting for me when I returned from Kansas. In the letter she said she thought I was a nice guy and wanted to go out with me. She was no longer working at Jefferson, so I didn't run the risk of getting into trouble for seeing her. As we had coffee together one day, she asked me what I was looking for. I told her I wanted what I thought everyone wanted: love. She said she was looking for a "friend." I thought she meant a non-sexual relationship, but she didn't. She wouldn't go out with me again. She called me several months later and said she wanted to see me again. I was interested in a monogamous relationship, so we got together and went to dinner at a Chinese restaurant near her apartment. She wore very sexy white short-shorts. As the dinner conversation progressed, she said she wanted to have sex with me. We went to my apartment for a few hours and had a great time; later I drove her back to her car at the restaurant.

I thought she was interested in me, but I was wrong: She told me she was interested only in sex, and she told me in graphic terms what she wanted me to do to her. In essence, she said: "I want you to call me anytime you want sex." The last time I saw her she said she was still with her boyfriend but wanted to have sex with me on the side. That was the last time I saw her. I was still going to the sex addicts' meetings. I thought it quite ironic that the 12-step program was teaching that sex had to be engaged in with respect for one's partners, but here I was, encountering lack of respect from the women I met.

During the summer and fall of 1997, I focused on finding a solid, loving relationship. I answered personal ads and put one of my own in the newspaper. I paid $1,400 for an upscale introduction service, without any success. I answered one personal ad from a 46-year-old middle school art teacher named Becky, and we hit it off right away. We dated each other exclusively from then on. She had never been married and had no children. After my experiences, I was very cautious about pushing any sexual intimacy, so we waited three months before sleeping together. Soon I started to talk to her about moving in together. She said she wanted a man to take care of her because she had had to take care of herself for so many years. Her last boyfriend was a banker with millions of dollars. They were engaged when she found him in bed with another woman. (That's one way to call off an engagement!) She told me repeatedly that I didn't have enough money to suit her.

One morning I woke up at her house, needing to be at the hospital for a 7:30 a.m. stress test for one of my patients. Becky's car wouldn't start and she wanted me to drive her to school, which was in the opposite direction from the hospital. I tried to explain to her that my patient was counting on me to be there on time, but she insisted that I had to drive her to work instead. I suggested she call a taxi and left. She was furious. She later told me she had spoken to her parents and to her best friend, who all told her that a man's first responsibility was to his woman and that I should have blown off my responsibilities to my patients. Obviously, she was extremely immature and self-centered. We had a shouting match on the phone and that was the end of the relationship. Three months later, she called me and apologized, saying she had acted like a selfish brat and wanted to get back together. I decided to give her another chance and we dated for a few more months, but it was never the same.

By the spring of 1998, I realized that women without children tended to be too immature for me, and I thought I should try to find someone with children from a previous marriage. One day I saw a beautiful woman at a fair, escorted by a tall, handsome man. To my surprise she waved at me and smiled. I was perplexed until she came over to talk to me. She had been a nurse with whom I had been friendly at Jefferson in the 1980s, and her name was also Becky. Since I knew we had had chemistry between us, I took her out to dinner some months later. I was definitely interested, but she said I was different from the happy, outgoing person she had known ten years before. My mood was clearly subdued, as I was still on too much medicine. I had strong feelings about her and continued to court her as best I could.

Becky had had a strange life, having had her first child at 15. She went on to have three more children with three other men. She was still married to her fourth husband and having an affair with her current boss, a gynecologist, who was also married. She was very ambivalent about me, and we never had sex. Becky was extremely charming as well as beautiful, and I fell hard for her. Being with her reminded me of my crazy relationship with Carla decades earlier. One day, in the summer of 1998, we made a date to go to the yearly Brentwood Medical Group picnic, which I was invited to every year. I considered it a privilege, because they only invited the specialists they favored. I was going for professional reasons. At that point I realized that Becky was poison for me and broke the date. I told her the picnic was business and that I didn't want to stir up the feelings I had for her, as I was just getting over her. Two years later she called me and said that she wanted to see me again, since she was having trouble finding men she liked. I was involved with someone else by then and respectfully declined. I felt I had dodged a bullet by not getting involved with her in the first place.

During the summer of 1998, after I decided not to see Becky again, I came to the conclusion I would never find what I was looking for in a relationship and was destined to live out my life alone. I wasn't going to stop dating, but I would no longer have aspirations of finding "ideal love." Besides, the Farley Center had accused me of having "preoccupation with fantasies of ideal love." What I had forgotten was what the Shirelles had sung about more than 30 years before, that the bleakest times are usually just before the best.

CHAPTER 56

THE SECRET DOSSIER

During the discovery phase of my lawsuit against the hospital, in 2003, Mike Cassidy and I received documents indicating that the hospital started keeping a secret dossier on me since 1997. Mike explained to me that the confidentiality of my file prevented the hospital from giving out any information about me to third parties, but the law did not allow them to keep my file secret from me. We discovered a checklist and table that referred to 112 separate events. Unbeknownst to me, they were having various hospital employees observing me and writing reports about me. In 2002, the hospital attorney, Paul Verardi, wrote to the Pennsylvania Human Relations Commission, stating that I had been designated a "Problem Physician" in 1997. The only person designated by the hospital to develop this dossier, as far as I know, was Terry Kostrub. Some of the entries in this dossier concerned my legitimate complaints about the care of my patients at Jefferson.

Several events that occurred in 1998 are worth noting in detail. These events are all related to serious life-threatening episodes caused by negligent care by nurses and other physicians. I should mention here that I never complained to authorities about inadequate care by any other physicians at Jefferson or any other Pittsburgh hospital. The physicians involved in these episodes were powerful people at Jefferson Hospital.

The first episode occurred on May 18, 1998. Mrs. N. was an 80-year-old patient of Stanley Wetschler. I had been taking care of her cardiac problems for many years and we had a close relationship. Mrs. N. was admitted to the Jefferson ICU in critical condition, having developed simultaneous problems of congestive heart failure, kidney failure, and respiratory failure. I was treating her heart failure. The nephrologists were treating her kidney failure with a hemodialysis machine, and she was on a mechanical ventilator managed by Dave Laman's group. She had been in the hospital for several days on the ventilator. When I saw her at 11:30 on the morning of May 18, she had been weaned off the ventilator as of the previous evening. Initially she had tolerated this reasonably well, but by the time I saw her she was slipping back into respiratory failure. I knew that if she had to be placed back on a ventilator, her chances for survival would be seriously impaired.

Her chest x-ray that morning revealed a large amount of fluid between her lungs and the chest wall on both sides of her chest. These fluid accumulations are called "pleural effusions," which can occur in many different diseases. In Mrs. N.'s case, the fluid was due to her congestive heart failure. I had treated hundreds of patients with pleural effusions from this condition, and one thing I knew for sure was that this type of pleural effusion would not resolve with hemodialysis or additional diuretics. Sometimes small effusions will resolve over time with proper medical therapy, but in this patient's case, the effusions were very large and were definitely limiting her ability to breath. I was certain that, without direct removal of the effusions, her breathing would worsen and she would have to go back on the ventilator.

I no longer felt comfortable doing thoracenteses by myself and the pulmonary group was already on the case, so I called Dave Laman from the ICU; Dave was in his office. I knew the pulmonary group did not like coming back to the hospital after their office hours because they frequently had other, non-medical commitments. Since it was still morning, I thought they would assign a member of their group to come in to do the procedure that afternoon. When I told David that I thought Mrs. N. was critical and needed the fluid taken out of her chest as soon as possible, he replied, "Richard, you are not my boss. I will see her tomorrow morning and decide whether or not she needs to have it done."

I can honestly say that in my career no other doctor has ever been so dismissive of my concerns, especially in a life-threatening situation. I repeated why I thought she needed the procedure urgently. I told him that I agreed I was not his boss. I said that Stanley was in charge of this patient and said I was going to call him to get someone else to do it. David did not like this at all. “Fuck you, Richard. Fuck you. Fuck you!” he snapped.

At this point I raised my voice and said, “David, you know the difference between me and you is that I care.” He asked if I was actually going to call Stanley, and I told him I had no choice because I thought Mrs. N. would probably die if the fluid stayed in her chest. He said the fluid would resolve with hemodialysis, but I knew that was impossible. The effusions were due to heart failure, and he was a lung doctor, so I thought he was not qualified to disagree with me on this issue.

The nurses thought I was being a little too loud and asked me to take the call in the conference room so as not to upset the patients. When I got off the phone with David, I asked the nurses to check the nearby patients and found that none of them had overheard the conversation. Despite the fact that the patients had not been disturbed, the head nurse still wrote me up for the incident. No one ever asked me what happened, and I didn’t know I had been reported until I got most of my records in 2003. The fact that I wasn’t told clearly indicated to me that the hospital was trying to build a case against me without my knowledge.

I called Wetschler and told him what was going on. He agreed to consult a thoracic surgeon to do the procedure, and I called the surgeon personally to express the urgency of the situation. The surgeon, Dr. Phitayakorn, was very dedicated, and I knew I could count on him. At around 2:30 that afternoon he removed a total of almost three quarts of fluid from Mrs. N.’s chest. This amount of fluid certainly would interfere with anyone’s breathing. Mrs. N. improved so dramatically that she didn’t have to be put back on the ventilator, and I was able to discharge her from the hospital in good condition about a week later. Mrs. N. saw me in the office for another three years before she eventually died. Every time she came to the office she thanked me for saving her life. And I was the one who got written up!

Another episode occurred at about the same time, again with a powerful physician, this time Buzz Fingeret. The patient was a 73-year-old man named Mr. J.B. He was in the hospital for congestive heart failure due to a leaky mitral valve, a weak heart and generally poor health. He could not survive heart surgery, so I was reduced to doing what I could for him with medical management. This presented quite a challenge because his fluid balance was extremely precarious. If he got a little too much fluid, he would go into life threatening heart failure. If he didn't get enough fluid, his blood pressure would drop precipitously and he could go into shock and die. Complicating his condition was an inability to take food or liquids orally, so we had to put a feeding tube directly into his stomach through the skin of his abdomen, a surgical procedure that required a surgical consult. For some reason, which I cannot recall, Buzz was consulted to evaluate Mr. J.B.'s abdomen and maybe to place the gastric tube. Once the tube was in, I was able to adjust his fluids and tube feedings to the narrow range he could tolerate.

Mr. J.B. was able to be discharged to a skilled nursing facility where he would receive the level of care he required. Prior to his discharge his tube came out and the radiologists were asked to put the tube back in place under x-ray guidance. I no longer needed Buzz's help with the patient. As he was out of town, I told his partner, Alice Rocke, that they were off the case, and she didn't express any objection. A week or two later, when Mr. J.B. was in the nursing facility, I received an urgent phone call from the Short Stay unit at Shadyside. I was told that Mr. J.B. had been sent there by Dr. Fingeret when the nursing facility called him by mistake, instead of calling me or his primary care physician, when his tube came out.

The nurses at Shadyside were panic stricken. Mr. J.B. had arrived unannounced and his blood pressure was only 70. Furthermore, the nurses told me that Buzz's partners at Shadyside, two prominent general surgeons there, were refusing to see the patient. The interns and residents were also refusing to see the patient. I guess they didn't want to get involved and take a chance that, if he died, they would in some way be held responsible. I was in my car, almost at Jefferson, around 8:30 a.m. when I got the call. I knew the patient was very tenuous and needed me to take care of him. Had I been called first, from the nursing home, I would have sent the patient to Jefferson, where the radiologists, who knew his difficult case, would be. As I couldn't go to Shadyside immediately, I told the nurses to put the patient in an ambulance and send him to Jefferson without delay.

When Mr. J.B. got to Jefferson, his tube was inserted by the radiologist and I was able to stabilize him. I knew that any other cardiologist would not know this man's case well enough to walk the fine line between shock and heart failure. He eventually went back to the nursing facility. This man was mentally alert and wanted us to do everything we could to keep him alive. Buzz's misbehavior had certainly put the patient at risk. In addition, at least six physicians were incensed at him over the incident, including doctors at Shadyside and the radiologists at Jefferson.

I called Buzz to ask him what had happened. He said he was in the operating room when he got the call around 7 a.m. Because he was busy, he told the nurses at the nursing facility to send the patient to Shadyside. I told him he knew the patient was not his and he should have told the nurses to call me. I told him I had told Alice Rocke the previous week that he was off the case. His attitude seemed to be that he was above any criticism from me because he was the President of the Medical Staff. I didn't think what he did could be justified, regardless. I thought that his behavior had been reckless and negligent, and he was not happy with me. I didn't care; my job was to protect my patients. Shortly thereafter, I spoke to Alice and asked her why Buzz would send the patient to Shadyside. She said it was not unusual for Buzz to send patients to other hospitals, expecting his partners to do the work without first notifying them. She told me a similar episode had occurred at West Penn Hospital. This behavior is called "dumping." I wasn't surprised when, a few years later, everyone in Buzz's group abandoned him, leaving him reduced to joining Chuck Cline, one of the young surgeons at Jefferson.

Buzz was very critical of me for calling him on his behavior. In my presence, on more than one occasion, Buzz said to other doctors that, "Richard ripped me a new asshole." I really didn't care what he thought. No doctor should be able to avoid some form of accountability for negligent behavior, especially people who are entrusted with the medical staff leadership. Those in a position of leadership should set standards of excellence for the rest of the medical staff. I didn't write him up for what he did. In fact, I made it a point never to complain to any authority about any mistakes any doctor made. I always felt it was best to talk to the person privately. But this time even my private conversation resulted, in my opinion, in Buzz taking retribution against me. This retribution involved an incident in which a nurse's negligence almost resulted in a patient's death in the Jefferson ICU.

CHAPTER 57

A LARGE MALE NURSE

On June 11, 1998, Mrs. R., an 82-year-old woman, was admitted to the Jefferson ICU with a severe heart attack. The pain she described was in the area of her upper abdomen and lower chest. She had been taking an antacid for the pain, thinking it was indigestion. Elderly people frequently complain of unusual types of pain during a heart attack. Her EKG was severely abnormal and the diagnosis was not in doubt. I explained the circumstances and the nature of the pain to the nurse in charge, Carol, a woman I had worked with in the ICU for many years. I specifically told her that the patient's symptoms were from her heart, not her stomach. That night at midnight the patient began to complain of recurrent discomfort. Under these circumstances, it is absolutely imperative for the nurse to notify the cardiologist caring for the patient about the change in the patient's condition. I was not notified and the patient was treated by the nurses with ginger ale. She continued to have intermittent discomfort for the next eleven hours, during which I was not notified.

The next morning I rounded at Shadyside first and did not arrive at Jefferson until 11 a.m. I saw Mrs. R. first. When I arrived at her room in the ICU, several nurses were sitting at the desk, shooting the breeze. The nurse caring for my patient was a large man approximately 6'2", 225 pounds—at least 60 pounds heavier than me. I will call him Nurse M. I didn't know him; apparently he had been a nurse for one year at that time. I asked him how Mrs. R. was doing and he said she was fine. I went into her room and was appalled when she told me that she had been having pain for many hours. Given her age and the large size of the heart attack, I knew immediately that she could go into shock and die at any moment. She needed immediate treatment with intravenous nitroglycerin and consideration for emergency cardiac catheterization and angioplasty or bypass surgery.

I hurried out of the room, took the nurse aside and quietly told him what was going on with the patient and that he should have called me and given the patient nitroglycerin. In no uncertain terms he told me I was wrong. I repeated myself several times, but he continued to tell me I didn't know what I was talking about. "You're wrong, you're wrong," he repeated over and over again. I couldn't believe my ears. No nurse had ever spoken to me like that in my entire medical career. Of course, I had had to criticize nurses many times in the past, but I always tried to do this quietly and out of earshot of others. I wasn't treating him any differently. I knew I had to persuade him that I was correct in order for him to continue to care for the patient. He must have told me five or six times that I was wrong, and I got so frustrated that I inadvertently raised my voice. I told him I was going to have to remove him from the case and walked away.

I went to look for Carol, who was supervising Nurse M. at the time. I tried one other room and, when I couldn't find her, I went into the adjacent nurses' lounge. As soon as I was a few feet into the lounge, I heard Nurse M. right behind me, saying that if I ever spoke to him like that again he was going to harm me physically. I turned around to find him bearing down on me like a grizzly bear, his face contorted with fury. He pushed his chest and abdomen against me as he threatened me, then closed the door to the room. I was now alone with him in the room and scared out of my wits. I yelled for help, ran to the phone and called security. He backed off. I was severely shaken and went back into the ICU, waving my arms and telling people he had attacked me.

I knew immediately that Buzz, as President of the Medical Staff, would try to blame me for the incident. I had to take steps to blunt his retaliation. I went to the office of the Vice President in Charge of Nursing, Cindy Roth, and told her what had happened. I asked her if the hospital would mind if I filed a report with the police. She said that was my right and the hospital wouldn't object. Fortunately for me, the local chief of police had been my patient since his bypass surgery several years previously, and he sent an officer to my office to take the report.

As I expected, Buzz tried to blame me for the incident, saying I had yelled at Nurse M. Buzz launched a full investigation into the incident, and I was not allowed to see the witnesses' statements. I called the chief of police and explained my situation. He told me the nurse had a previous criminal record, and I was able to get copies of all the statements. Of six witnesses, only one or two said I yelled; the others used the word "spoke" or "talked." I interviewed one of the witnesses, another nurse, who admitted to me that she had lied about what happened and lied when she said I had a history of yelling at nurses. Not only did she formally retract her statement, she and the head nurse in the ICU confirmed that I had never yelled at any nurse in the ICU during the 14 years I had been at Jefferson.

And the patient? Because Mrs. R. was elderly and not entirely mentally competent, I could not immediately get informed consent from her for the cath. The next of kin was her son, who lived in California. She remained pain-free on the IV nitroglycerin, so I was able wait a few hours for the son to call me back that evening. I asked him if he wanted me to treat his mother aggressively or just allow nature to take its course. He said he wanted everything possible done to save his mother's life. He spoke to her directly and persuaded her to agree to the procedure. The next morning she was in the cath lab at Shadyside and had an emergency angioplasty. All her coronary arteries were either partially or completely blocked. There was no doubt that my clinical assessment had been correct. The angioplasty was a success and the patient was subsequently discharged in good condition.

The family members were extremely pleased with the care Mrs. R. had received, and several of them told me they wanted me to be their doctor if they got sick. These people lived near the hospital, so I knew I had done a service for the hospital by creating good will.

Despite this, Buzz still tried to twist what had occurred to engineer a reprimand against me, even in the face of indisputable evidence that I had done nothing wrong. I asked to present my case directly to the Medical Executive Committee and wrote a letter to the committee, asking that Buzz recuse himself because of his grudge against me for calling him on his negligence about his care of Mr. J.B. I asked that the Vice President of the Medical Staff, Richard Collins, chair the executive committee meeting in his stead. Buzz refused and misused his power to issue a reprimand against me. Fred Boehm, the hospital's legal counsel at the time, told me on March 15, 1999, "That was nothing," referring to the incident. On July 31, 1998, Gary Perecko, the Executive Vice President of the hospital, and Cindy Roth wrote to Fingeret that Nurse M. and the other ICU nurses involved did not fulfill their obligations to me and the patient and that my complaints about the poor quality of care were justified.

I don't remember ever yelling at a nurse or being accused of yelling at a nurse at any time in my career, but I know that many other doctors would occasionally act inappropriately in the ICU at Jefferson. For example, one day Dave Laman got angry with me and yelled out right in the middle of the ICU, "Fuck you, fuck you, fuck you!" Of course, since he was powerful, he incurred no criticism for doing so. In fact, in 2000, David took the opportunity the yell the same thing at me for the third time on one of the medical floors at Jefferson, again without consequences. The hospital would always try to protect doctors whom they perceived to be bringing a large amount of business into the hospital. Since I was only working part time and was not in a powerful group, Buzz knew I was fair game for his retribution. These same attitudes led to the events of 2000 and 2001 that subsequently led to my lawsuit against the hospital.

CHAPTER 58

FINISHING UP 1998

Subsequent to what I felt was the outrageous and negligent behavior of Dave Laman in the case of Mrs. N., I felt trapped in a situation with the pulmonary group that prevented me from caring for patients at Jefferson Hospital. It seemed that no matter how I expressed my concerns, the pulmonary group would use their power to deflect even the most serious lapses of patient care responsibility. I did not want to create a ruckus by writing a formal letter of complaint. Instead, I tried to handle the matter privately. Talking to Laman was clearly useless and his response was always indignation and vituperation.

The junior member of the pulmonary group had quit them a short time before the incident with David, and they had recently hired a new pulmonologist by the name of Jean Weaver. One day, I approached her privately and expressed my serious concerns over what had occurred with Mrs. N. and similar events. She seemed as appalled by what occurred as I was. I asked her to help me take care of my patients, since frankly I was getting a little desperate. She was very agreeable and I felt reassured.

What I didn't find out until I received the documents in the discovery phase of my subsequent law suit was that Sims had written a letter to Fingeret, as President of the Medical Staff, on June 25, 1998, accusing me of "intellectual and character assassination of the members of our group." He continued, "I am sure you agree that such conduct from a member of our Medical Staff is deplorable and intolerable. Please consider this letter a request for an investigation…." I guess he thought David's refusal to see Mrs. N. in a life-threatening situation was not "deplorable and intolerable." Neither, apparently, was Laman's totally unprofessional behavior, cursing repeatedly at me during my telephone conversation with him. I don't think Dr. Weaver was very happy with her group, as she left after a brief period of time.

Fortunately, Rick Collins was substituting for Fingeret as chairman of the Executive Committee, or else Fingeret had finally recused himself in matters concerning me. Collins responded to Sims in a letter dated July 2, telling Sims that the Executive Committee refused his request. Dr. Collins seemed to be the only fair-minded, rational human being in the Medical Staff leadership at that time. I was pleasantly surprised when, a few years later, he was appointed Chairman of the Board of the hospital.

After being falsely accused in the Nurse M. affair, and after the false accusations made about me in 1997, I knew I had a responsibility to see the same injustices were not visited on other innocent doctors. I felt that only physicians without political power (read "money for the hospital") would be subjected to such discrimination. On July 10, I wrote to Stanley Wetschler, Chairman of the Bylaws Committee at the time, requesting that physicians accused of infractions of the bylaws be given rights of due process in order to be able to defend themselves. I offered to attend the next Bylaws Committee meeting, scheduled for July 23. I had hoped to be able to address the committee to use the events of 1997 as the reason for my request. Wetschler replied on July 16, saying he was refusing my request. It was a continuing pattern of behavior by the hospital to refuse to actually listen to anything I had to say about what had happened to me. True to form, Wetschler wrote to me on July 23 that the committee decided the current procedures "provide adequate protection to safeguard the rights of the accused…and [changes] would not be practical." I guess it was more "practical" to destroy a doctor's career for no apparent reason. This pattern was to continue.

The remainder of 1998 was uneventful in the hospital. By the end of the year I was able to pay myself back the $30,000 I had lent my practice. Other than the difficulties with Fingeret and the pulmonary group, I was enjoying the practice of cardiology more than ever. I was getting along well with all the other cardiologists who were covering for me. I didn't have to worry about being attacked by them as long as I continued to refer procedures to them. I even hoped to make a little money going forward. As it turned out, the operative word here was "little," not "money." I even bought a new set of golf clubs and started enjoying life a little more.

In August, I took a week off and went on a cruise for the first time, sailing from Anchorage, Alaska to Vancouver, British Columbia along the inland water route. I had never seen such beauty, not even in the Rocky Mountains. The ship stopped at different places for us to get off and do other activities. I went white water rafting twice and flew over the glaciers in an airplane. We paddled canoes in a beautiful lake. I saw bald eagles and their nests. I even met a woman on the ship, but again, she was only interested in sex. After I got home I sent her some flowers, and that's how I found out she had a boyfriend. As I mentioned before, at that point in my life, I just gave up and resigned myself to spending the rest of my life alone. Then, to paraphrase the Monkees, I saw her face.

CHAPTER 59

THE POT OF GOLD AT THE END OF THE RAINBOW

One day in August, 1998, I was working out at the gym I have belonged to since 1984, when I noticed a very pretty woman walking on a treadmill. From where I was I could only see her head and shoulders. She had medium length dark blonde hair and looked to be around 35. I didn't think much about her after that. Then a few weeks later, in early September, I saw her exercising in the gym's indoor swimming pool. She was wearing a modest one-piece bathing suit. I watched her pushing a kick board. After I got into the pool, I saw her walking along side it. I couldn't believe my eyes. She had the body of a teenage gymnast. I said to myself, *I would marry that woman.* I knew it was unlikely I would be sexually compatible with any woman, so I had no hopes along those lines. I watched her walk over to the whirlpool and get in. She was alone in it, and I saw an opportunity to meet her. I walked over to the whirlpool and took my usual spot which was a respectable distance away from her but close enough to talk to her. I started a conversation and we exchanged names. Her name was Linda Rose. I knew I might not have much time, and I didn't want her to think I was an axe murderer, so I mentioned I was a doctor. She told me she was a school teacher and promptly got up and left. I watched her as she walked away, smitten with her beauty.

A week or so later, on a Saturday afternoon, I saw her again at the pool, this time with her 10-year-old daughter and 5-year-old son. She was sitting on the side of the pool, watching them as they played in the water. As I walked behind her, I looked to see if she was wearing a wedding ring. She wasn't, so I felt at liberty to talk to her again. I sat down at the edge of the pool a couple of feet away from her and we started to talk—something I'm good at. She told me she was separated from her husband and contemplating a divorce. In reality, I learned later, she had already decided to get the divorce. My divorce from Barbara was still not finalized, so we were both in the same situation. As we sat there talking I couldn't believe a woman her age could have such a perfectly flat lower abdomen. I didn't think I had much of a chance with her. After ten or fifteen minutes, figuring I didn't have much to lose, I asked her if she wanted to go out for dinner. She responded emphatically: "No! I'm not ready for that."

I didn't let that faze me and continued the conversation for a few more minutes, after which I went about my business. Before I left the pool area, I saw her lying on one of the poolside chaises. As I walked by, I wanted to say something nice. I told her she had beautiful children, which was absolutely true. I also asked her if she was an athlete. She said that she wasn't—which, in reality, she said out of modesty.

The following Saturday afternoon was Ben's thirteenth birthday party at a paintball facility. I attended and had a great time playing paintball for the first time with Ben and Sarah and their friends. Barbara was also there, so I felt comfortable leaving a little early. I wanted to get to the gym in the hope that Linda would be there with her kids. As I walked to the men's locker room, Linda came out of the women's locker room. She didn't see me as she walked about five feet in front of me in the same direction. I couldn't help but notice that her shoulders were wider than her hips. "Linda, if you don't feel comfortable talking to me in front of your children, I won't," I said. She responded that it wasn't a problem. I went to get dressed to work out. I was in the gym, standing on one of the machines doing my exercises about ten minutes later when I heard a voice to my right and a little behind me. It was Linda. She seemed somewhat nervous as she asked me if I would have lunch with her. I responded: "With you! Of course I would. When do you want to go?"

She said: "Meet me at Pino's (a pizza place) when you finish working out." Somehow, my workout that day was exceptionally short.

Linda was sitting at one of the outdoor tables eating pizza when I arrived, and we started to talk casually. I remembered that the first

Becky had told me I was too intellectual for her. I didn't want to take any chances representing myself to Linda as not being an intellectual, so as not to get started under false pretenses. I was up front with who I was and what I cared about. We discussed history, economics, politics and any number of other topics about which I felt passionately. I did almost all the talking in a conversation lasting two hours. She was a great listener and obviously quite intelligent, and she seemed genuinely interested in what I had to say. I had plans to have dinner and a movie with Ben that night. When I got up to leave, I deliberately did not ask her for her phone number. Instead, I gave her my business card and wrote my home phone number on the back. What I didn't know at the time was that Linda was not the type to play games. Once she decided to ask me to lunch, she had pretty much decided she wanted to have a relationship with me.

I didn't see Linda again at the gym. I didn't think being more aggressive would serve any useful purpose. I had already asked her out once, and she had said she wasn't ready to start dating. She had my number and knew I was interested, and I figured she knew where I was if she were interested. I wasn't trying to manipulate her feelings; I was just trying to be a gentleman. A week later, at 11:15 on a Sunday night, my phone rang. Usually a call that late at night would almost certainly be from my answering service, so I was a little shocked when it was from Linda. She said she had been thinking about me every time she went to the gym. After my experiences with Sue and everything that occurred in 1997, I was more than a little paranoid about women. At first I thought she was calling to tell me to stop harassing her or she would call the police. We went back and forth for a few minutes, with me trying to figure out why she called. Finally I said, "Did you call to ask me out on a date?" When she replied in the affirmative, I suggested dinner on Tuesday evening, and she accepted.

A new French restaurant had recently opened in my neighborhood and I had not eaten there before. The place was small, with an ambiance reminiscent of my times in Paris. I arrived first and was seated. A few minutes later Linda walked in wearing a knee-length slinky black dress and high heels. I said to myself, *What is this woman doing with me?* This was a chance of a lifetime, and I was resolved to do everything I could not to screw it up.

We fell into easy conversation, and this time it was two-way. She told me she didn't believe in marriage. She really didn't want to get married the first time and felt that marriage was just an excuse to enslave women. She asked what I was looking for. This time I was smart enough not to repeat what I had said to Donna about looking for love. Instead I said I just wanted to have fun for the rest of my life. At first, she took this to mean I was looking for sex with many women. I explained that my idea of having fun was to share it with one woman.

Linda had gone to France for six weeks at age 19. I had been to Paris three times, and we got to talking about our experiences. When I mentioned the Louvre, she said she liked the Jeu de Palme better. The Jeu de Palme, a small museum near the Louvre, is dedicated to Impressionist art. I jokingly refer to her mention of it as those "three little words." Since I moved to Pittsburgh in 1984, no one had ever uttered those words to me. Suddenly, she was not only beautiful, but cultured and worldly. That was it; I would do anything (almost) to have a relationship with her. As we left the restaurant, she seemed to want to take my hand. As we walked hand in hand, I told her I wouldn't put any sexual pressure on her. When we got to her car I was about to shake hands, say goodnight and add that I wanted to see her again. Instead, she put her arms around me and kissed me on the mouth, passionately.

CHAPTER 60

TRUE LOVE

All of my research, all of my personal experiences with women, all the nonsense I was fed at the Farley Center and Menninger, and all my writings about sexual relationships could not even begin to describe my relationship with Linda. Everything Pandya, Hedberg, Irons, and Cobb had said about sexual relationships was proven, by the reality of Linda Rose, to be utter nonsense. I hate it when people say things authoritatively with absolutely no scientific data to back it up. As far as I'm concerned, all the people I just mentioned above were little more than charlatans and hucksters. They had no understanding of human sexuality whatsoever.

After Linda kissed me that evening, she accepted my offer of a date for the next Saturday night. She was to meet me at my apartment because neither of us thought it would be a good idea for me to meet her children so soon after we met. I saw her at the gym the Thursday before; she needed directions to my place. I lived near the gym, so I offered to show her rather than just give directions. In New York, people seemed to have a "three date rule" before sleeping together. In Pittsburgh, the rule seemed to be the "three month rule." That's why I told Linda I wasn't going to put any sexual pressure on her. What I didn't expect was that Linda was more like a New Yorker. I caught on pretty quickly when we got to my apartment that evening.

Before I try to describe the nature of our sexual relationship in general terms, I want to tell you a little bit about Linda. In reality she was 40, not 35. She is 5'5" tall and weighs 105 pounds. She is from Fort Wayne, Indiana and graduated from high school in 1976, third in her class of about 300 students. A teenage gymnast, she had qualified for and competed in the Indiana State high school girls' gymnastics championship in the balance beam. Like me, she did better on the math SAT (750) than on the verbal (660). She was the first girl to be named "scholar athlete" at any high school in the history of Fort Wayne. She graduated from Indiana University with a major in anthropology and subsequently got a master's degree in library science from Ball State. When her then-husband got a job as a reporter with the *Pittsburgh Post-Gazette*, she moved with him to Pittsburgh, where she worked as a reference librarian. When her daughter was born in 1988, she went back to school to get her certification in elementary education. At the time we met she was teaching second grade in the Pittsburgh Public Schools. Linda's dedication to her students is very similar to mine for my patients. She is completely guileless. She is a very responsible person in both her professional and personal life, and is as fine a human being as anyone I have ever met.

Linda and I share so many personality traits that I joke we must be distant cousins. She is mostly of German descent, and I have a German last name. One big difference, however, is that she is completely normal mentally. She may be the only person I know who has never been in therapy, and is, in my opinion, one person who doesn't need it. While she has normal ups and downs, she is not predisposed to clinical depression. Very soon after we started dating, it became apparent that she did not have trouble with commitment or intimacy. I certainly didn't with her. But I was concerned how she would feel about me having bipolar disease. I didn't wait very long, a week or two, before I told her about it. I expected her to react to this information and draw some negative conclusions. Instead, she said: "So?" She is very tolerant. On the other hand, she has extremely high standards of behavior for her romantic relationships.

She demands total honesty, trust, commitment, and respect, as I do, and in return, she holds nothing back. She loves me in a way that I didn't think possible. In a very real way she has taught me what love is. Not in my wildest fantasies did I think a woman like her existed. Because of her I have come to believe, without any equivocation, that the *best* sex can only occur in the context of total trust and total commitment. Total trust and commitment are not things that one can declare; they must be lived on a daily basis, and they must be continuous. Once trust is violated, the same level of trust can never be achieved again. I'm not saying that small violations of trust will always cause a couple to break up; however, once trust is violated, that breach will adversely affect sexual intimacy permanently. Without total trust and commitment, the ability for each person to be themselves in bed is intrinsically compromised. One must feel secure in order to take the risk of exposing one's inner sexual self without fear of rejection.

Despite all my sexual experiences, I have never had a sexual relationship that is even in the same league with what I have been living with for the past nine years. I don't mean that we have a physical relationship that is necessarily better than that of many adventurous people. The difference is the mental part. I have come to believe that sex is actually between the ears, not between the legs. At first, we played around in ways that most people would find a little too far out, but after a few months, the mental aspect of our sexuality began to take over as the most exciting part of sex. This is not to say that the physical aspect suffered in any way. Linda's sex drive is actually stronger than mine. As I mentioned before, the person with the lesser sex drive always controls the sex life of a couple. Barbara, for instance, controlled our sex lives. With Linda, I did. Because I knew very well how it felt to be sexually rejected constantly, I was very aware of how Linda would feel. We didn't have any conflicts over frequency. It was at least once a day for the first five years. By age 56 or 57, I started to slow down physically, and we had to decrease to four times a week, except on vacations. Since I met Linda, I have had the incredible good fortune to live in a state of continuous sexual satisfaction.

But frequency is not the exceptional nature of our sex life; it is quality and mental stimulation. To paraphrase Lone Star, every time seemed like the first time. I know the only way my life was able to take this turn for the better was because I was no longer working full time. I certainly didn't plan it that way. It just happened. I guess you could say it was dumb luck, and I couldn't disagree. But some people say luck is just opportunity meeting a prepared mind. In that sense, I must concede that the first 51 years of my life were just preparation for meeting Linda.

What is the mental part of sex? It's those fantasies that excite one sexually. While I won't reveal what sexual fantasies excite us, one thing I will say is that our fantasies never contain thoughts in which we are unfaithful to each other. Other than that, pretty much anything goes. I know that the fantasies I express to Linda in bed I have not ever revealed to another human being, not even any of my therapists. Actually, I doubt seriously that any other woman would be interested or turned on by my fantasies. On the other hand, I'm sure that Linda's fantasies would probably not be thrilling for any other man. However, Linda and I encourage and fully appreciate the other's sexual fantasies. I feel totally free to express myself, and I do everything I can to make Linda feel comfortable expressing herself. Linda has so much self-respect that she allows herself complete freedom to be herself, sexually.

I have coined a phase to describe the nature of our sexual relationship: "Cortical sex," referring to the cerebral cortex. We explore all the nooks and crannies of our cortical convolutions. Sometimes we go to places we don't want to be, in which case we back up and go down a different path. Our foreplay is equal parts physical and verbal, and usually goes on for 30 or 40 minutes. I do most of the talking (naturally), but Linda talks as well, and nothing arouses me on more, sexually, than her telling me her fantasies. I know this type of relationship would be impossible in the absence of total commitment and trust. Or course, it goes without saying, it would be impossible without monogamy. The result is sexual intimacy of an intensity I never imagined existed.

This level of human interaction also depends upon the nature of the relationship outside the bedroom. It is necessary to share common goals and values, and conflict in these areas can present insurmountable barriers to intimacy. Linda and I share the basic philosophy of equal power in all aspects of our lives. Money and children are frequent causes of discord in marital relationships. In this regard, Linda and I are in full agreement that the children's welfare, both mine and hers, have first priority. Our needs come second. Linda also insists on financial parity. I had always assumed that the only way I would be able to attract a woman I wanted would be to use my wealth, but in our case, my wealth sometimes actually gets in the way.

The question of commitment was moot for us. From the first time we slept together there was never any question on either of our parts that we both wanted to spend the rest of our lives together. So far we've been successful. I won't know for sure if our marriage will last for the rest of my life because I can't know that until I die, but I have no reason to believe it won't. Ironically, neither one of us ever anticipated what we have found together. Linda once told me that, just before we met, she had had the same sense of resignation that I had about never being able to find a partner with whom she could be happy.

By December, 1998, we were sure enough of our intentions that we felt it was appropriate for us to tell our children about our relationship. We also knew we wanted to live together. My divorce was finalized that month, but I thought it best for us to live separately until Linda's divorce was final. We both thought this wouldn't take as long to complete as my divorce because much less money was involved. Unfortunately, Linda's divorce wasn't completed for almost four more years. By the spring of 1999, it was clear to me that waiting any longer would be counter productive. The pain of living apart was becoming too much for both of us, so I suggested that we buy a house together. I could have bought one myself, but I wanted Linda to have an equity position in the house so she could also benefit from the financial aspects of ownership.

Because I felt that most women would want me to support them and their children, the idea that she would be able to share the expenses was quite welcome. I figured I could afford two thirds of the expenses and mortgage payments for a house in a nice neighborhood with enough room for four. Linda was hoping I would be willing to pay for less than half because she and her kids would be using more than half the house, so when I suggested we share expenses 60/40, she was agreeable. But because I would be paying 60%, she insisted that she make up the difference by doing more of the household work. I was delighted when she thought it was a great deal for her. We started to look for a suitable house, and by May we had made a decision: We found a lovely three-bedroom contemporary for $295,000.

Before the closing we felt the need to put our agreement in writing. This was a collaborative effort, not adversarial. Joel wrote it up according to our specifications. I knew from my experience with "medical marriages" and my divorce that it's best to agree in advance what will happen in the event of a break-up. A house is a major investment, and a clear mutual agreement reached when you are on good terms avoids a lot of mutual pain if the relationship falls apart. The agreement we reached included keeping all our money separate, even if we decided to get married. At the time, Joel thought this was a bit too Draconian, but we insisted. (Pittsburgh culture is quite conservative in this way). Our agreement was 24 pages long.

We moved into our new home by August, and for the first time in years I felt as if I were part of a family again.

CHAPTER 61

SETTLING IN AND THE LOW CARB DIET

The year 1999 was mostly uneventful in the hospital. I settled comfortably into my new life and was enjoying the practice more than ever. I had good coverage and complete control over my patients. I found getting along with the cardiologists I had worked with in the past to be much easier now that issues of money and control were no longer in play. Also, since I didn't work full time, I wasn't a competitive threat. They valued my patient referrals, and I was happy with the quality of their work.

I had a trip planned to Arizona for late January, 1999, and I asked Linda to come with me. She was able to take a long weekend and came along for those days. We went to the Grand Canyon and Sedona then stayed a couple days in Scottsdale to play golf. Linda and I both played tennis and golf. I never enjoyed playing golf with "the guys," so it was a real treat to be with a woman who liked the sport. I had gotten her a new set of golf clubs for Christmas. One day we played with a couple a little older than us. The husband was a retired engineer who had been bought out for several million dollars and felt miserable about not working. A few years later I would have to cope with early retirement. For successful people, retirement can be a very difficult adjustment, and having a lot of money does not make it that much easier.

After Linda went back to Pittsburgh, I stayed a few more days in Arizona, where I had my first experience with discrimination related to my illness. I met a nice couple and we spent some time together, but as soon as I mentioned my diagnosis, I didn't see them again. I also felt the temptation to cheat on Linda. While I was working out in the hotel's gym one afternoon, two attractive female employees in their twenties made it clear to me that they were interested in me. I felt flattered, as any healthy man would, but I consciously told myself that I was being tested. As easy as it might have been to have sex with either one and not let Linda know what happened, I knew that *I* would know, which would create a barrier to intimacy and ruin our relationship. I knew I couldn't have my cake and eat it too, so I did not take advantage of the situation. This wasn't a new experience for me. I have always demonstrated good will power in turning down sex in inappropriate circumstances.

In 1999 I also became aware of a serious health problem. The previous fall, Linda and I had gone to a Halloween party given by the couple who bought my house. Pictures of the party included one of me standing on the stairs to the second floor. I didn't recognize myself. I was fat, even though I only weighed 167 pounds. I went on a diet and was down to 156 by the time we went to Arizona, but I also discovered that my blood pressure was up to 180/110. My triglycerides had skyrocketed to 441, with normal being less than 150. My good cholesterol (HDL) was very low at 23, with normal being over 40. My total cholesterol and bad cholesterol (LDL) were in the normal range. Luckily for me Jim Burke, the head of the Jefferson emergency department at the time, told me I had to read the book *Protein Power* by Michael Eades and his wife, both physicians. The book was on the N.Y. Times best seller list at the time. It allowed me to understand that I had a condition called "Syndrome X," or "metabolic syndrome," a hereditary condition that affects up to a third of the U.S. population. Commonly referred to as pre-diabetes, the condition imparts a high risk for subsequent heart disease.

The book described the physiology of glucose metabolism. As some people age they develop resistance to the effects of insulin. For this reason, the body has to produce more insulin to keep the blood sugar in the normal range. In this process more sugar is turned into fat and stored in the body's fat tissue, which leads to worsening insulin resistance and higher insulin levels. The higher insulin levels lead to worsening high blood pressure. Sugar is a carbohydrate, and simple carbohydrates, such as those found in potatoes, white rice, pasta and other high carb foods, are converted into glucose by the body, causing more insulin to be secreted. I didn't want to die at 68 as my father had, so I started a low carb, high protein diet in Arizona after I finished reading the book.

The book recommended a maximum carbohydrate intake of 30 grams per day, but I ate even less. Within two months my triglycerides were down to 115, my HDL was up to 43, and my blood pressure had normalized with drug therapy. By mid year I had lost additional weight and was down to 144 pounds, similar to my weight when I graduated from medical school. I thought this diet could benefit some of my patients if used appropriately.

One patient in particular exemplifies how the low carb diet can be extremely beneficial in patients with diabetes. Dave Laman referred a patient to me who had very severe lung disease from smoking. Mr. M. was in his mid sixties and weighed 320 pounds. When I first saw him, all he could do was sit in a chair with his oxygen prongs in place in his nose. He had insulin dependent diabetes, which required 120 units of insulin daily to control. I was consulted because he had severe angina pectoris, heart pain due to blockages in his coronary arteries.

Although I pushed his medications as aggressively as possible, Mr. M. progressed to the point that he had chest pain at rest, but his lung disease was so severe he would not have been able to survive bypass surgery. I took him to Shadyside for a cath because he was a high-risk patient and the Jefferson cath lab was only certified for low-risk patients. I hoped to find blockages that would be amenable to angioplasty. He had multiple blockages, two of which were very severe and in large arteries. He continued to have chest pain at rest, so I couldn't even send him home. I asked Jim O'Toole to see him for possible angioplasty of those two arteries, and we reviewed the film together. Jim felt angioplasty would be too risky. Because the patient was an insulin-dependent diabetic, angioplasty was relatively contraindicated because of a high probability that the arteries would narrow down again fairly soon after the procedure. I explained my predicament and practically begged him to dilate both vessels. He finally acquiesced. Jim was the best and I had a lot of confidence that he could pull it off, which he did. The patient became pain free and I was able to send him home.

I wanted to use the low carb diet for Mr. M. in the hopes he could benefit from it as much or more than I had. I called the endocrinologist who was taking care of his diabetes, who thought I was crazy and refused to participate. I felt the diet might be his only chance, and he decided to go along with it. I watched him very closely. The diet can have very annoying side effects, such as lightheadedness and ketosis, which have to be managed aggressively. One year later he was down to 215 pounds and was completely off his insulin. He was able to work outside in his garden without his oxygen. He did develop some recurrent chest pain at that time, so I admitted him directly to Shadyside for another cath. He was not able to do a stress test. I asked Jim to do the cath in case he needed another angioplasty. Remarkably, both angioplasty sites were still wide open. His chest pain turned out to be from his esophagus, and he responded well to medication for acid reflux.

Dave Laman was amazed when he saw Mr. M. again in the office. "Richard, what did you do to him?" he asked. I hoped that David would have gained some faith in my clinical judgment because of this case, which would help me win his confidence in how I treated heart failure in the ICU. It didn't. However, Mr. M.'s endocrinologist told me the next time I spoke to her that low carb diets were becoming more mainstream and that she herself had started using them for some of her patients.

I considered Mr. M. a miracle case and wanted to spread the word. No serious research was being conducted to assess the efficacy of the low carb diet for treating diabetics. I was in no position to do my own scientific research, so I called several academic endocrinologists, urging them to do the research. I attended a cardiology review course in Chicago in 2000 and spoke privately to the professor who gave the lecture on lipids. I asked him about my personal experience with my condition. He said I was especially sensitive to carbohydrates, but expressed no intellectual interest. In fact, none of these academics were the slightest bit interested. I guess no one thought they could get funding. Drug companies sponsor a disproportionate amount of medical research. I knew a diet could not be patented, so no company would fund such research. In fact, if the diet was found to be effective the drug companies would not be able to sell as much medicine to diabetic patients. This might have scared off the doctors, who might have become a target of the drug companies and suffer retribution if the research proved that a low carb diet was more effective than the medication the companies were peddling. *The New York Times* published a letter of mine in January, 2006, which was about this conflict of interest. I have maintained my weight loss and other benefits of this diet without difficulty for the past seven years. I still maintain that low carb diets could help enormously in the global fight against obesity and diabetes.

My relationship with Linda continued to blossom in 1999. I wanted to show her the beauty of the American Rockies, which she had never seen. Also, I had purchased a new car, a BMW 540i, and was anxious to get it on the open road. Linda was concerned that the U.S. was running out of room and becoming overpopulated, so that summer I thought a road trip would impress her with the vast open spaces of the Great Plains and Mountain States. Some of my fondest memories were of my trip out west in 1971. That summer, we had 11 days for our vacation. We visited the Black Hills, Yellowstone and the Grand Tetons, covering 4000 miles *in toto*. It was a thrilling trip, but when we returned, we concentrated on moving into our new house. It was an exciting time. Later that year I developed acute appendicitis and had emergency laparoscopic surgery on a Tuesday morning; I was back at work that Friday. I couldn't stand sitting around the house doing nothing. Life was very good, but by the end of 1999, things began to heat up again at Jefferson.

CHAPTER 62

A HOSTILE WORK ENVIRONMENT

In December, 1999 a change in the hospital bylaws was suggested by the new lawyers hired by the hospital to replace Fred Boehm. The new firm was called Horty and Springer, and their specialty was hospital law. The new proposal had to be approved by a vote of the medical staff. The new rules would allow the hospital to summarily dismiss any doctor accused or convicted of various offenses outside the hospital. All due process protections for a doctor so accused were to be removed.

After my experience in 1997, I thought this was a bad idea. At the Quarterly Medical Staff meeting that month, the new rules were to be put to a vote. I stood up and spoke against the adoption of these rules and gave my reasoning. The bylaws vote was tabled. After the meeting, several doctors came up to me to praise my actions, including Rick Collins, President of the Medical Staff at that time. He asked me to put my concerns in writing so he could accurately present them at the next bylaws committee meeting. I wrote him a three-page, single-spaced letter, stressing the importance of due process and the potential pitfalls of the proposed bylaws. My letter was the main point of discussion at the meeting. The committee voted down the new bylaws. Fred Boehm attended the meeting. Subsequently, the medical staff office told me that Fred had said, because of my letter, the meeting was the best bylaws committee meeting he had ever witnessed at Jefferson. I hoped I was making progress in my quest to require that doctors be granted due process procedures so they would be able to defend themselves against false accusations.

At the end of 1999, I found that I had only been able to earn $35,000 dollars that year from my practice. This was only ten percent of my salary in 1996, before I got sick. I was in good financial shape, but I couldn't help thinking how another doctor, subjected to the same nefarious behavior as I had experienced in 1997, and with fewer financial resources, could have had his or her life and career destroyed. If I had not had my disability insurance, the depression I would have gone through could very well have resulted in my suicide. That's one reason why both state and federal law prohibits creating a hostile work environment for people with disabilities.

That year, 1999, was my full first year of practice after paying off the money I had lent my practice to get restarted in 1997. Now I had unequivocal evidence of the monetary damages I had incurred by the illegal action of the hospital and medical staff leadership. I was angry, as anyone would be under the circumstances. I confronted Buzz, told him the outcome of his behavior, and asked him why he had done what he did. He refused to answer. I asked him what was in my file that could have caused him to do it. He refused to tell me. He said it was up to Collins to tell me because he was now the president. Collins sent me a letter on January 20, 2000, in which he asked me to outline my specific issues and questions in writing. The next day, when I saw Rick in the Medical Staff office, I asked him what was in my file. It was like pulling teeth to get the truth out of these guys, but Rick was a man of honor and told me there were no complaints in my file other than those I already knew about. I think that's what he actually thought, so I don't think he lied. Because I was not allowed to see my file, I didn't know at the time that what he said would turn out to be untrue.

If there was nothing else in my file, why was I sent away for six months? I was determined to get to the truth, so I started my own little investigation. I spoke to Madhavan, Tauberg, Bob Werkin, the head nurse in the cath lab, and Dr. Borrero. I found out that the hospital had had no interest in finding out what actually happened in the cath lab in March of 1997. I also found out that Adler had injected himself into the process. Now things were becoming clear to me. I started looking for a lawyer to help me sue the guilty parties. I called a law firm in Topeka and was laughed at when I said I wanted to sue the Menninger Clinic for malpractice. I tried to figure out a way to sue the Farley Center, but it became apparent that suing someone in another state was extremely difficult. I interviewed with one lawyer in Pittsburgh to help me sue Jefferson, but he never even called me to tell me why he wasn't going to take the case, nor did he ever return the multiple documents he had asked me to leave in his office after I met with him. I wondered if other cities were populated with such people. At the time, I wanted to find a lawyer who would take the case on a contingency fee, but no one would. I didn't think I could afford to pay a lawyer an hourly fee for such a large undertaking, so I gave up. At least I knew the truth about most of what had occurred.

I was quite happy with my life and was just going to let bygones be bygones. However, in January, 2000, someone else decided to use me as a political football to achieve their own selfish agenda. Now I was just a part-time solo practitioner with no political or financial power, and my only source of protection was the quality of my patient care. One doctor, the new director of the Jefferson Cath Lab, thought it would be useful to his career if he attacked me. (I'll call him Dr. KIA for "know it all.") He was a product of a second-tier medical residency program in New York City and had done his cardiology training at a procedure-oriented hospital in Texas. I had had problems with Dr. KIA in the past. Larry Adler repeatedly told members of our group that this guy was the most treacherous cardiologist in Pittsburgh. He got the cath lab director's job because he was with a large, powerful group. It was Dr. KIA who had lied to Dr. R. in the 1980s, telling him that I had tried to recruit him out from under their noses. He was vicious.

I never worked with Dr. KIA, but the few experiences I had with him were not good. In the 1980s he presented a case of his at the monthly Department of Medicine meeting at Jefferson. (The meetings were subsequently changed to quarterly.) The patient he presented was a man who came to the Jefferson ER with a dissecting aneurysm of the ascending aorta, a tear in the wall of the aorta just above the heart. The dissection had opened a channel from the aorta into the sac covering the heart, the pericardium. Because of the high pressure in the aorta, the blood was blowing up the pericardial space as if it were a water balloon. The result was what is called "pericardial tamponade." The pressure in the sac compresses the heart and prevents it from pumping properly. Other disease states can cause the pericardium to fill with fluid and result in tamponade. The most common would be an infection, an inflammation, or a tumor that has metastasized to the pericardium. The treatment in these conditions is to drain the fluid with a needle or perform an operation to remove the fluid and part or all of the pericardium. This should *not* be done if the cause of the tamponade is an aortic dissection directly into the pericardial space. In that circumstance, the blood in the pericardium is at the same high pressure as the blood in the aorta. If you open the pericardium in this condition, it's just like putting a hole in a water balloon: The patient will bleed to death in a matter of moments. Most medical residents know this. A cardiology fellow should know this. An attending cardiologist must know this.

Dr. KIA proudly presented this case as a manifestation of his clinical expertise. The only way this patient could have had any chance for survival was to have been taken immediately to a hospital that had the ability to do open heart surgery. At Jefferson, we routinely sent such difficult patients by helicopter to one of the major heart hospitals in Pittsburgh. He would have then been whisked directly to the cardiac operating room where a team of surgeons would be waiting for him. The first thing they would have done would be to put the patient on a heart-lung machine to control his circulation. Then surgery would have been performed to correct the problem. Since this man had survived long enough to get to Jefferson, he might have been able to survive the trip in the helicopter. Even with the best of care, though, his chance of survival would probably be no more than 25%.

However, Dr. KIA did not send the patient to a hospital that did heart surgery. Instead, he decided to have the man's pericardial sac drained at Jefferson. He consulted the surgeon who had the most heart surgery experience at Jefferson, who was definitely the best vascular surgeon at the hospital. He was also a very accommodating man and would almost always do what any of the cardiologists asked him to do. In this case, Dr. KIA said he had made the decision to treat the patient at Jefferson and told the surgeon exactly what he wanted to be done. The patient was taken to the operating room. When the surgeon tried to drain the pericardium, the patient promptly bled to death.

I couldn't believe Dr. KIA made this decision. About 30 or 40 doctors were at the conference, but no one said anything. I felt a responsibility to say something because these conferences were supposed to be educational, and discussion of the case was appropriate. I wanted to inform the other doctors of how the patient should have been treated so that some other, similar patient in the future would be handled properly. I spoke up and explained my reasoning. Dr. KIA responded by saying, "That's my clinical judgment and I stand by it."

No one in the room spoke up to support my position. In retrospect, I don't know why the other doctors remained silent. I may have been the only cardiologist in the audience, so it's possible the other doctors had forgotten what they had learned during their residencies. Perhaps they had never been taught about dissecting aortic aneurysms. Or maybe they were just being polite. I know that if this case had been presented at Mt. Sinai, there would probably have been an uproar in the room.

Another experience I had with Dr. KIA occurred in 1995 at Shadyside. I had a case scheduled for the cath lab one morning. I don't remember whether I got a call from Dr. KIA or if I was told by the staff in the cath lab that my case was being bumped and a case of Dr. KIA's was to be done first. I spoke to KIA about this on the phone and tried to explain that the cath lab rules did not allow for anyone's cases being bumped except for true emergencies. His case was not billed as an emergency. He told me that because he did more cases than I did at Shadyside, he had the right to cut ahead of me. I told him that he didn't. He responded: "Fuck you, Richard. Fuck you." That was the end of the conversation.

This was the only instance I can recall in which I actually called a hospital administrator to complain about another doctor's behavior. I got to do my case as scheduled. A few days later I got a letter from Henry Mordoh, the president of the hospital, not the medical staff president. He apologized to me for what had occurred and said that he had called Dr. KIA to his office and explained the rules of the cath lab to him. I should also mention here that the cath lab staff at Shadyside had told me that Dr. KIA frequently did multiple repeat angioplasty procedures on some patients instead of referring them for bypass surgery. This event portended Dr. KIA's treatment of me when he became cath lab director at Jefferson.

Madhavan had been the head of the Jefferson cath lab since 1994, when I turned down the job and asked that he be given the position. Every two years, every doctor at all the hospitals had to apply for reappointment and for his specific clinical privileges. At the time, the state had a requirement that cardiologists needed to do one hundred cases a year to be credentialed to do cath. An exception was made for doctors who had extensive experience and proven safety doing caths. The cath lab director had to sign off on a doctor's credentialing. I had cath privileges at West Penn and Shadyside since 1984 and was routinely approved at those institutions, despite the fact that I may have done fewer than a hundred cases. At Jefferson, Madhavan had also routinely renewed my cath privileges under the exception for experienced doctors. I was the senior doctor in the cath lab and, when Dr. KIA got the job, he assured me that he would follow suit and approve my privileges. He didn't.

In January 2000, as part of the routine biennial reappointment process, I was informed that Dr. KIA was considering not renewing my cath privileges. The supposed reason for this was that five of the cases I had done at Jefferson should have been done at Shadyside because they were too high-risk to be done at a hospital without angioplasty or heart surgery capability. The Jefferson cath lab had been licensed by the state to do relatively low-risk caths. The cath lab had a list of the circumstances under which a cath could not be done there. We had to fill out a checklist on every patient, which was then reviewed by the head nurse in the cath lab before the procedure could be done. If there was any question, the lab administrator and/or director would be contacted.

I knew the rules like the back of my hand and was meticulous in following them. All five of the cases Dr. KIA questioned had gone through the pre-cath authorization process. Only one of the cases had been reviewed by the Peer Review Committee, and that had not been found to have any clinical errors. When I tried to talk sense to KIA, he said he had to show the hospital that he could protect them from me. Then he said he was doing me a favor because the easiest thing he could have done was just take away my cath privileges. At this point I concluded that he was out of touch with reality. Some time later I spoke with him again and, in a nice way, tried to get him to understand that all my cases had been pre-approved under the procedures already in place. He told me I was being inappropriate for talking to him. I told him, "I don't need you to tell me what is and is not appropriate." He then said he was going to write me up.

He was arrogant and hostile, and I had had enough. No one was within earshot and, remembering what he had said to me at Shadyside in 1995, I told him: "Fuck you!" That was the only time in my career I had ever said that to anyone. I still feel he deserved it. He wrote me up. I told Wetschler what occurred and he told me to put it in writing, which I did. A few years later, Michael Monseur, the attorney writing up the legal complaint against the hospital, asked me if I really said that to KIA. I told him I did. Michael replied, "Good for you!" My sentiments exactly. Michael included an entire count about this episode in my legal complaint.

The odd thing about this episode was that I wasn't even told who the other four cases were. Not only was I not told about them, the cases went directly to the Credentials Committee without first being reviewed by the Peer Review committee. When I was Chief of Medicine, I made the decision as to whether or not a case should be referred for peer review. If it was, the doctor involved would be given written notice, which included the issue under review. Usually the doctor was given two weeks to respond. The doctor would usually review the hospital and office records in depth and jog his memory of the case. Dr. KIA had arranged for the cases to go to the Credentials Committee without first being reviewed under the usual peer review process. This was a clear violation of the Bylaws of the Medical Staff. In other words, this was a hatchet job by Dr. KIA. I think it was in retribution for the 1995 event at Shadyside.

Stan Wetschler was the Vice President of the Medical Staff at the time. The Vice President also was chairman of the Credentials Committee. Stanley sent a letter to the Board of Trustees, asking them to consider abridging my cath privileges. I found out about this in time and wrote Stanley a letter asking him to rescind the letter because I had not had a chance to answer the charges. He wrote to the Board, asking them not to act. I knew the charges were ridiculous; so did Madhavan and Mike Nathanson, who was also an invasive cardiologist and Chief of Medicine at the time. Mike wrote a letter to Wetschler, on February 21st, 2000, clarifying the situation by saying that I had always had a low volume of cases, and that my technique and complication rate was at least as good as those of the other cardiologists. He said that the issue of quality and the issue of whether or not a patient should have their cath at Jefferson or Shadyside were entirely separate, and that he objected to anyone's cath privileges being changed in the absence of any evidence of poor quality. Madhavan told me he actually called Dr. KIA and Dr. Wetschler to tell them that my judgment in case selection was excellent.

I wrote a letter to Wetschler on May 8, 2000, delineating eight reasons why the action of his Credentials Committee was wrong. I spoke with Wetschler afterwards, and he agreed that all the cases should have gone to peer review first before going to credentials. He then acquiesced to actually tell me who the patients in question were and said that I could write a written response regarding the cases. He gave me only 24 hours to do it. This was the first indication to me that Wetschler was severely challenged ethically. I replied in writing to all four cases in question in a letter to Wetschler on May 10th. Of course, I talked to Bob Werkin, Terry Riffer, the cath lab administer, and Wetschler and Collins. Riffer told me that Dr. KIA had been instructed by him to discuss all the cases with me personally. He also asked me not to tell anyone about this because he didn't want to get in trouble for telling me. (Riffer no longer works there, so I am not violating any confidences.) I told Wetschler and Collins that KIA had been instructed to talk to me about the cases and that he had not done so. They asked from whom I learned this, but I wouldn't say because I wanted to keep my word to Riffer. They asked if I wanted them to overrule KIA, and I responded in the affirmative.

By this time, Mike Nathanson had told me that the State of Pennsylvania had completely eliminated any volume requirements for diagnostic catheterization making the entire issue moot. This was probably because diagnostic caths, as opposed to angioplasty, had become much safer due to improvements in the dye and equipment. In any case, after

I had a chance to respond, none of my cases was found to be inappropriate. In fact, Mike Nathanson told me that he doubted that any other invasive cardiologist could have withstood the degree of scrutiny I had been subjected to. I think he was correct. It also became clear that KIA had not even reviewed the patients' charts prior to making his allegations. Eventually, Wetschler negotiated a compromise in which I was asked to get prior approval for each of my next twenty cases. This was ridiculous on its face, as pre-approval was also required for all the other cardiologists, although in their cases, approval had only to be given by Werkin and Riffer. In my case, I had to get approval from Madhavan, Nathanson, or KIA. Of course, I complied, and none of my cases was found to be inappropriate.

I found out later that Tom Pinto, the second senior invasive cardiologist after me, was asked to review the cases. Tom told me that KIA told him that the cases had been discussed with me first, which of course wasn't true. KIA was treacherous indeed, but he was also pretty stupid. By saying my cases should have been done at Shadyside instead of Jefferson, he clearly implied that Werkin and Riffer had not been doing their jobs. They were furious with him. Even worse, as director of the cath lab, it was KIA's job to have as many cases done at Jefferson as possible in order to meet the state requirement for the cath lab to do 400 cases a year to maintain its certification. This was the same responsibility I had had at Elmhurst. Riffer told me that he wanted KIA to be fired from his job and asked me if I would be willing to take it. I was flattered, but I explained to him that I didn't do enough cases to be qualified to be the cath lab director. Also, I felt that the cath lab needed someone who did angioplasty and did cath as their main professional activity. As it turned out, KIA was not fired, but his contract was not renewed when it came up for renewal after he had been on the job for two years.

The reason I was able to be attacked by KIA was that I was not in a powerful group and because I was not bringing much money into the hospital as a part-time practitioner. This is one example of how money is frequently more important than quality in today's medicine. It's also an example of how the hospital was creating a hostile work environment for me. There were more to come.

CHAPTER 63

FIGHTING FOR MY PATIENTS

In early 2000 I was taking care of an elderly woman in the ICU. She was extremely ill with congestive heart failure, kidney dysfunction, and large amounts of fluid in both sides of her chest between the lungs and chest wall (bilateral pleural effusions). She was requiring 100% oxygen to stay alive. I knew if we could take out the fluid from her chest, her breathing would improve, as would her general condition. As I mentioned in the case of Mrs. N., pleural effusions cannot easily be removed with hemodialysis. We needed to remove the fluid directly, with a needle.

I was off for the weekend and being covered by one of the cardiology groups. Bill Sims was rounding for the pulmonary group that weekend and was taking care of my patient's oxygen requirements. I was so concerned about her that I called Sims myself on Saturday morning and discussed the pleural effusions with him. He said the patient did not need a thoracentesis, but rather she needed urgent dialysis. He assured me he would take care of this and not to worry. I took him at his word. However, when I saw the patient on Monday morning, she was still on 100% oxygen and clearly in severe distress. No hemodialysis had been done, nor had she had a thoracentesis. I was appalled. I actually feared being sued for malpractice. I documented my call with Sims and the patient's status on the patient's chart. Subsequent to that, Sims wrote an angry note in the chart, denying that he had ever said the patient didn't need a thoracentesis.

While I was sitting just outside the patient's room, Laman and Sims approached me. Standing over me, they berated me in loud voices, saying the patient did not need a thoracentesis. I responded that I disagreed with them, but that it was not appropriate to discuss this in front of the patient's room and in front of the nurses. I asked Sims to step out in the hall to continue the conversation. He said that he did not want to step out into the hall but preferred to go out and "settle this in the parking lot." This was clearly a threat of physical violence. I again said we should discuss the situation in the hall. He again refused, reiterated his desire to settle it in the parking lot, and left. (I should mention here that Sims is a least four inches taller than I am.) I then went to talk to Deliere, who was also in the ICU, and practically begged him to do the thoracentesis on the patient. He grudgingly complied. The patient improved dramatically and no longer needed 100% oxygen. Her blood oxygen level rose simultaneously. I did not report Sims and Laman's behavior to anyone at that time.

Later that year, the pulmonary group found another doctor to replace Dr. Weaver. She was a tall, large woman who was trained as a critical care specialist. I will call her Dr. C. The hospital had a small reception for her, and I took the opportunity to discuss her understanding of the role of blood proteins in congestive heart failure. I mentioned my conversation with the course director at the Critical Care course in 1992. She seemed to agree with me on all points and I felt reassured. Later events proved I was wrong to feel that way.

Before I continue my story, I need to explain a little bit about the relationship between blood protein and congestive heart failure. These ideas were published by Dr. Guyton before I started medical school in 1969, and every medical student is taught about this in the freshman year physiology course. The concept is fairly simple. Normal blood contains protein. This consists of globulins, which are large molecules, and albumin, which is a smaller protein. As blood passes through the lungs from the right side of the heart to the left side, it passes through the pulmonary capillaries. While the blood is in the capillaries, oxygen passes from the alveoli in the lungs into the blood. Simultaneously, carbon dioxide passes from the blood into the alveoli and is then exhaled. The capillaries have very thin walls that allow this gas exchange. The walls are too thin to keep the water in the blood from oozing through them into the lungs.

The water pressure in the capillaries is pushing the water molecules out of the capillaries into the lungs.

The reason we don't drown from our own blood is because the protein in the blood attracts the water molecules and keeps them in the capillaries. The protein molecules are so large they cannot get through the capillary walls into the lungs. This attraction of the water molecules to the protein molecules in the capillaries is expressed as a pressure. When I was in school this was called the "plasma oncotic pressure" and is expressed in millimeters of mercury (mmHg). The more protein in the blood, the higher is the plasma oncotic pressure. With a normal amount of protein in the blood, the plasma oncotic pressure is about 25 mmHg. This is the pressure pulling the water in the blood into the pulmonary capillaries. The normal water pressure in the capillaries is less than 12 mmHg. Because the oncotic pressure is normally greater than the water pressure, the water stays in the capillaries and doesn't leak out in the lung tissue.

When the heart is weakened or too stiff (non-compliant), the pressure in the heart during relaxation (diastole) increases in order to maintain adequate pumping of blood. If the heart becomes so weak that that the pressure goes above 25 mmHg, the water pressure in the pulmonary capillaries will rise to this same level. Once the water pressure in the capillaries rises above the oncotic pressure, the water in the capillaries is pushed out into the lung tissue, and the lungs begin to fill up with fluid. This fluid accumulation in the lungs is what we call congestive heart failure. This is treated by lowering the pressure in the heart with various medications, most commonly a diuretic that causes excess water in the body to be eliminated through the kidneys.

Here's the problem. If the plasma protein is abnormally low, water will be pushed into the lungs at a lower capillary water pressure. Because the albumin molecules are smaller than the globulin molecules, albumin contributes most of the oncotic pressure. The reason for this is complicated, so I won't go into it here. For example, if the albumin is only 50% of normal, the oncotic pressure will be about 50% of normal, i.e. about 12-13 mmHg. So, the water molecules in the blood will leak into the lung tissue at a water pressure of only 12 instead of 25. The normal amount of albumin in the blood is 3.5-5.0 grams per 100 ml (grams %) of blood. The amount of albumin in the blood goes down in people with poor nutrition. Patients who cannot get adequate nutrition will consequently have less albumin in their blood. This is a frequent problem in very sick patients in the intensive care unit. While these patients can be fed with a stomach tube or intravenous line, it is not always possible to keep the albumin in the normal range.

One such patient was Mrs. L., who was in her late sixties or early seventies. Jim Brooks referred her to me because she had an abdominal aortic aneurysm. The aneurysm was so large that it needed to be treated with surgical removal and replacement of part of the aorta with a length of Dacron tube. Jim sent her to me at the office to evaluate whether or not she was healthy enough to survive the stress of this dangerous surgical procedure. She was otherwise healthy except for high blood pressure, which was well controlled, so I cleared her for surgery. Since I was now her cardiologist, I was responsible for her care during her hospitalization. Her surgery was performed in mid August, 2000.

Post operatively, Mrs. L. was unconscious and needed to be on a ventilator so it could breath for her. The pulmonary group was caring for the ventilator. Her blood pressure became extremely high at 260 mm Hg and was causing her brain function to be impaired. This is called "hypertensive encephalopathy" and is a very serious condition. For several days post operatively she had to remain on the ventilator, and I had to keep adding medication to lower her blood pressure. I got to the point where she was being treated simultaneously with five different medications. Despite this, her blood pressure stubbornly refused to come down. She was so sick the nurses were sure she was going to die. At around 2 a.m. one night, they called her husband at home to come to the hospital. This was normal procedure if a patient's death was imminent. I was on the phone with the nurses almost constantly throughout the night. I was racking my brain trying to figure out what the hell was going on with this lady. Finally, in a flash, I realized the problem was the Dacron graft.

The normal aorta is very elastic, so it expands when the pressure and flow in its lumen increases. This expansion limits the pressure increase. A Dacron graft is not as elastic. Once I realized what was going on, I knew the problem was that she just had too much fluid in her body. With a normal aorta, its expansion would ameliorate the rise in blood pressure caused by the excess fluid in her body. Because I had never seen or read about a similar problem, I had to deduce all this from basic principles and my knowledge of hemodynamics and physics. I came to the conclusion that the only way I was going to be able to lower her blood pressure was to get as much fluid as possible out of her body. I was treating her with a diuretic, just not enough.

At that point she had a catheter passed through a vein into her lungs to measure the water pressure in her pulmonary capillaries. By August 21st this pressure varied between 16 and 22 mmHg. Unfortunately, her blood albumin was down to 2.4. Because of the low albumin, this level of pulmonary capillary pressure would result in water being pushed into the lung tissue from the capillaries, resulting in congestive heart failure. If her condition was further complicated by heart failure, I thought she would have no chance of survival. Because I was having such a hard time lowering the capillary pressure, the only recourse was to raise her blood albumin level by infusing albumin directly into her bloodstream intravenously. I wrote an order for this.

The nurse caring for the patient that morning was Paula Gaffney. At around 9 o'clock that morning, Paula approached me and told me she thought my treatment was incorrect. Recalling my experience with Nurse M. in 1998, I made sure I didn't get into an argument with her. Instead, I took her out of earshot to explain what I was trying to do and why. She didn't agree, but I refused to change my treatment. It seemed to me that she didn't trust my judgment. Because I was only practicing part time, I didn't have as many patients in the ICU as I once had. She was fairly new, so I felt I had to take a little extra time with her so she could get to know me. I was obviously very concerned about Mrs. L., so I went to see her again at around 11 o'clock. Again Paula told me my treatment was wrong and that I was "over-diuresing" the patient. Again I took her aside to explain what I was doing, to no avail.

I went to the office to see patients and got back to the ICU around 2:30 p.m. Paula told me the patient's blood pressure had gone up after the intravenous albumin. Paula had spoken with Dr. C. about the increase in blood pressure, but neglected to call me about the problem. Dr. C. had taken it upon herself to discontinue my order for albumin without calling me first. In my 16 years at Jefferson at that point, no one had ever cancelled one of my orders without discussing it with me first. This was especially galling because the problem was heart failure and high blood pressure, clearly in my area of expertise. I felt Dr. C.'s behavior was outrageous and dangerous to the patient. I called her and told her that if she ever did that again, I would report her to the Chief of the Department of Medicine. I reordered the albumin at half the dose and pushed the diuretics.

Paula again told me that I was "over diuresing" the patient. By now the capillary pressure was down to 15. Her blood pressure was still very high, so I had to get more fluid off. Even though a normal capillary pressure is less than 12, the usual in you or me at rest would be around 6, so I had a lot more to do to get Mrs. L.'s blood pressure down. At this point Paula told me 15 was a "normal" capillary pressure. Now I felt that her ignorance was dangerous, not just for Mrs. L., but for all the patients Paula might care for in the future. I also thought that she had been indoctrinated by the pulmonary group. I felt it was my responsibility to teach Paula the truth about congestive heart failure. I asked Brenda Veschio, the head nurse in the ICU, to meet privately with me and Paula in Brenda's office. This was exactly what Dr. Lipman, the medical director of the ICU, had told me I should have done in the Nurse M. incident.

We sat down in Brenda's office for 40 minutes. I hoped that, with Brenda's help, I would be able to get through to Paula. I was not successful, as Paula continued to insist that her education was the equal of mine and she knew as well as I did what was best for Mrs. L. I told Paula a little about my education, but this did not alter her opinion that her education was the equal of mine. I explained the physiology relating to blood proteins and congestive heart failure. She said she knew all about it. By this point, I had been told by some of the other nurses that they were afraid of the pulmonary group. These nurses were afraid of expressing any disagreement with them for fear of retribution. They would only discuss this with me in hushed tones for fear of being overheard. It became clear to me that Paula was closely aligned politically with the pulmonary group and had adopted Deliere's stance on fluid management. I hoped that not too many of the other nurses in the ICU had bought into this nonsense. Here was a clear example of "might makes right." I resolved to educate the nurses, so I copied multiple articles and book chapters to give to the nurses and to Dr. C. I began to give lectures to the nurses about the issue, as I was told that the nurses were not taught the relationship of plasma proteins to the physiology of heart failure in nursing school.

By the day after my conversation with Paula and Brenda, Mrs. L. had urinated out eleven quarts of fluid. Her blood pressure had normalized and I was able to begin discontinuing her medications. She had woken up. Her breathing tube had been taken out and she was up sitting in a chair. She went home about a week later in good condition. I saw her in the office more than a year later, in November, 2001, with her husband. It was only then that I learned that he had been called to the hospital at 2 a.m. When I told her that I was going to retire from medicine, she asked me what she should do if she got sick again. She felt I had saved her life. I told her I couldn't recommend that she should return to Jefferson.

This is not the end of the story. Unbeknownst to me, Paula wrote me up for what occurred. The story she told was out of touch with reality. I didn't find out what she actually said until I got a copy of her letter as part of the discovery phase of my lawsuit. She distorted the truth in retaliation for my audacity in thinking that a cardiologist might know a little more about congestive heart failure than a young nurse. Her arrogance was amazing. It was only superceded by the arrogance of the pulmonary group in the months ahead. I also discovered that the medical staff leadership was tracking whether or not I spoke with Paula again. When I told the supervisor of the ICU, Louise Urban, about the articles I had copied for Paula and Dr. C to read, she told me not to give them to Paula directly. Instead, she asked me to put them in the nurses' lounge in the ICU for all the nurses. She said Paula felt "singled out." No one in the medical staff told me I wasn't supposed the talk to Paula again. Nevertheless, in my secret dossier, I found sequential entries asking whether I had spoken to her again. I didn't, but it was obvious that someone on the Medical Staff leadership was deliberately trying to entrap me. Dr. C. responded to the articles I gave her by sending me articles about the use of albumin in the ICU. These articles made no reference to the use of albumin for patients with congestive heart failure. She refused to discuss any of this with me, and it became obvious to me she had no idea what I was talking about.

CHAPTER 64

THE FIGHT CONTINUES

My attempts to reform the medical staff procedures having failed, I decided to try to work within the system. I was only working half time, so I thought I would have the time to do the duties of the President of the Medical Staff, which would require an eight year commitment. Prior to becoming president, a doctor had to spend two years each as secretary treasurer and vice president. After two years as president, he would serve two additional years as chairman of the Peer Review Committee.

Dr. Kris Gopal was chairman of the nominating committee. We had a good relationship over the years. He had treated me for a minor surgical problem, and I had been Chief of Medicine when he was President of the Medical Staff. On August 8, 2000 I sent the nominating committee a three and a half page letter outlining my qualifications for a position on the medical staff leadership. I asked Rick Collins and Stan Wetschler to read the letter before I sent it, and both of them thought it was good. They responded positively when I asked for their support for the position.

At the meeting of the nominating committee, Kris Gopal advocated for me. Unfortunately, Buzz Fingeret was also on the committee. Kris told me that Buzz objected to me because I was in the Department of Medicine and the last two people nominated were not surgeons. He used this argument to prevent my nomination. Instead, Chuck Cline, a general surgeon, was nominated. Chuck and I had an excellent relationship, and I thought he was a good choice. Kris told me that he thought my nomination would go through at the next two-year cycle. As it turned out, Chuck never did become president, and the next three presidents were from the Department of Medicine. I thought at the time that Fingeret's objections to me were related to the case of Mr. J.B. Considering I had displayed no deference to his being president when I voiced my criticisms of his care of my patient, I think he may have been afraid of me being in a position of power. As it turned out, I was forced to retire before the next election cycle.

My forced retirement, at the end of 2001, was in part related to my conflicts with the pulmonary group. After the episode with Dr. C. over Mrs.'s L.'s care, I felt reluctant to talk to her again. So, when Dr. C. wrote an order on an elderly woman patient of mine, I didn't feel comfortable calling her about it. I still wrestle with that decision in my mind, as the outcome was not good. Mrs. K. was in her late 70's or early 80's. She had had an episode of congestive heart failure and kidney failure in the past, which Bob Mitro, the nephrologist, and I had treated. Her kidneys had shut down at the time and she had required hemodialysis to remove the excess fluid from her body and lungs. Mrs. K.'s heart was able to pump well, but it was very stiff. This condition is referred to as diastolic dysfunction. Diastole is the period of time between heart contractions during which the heart relaxes. In a normal heart, the pressure in the left ventricle is quite low during diastole. As the heart stiffens over time, the pressure in diastole increases in order to fill the ventricle adequately to pump enough blood. However, the heart becomes very sensitive to the amount of fluid in the body. Therefore, it was imperative that Mrs. K.'s fluid status be kept within a narrow range. Too little fluid and her blood pressure would be too low. Too much fluid and the pressure in her heart in diastole would increase to the point that fluid would accumulate in her lungs. That is, she would go into heart failure.

When Mrs. K. was admitted to the hospital in early November, 2000, she was fluid-overloaded and in congestive heart failure. She responded well to diuretics, and in a few days her lungs had cleared, but she was still short of breath. I asked Emil Deliere to evaluate her pulmonary status. Emil wrote that her shortness of breath was due to musculoskeletal problems related to her advanced age, rather than due to any pulmonary disease. There was really no problem that required specific pulmonary treatment. She was getting her strength back and hopefully would have been able to go home soon. However, her blood work indicated that her kidneys were weakening slightly from diminished blood flow as her cardiac output went down with the removal of fluid from her body. In this circumstance, the diuretic needs to be reduced or discontinued. If this doesn't improve the kidney function, small amounts of fluid can be cautiously given orally or, if necessary, intravenously. Because the pressure in her heart in diastole could increase markedly with a small amount of additional fluid, too much fluid could cause her to go into heart failure. This was especially critical in Mrs. K.'s situation because her kidneys were weak and would not be able to excrete any excess fluid. If this treatment were unsuccessful, she would need another course of hemodialysis. Bob Mitro and I were watching her very closely.

When I saw Mrs. K. one afternoon, I was quite surprised to see that Dr. C. had seen the patient for the pulmonary group that day and written an order for intravenous fluids. Since the patient had a nephrologist and a cardiologist on her case, and she had no intrinsic pulmonary disease, it didn't make any sense to me that any pulmonologist would think it appropriate to address her volume status. Nevertheless, Dr. C. had ordered 1500 ml of saline solution to be given to the patient intravenously to increase her cardiac output and thereby improve her renal status. I thought this was way too much fluid, but I really didn't want to talk to Dr. C. about this, and it wouldn't have been right to change her order without first talking to her about it. Instead of calling her, I wrote a note in the chart saying we needed to observe the patient closely for recurrent heart failure. I thought at worst Mrs. K. would get some excess fluid in her lungs, which we could handle with diuretics or dialysis. I thought this would be a good opportunity for Dr. C. to learn when not to give excessive fluid to a patient. This was at the heart of the disagreement between the cardiologists and Dr. Deliere. I'm pretty sure the other pulmonologists in the group would not have taken it upon themselves to address the patient's volume status in light of the fact that Mitro and I were on the case. My supposition is that Dr. C. felt that, because she was trained in "Critical Care," she knew as well as a cardiologist or a nephrologist how to handle Mrs. K.'s complex fluid problems. I don't think that Dr. C. had ever seen Mrs. K. prior to that day and didn't have a firm grasp of her medical history and complex situation. In short, I thought Dr. C. had enormous chutzpah to do what she did.

Early the next morning, around five o'clock, I got a call at home from the nurses. Mrs. K. had gone into florid congestive heart failure and was transferred emergently to the ICU. She was now on a ventilator, which kept her alive. I didn't discuss the episode with anyone in the pulmonary group at the time. I hoped Dr. C. would see what happened to the patient after the fluid orders she gave. I spoke to the Chief of Medicine about the case. He advised me to submit the case to formal peer review, which I did. In the meantime, we could not get Mrs. K. off the ventilator. Bob Mitro was handling the renal problems. One day he wrote an order for albumin for the patient. I figured he had his reasons and didn't see any reason to object. Dr. C., on the other hand, took it upon herself to cancel Bob's order on November 26th. I couldn't believe it. I called Bob and told him what happened. Dr. C. had not spoken to him before canceling his order. When I asked Bob if he wanted the albumin discontinued, he said no and asked me to resume it.

I knew I was treading on thin ice, but something had to be done. I asked one of the nurses to listen in when I spoke to Dr. C., knowing that I might be accused of yelling at her if I didn't have a witness. I quietly told Dr. C. that her behavior was similar to what she had done in Mrs. L.'s case that August. I was going to keep my word and report her behavior to the Chief of Medicine. She responded that her group supported her on this issue. I said this had nothing to do with her group; it had only to do with her. I thought she was extremely disrespectful of Mitro and me. She seemed to feel she had license to act that way because she was in this powerful group. I later spoke to another doctor, an infectious disease consultant, who had had similar problems with Dr. C. changing his orders. Since the pulmonary group had no significant competition, they felt at liberty to behave as they saw fit. Had there been another pulmonary group with a substantial presence at Jefferson, no problem would have arisen. I would have just shifted my referral patterns to another group. I felt trapped. I felt the hospital should have made sure physicians would have at least two choices in every medical subspecialty. Every other medical subspecialty at Jefferson had at least two competing groups.

The next day, a Monday, while I was in the emergency department, I got a call from one of the senior physicians on the staff who told me he wanted to give me a "heads up." Laman had told him, "We are going to make his life miserable," referring to me. I told him I could take care of myself and not to worry. These guys seemed to feel they ran the hospital. I think they were also concerned that another pulmonary group was applying for privileges at Jefferson. I was told by a member of the other group and by at least one hospital administrator that Laman's group was doing everything they could to keep the other group out. As far as I was concerned I was fighting for my patients. I had absolutely no doubt that my first responsibility was to my patients, not to the hospital or to other doctors. Whether or not I was correct in my opinions is not the issue. I was convinced I was right, so I really had no other ethical course of action. More than a year later, on April 4, 2002, I was told by Bruce Payton, Vice President in charge of Clinical Services for the hospital, that the pulmonary group thought they were right and I was wrong. Regardless of who was right, I had an absolute right to express my honest medical opinion so long as I didn't violate a patient's privacy. During that same conversation, I told Bruce about Mrs. L. telling me her husband was called at 2 a.m. to come into the hospital because she was going to die. I told him I had been able to send her home in good condition. He responded, in a sincere tone of voice, "You are a great doctor who fights for his patients." He also volunteered that what had been done to me since that time was the fault of the Medical Staff leadership, not the fault of the hospital administration.

The retribution by the pulmonary group began almost immediately. I was called on the carpet for supposedly "harassing" Dr. C. She was the only doctor I had ever worked with at Jefferson who felt entitled to change other doctor's orders without talking to them first, and I was the one accused of being "unprofessional." As far as I was concerned, this was just the pulmonary group using their political muscle to carry out their stated intention of making my life miserable. I was going to speak the truth to the appropriate people and let the chips fall where they may. I didn't go around the hospital discussing the issue indiscriminately. I did mention the changing of orders once to one of the general internists who told Laman about it, but that was all. I certainly did not say anything that wasn't true.

On November 30, 2000 I was summoned to a meeting with Collins, Wetschler, Payton, Laman, and Donna Klos, an administrator, and was told I was harassing Dr. C. When I asked what I had said or done in this regard, I was told they didn't know what I did, but that Dr. C. had "perceived" harassment. I was asked to apologize to Dr. C. I was told to write a letter saying I was sorry that she perceived I was "harassing" her. I told the people at the meeting that many of the cardiologists I had worked with at the hospital felt very strongly that the pulmonary group gave too much fluid to some patients. We all agreed that we should have a conference with all the cardiologists, pulmonologists, and nephrologists to discuss the proper use of albumin and intravenous fluids in heart failure patients. Laman agreed to this conference in front of everyone. Of course, when I got a copy of the minutes of the meeting during the discovery phase of my lawsuit, this fact was conveniently omitted. I did, however, document this in a subsequent letter to Wetschler. I was elated about having the conference. It was what I had wanted for a long time. At that time at Jefferson, we had no conferences at which doctors were free to give their opinions about serious cases without fear of retribution. After the meeting, I told Wetschler that I thought the pulmonary group would not attend such a conference, and he said they didn't have a choice because he was going to mandate it. Two weeks later, Wetschler told me the pulmonary group was refusing to attend any conference.

The pulmonary group was not finished trying to make my life "miserable." The following week I received a letter from Bill Maruca, dated November 30, 2000. Mr. Maruca was a lawyer representing Dr. C. and the pulmonary group. He accused me of making "a number of false and defamatory statements regarding Dr. C." I was tired of this nonsense. I had had enough experience with the legal system to know one is never supposed to talk directly to the other side's attorney, but I didn't care. I wasn't going to waste time and money hiring a lawyer to respond to

Maruca. Instead, I immediately called him and told him in no uncertain terms that I was an honest person and did not lie. I said I had never said anything untrue about Dr. C. I told him that as long as I told the truth, my speech was protected. I was told later by Wetschler that I had said my speech was protected by the peer review law. I wrote back to clarify that I meant my speech was protected by the First Amendment to the Constitution of The United States. Maruca asked me what I said to Dr. C., and I told him I told her I was going to report her to the Chief of Medicine. I never heard from him again. I was going to stand up for my patients, period.

Mrs. K. remained in the ICU and could not be taken off the ventilator. Dr. Pandy, the primary care physician who referred Mrs. K. to me, told me that one day in the ICU Mrs. K. squeezed his hand and with her expression begged him to save her life. He started to cry when he told me this; so did I. One complication of prolonged ventilator therapy can be an esophageal tear. A tear of the lower esophagus is called a Mallory-Weiss tear. Mrs. K. suffered this complication and bled to death on November 30, 2000. It wasn't long before I had to fight for another one of my patients.

CHAPTER 65

THE LAST STRAW

I took to heart the need for me to get along with the pulmonary group. For people to get along, both sides have to make an effort. In my opinion, Dr. C. and her group were more interested in imposing their will on me than trying to behave civilly. This became apparent to me with the case of Mr. W. Mr. W. had been a patient of mine for about a decade before he was admitted to Jefferson Hospital in early December, 2000. His primary care physician was Tom Schaefer. Mr. W. had a history of blockages in his coronary arteries and a narrowing of his aortic valve. I had done a catheterization on him the previous January, at which time he had moderate narrowing of two of his three coronary arteries. His aortic valve was narrowed but not to the degree that it required surgical intervention. I had reviewed the films with Jim O'Toole and asked him to give me a formal consultation as to whether or not the patient would benefit from angioplasty, as the severity of the coronary disease did not warrant bypass surgery. Jim said it would be too dangerous to do an angioplasty because of the presence of a narrowed aortic valve. We decided to treat him with medications, and he did well, without symptoms of chest pain or shortness of breath until his subsequent admission to Jefferson.

On admission, Mr. W. had some fluid in his lungs. As I recall, Tom and I didn't know for sure if he had pneumonia or heart failure, but I think we initially treated him for both conditions. When he did not improve, he was transferred to the ICU. On a Thursday, I asked Bill Sims to pass a catheter through a vein into Mr. W.'s lungs to measure the pulmonary capillary pressure. The pressure was 24. Because of this high pressure, Bill and I agreed the patient had congestive heart failure. I reviewed the CAT scan of his chest with the chief of radiology, and we agreed that Mr. W. had both heart failure and pneumonia. I thought he had the pneumonia first and then developed heart failure because of the stress of the lung infection on his cardiovascular system. Infections are a known precipitating factor of congestive heart failure.

Given what was going on between me and the pulmonary group at the time, I went out of my way to communicate collegially with them, as I had been instructed to do. I saw Sims and Dr. C. together in the hospital on that Friday afternoon. Dr. C. was rounding for the pulmonary group that weekend, and I wanted to be sure we were on the same page in order to avoid any further disagreements. The three of us discussed Mr. W.'s case for a few minutes. We were in total agreement that the patient had congestive heart failure.

At this point I must digress to discuss a condition called "Acute Respiratory Distress Syndrome" or ARDS, a condition in which the walls of the pulmonary capillaries become diseased. The walls can no longer block the proteins from passing from the blood into the lung tissue. Water and protein will then accumulate in the lungs. On an x-ray it may be difficult to distinguish between congestive heart failure (CHF) and ARDS. The treatment of ARDS is done by pulmonary doctors, not cardiologists. During all the years I had been discussing the differential diagnosis of CHF from ARDS with the pulmonary group, I had read numerous scientific articles about ARDS. The diagnostic criteria always included the requirement that, for the diagnosis of ARDS to be made, the pulmonary capillary pressure had to be less than 19. Since Mr. W. had a pressure of 24, the diagnosis had to be CHF. That's why Sims had insisted that Mr. W had CHF and not ARDS after he placed the catheter into Mr. W's lungs on that Thursday.

Of course, the treatment of congestive heart failure requires removal of fluid from the body and the consequent lowering of pulmonary capillary pressure. In Mr. W.'s case, the capillary pressure had come down somewhat by Saturday morning, exactly what I was trying to accomplish. We were also treating his pneumonia with antibiotics. Since he had no underlying lung disease and his heart muscle was pretty strong, I felt he had a good chance to recover. So, when I got to the ICU on Saturday morning, I was appalled and deeply concerned to find that Dr. C. had changed her diagnosis to ARDS. I knew the pulmonary group liked to treat ARDS with more intravenous fluid. This therapy would be counterproductive to treating CHF, so the proper diagnosis was imperative. In addition, because of his illness, Mr. W.'s nutritional status was deteriorating and his albumin was low. To prevent worsening of his CHF, I felt he needed to be treated with diuretics, fluid restriction, *and albumin*. I thought the best way to handle the situation was to speak with Dr. C. and explain what I thought was going on with the patient.

I asked her, on the phone, why she thought the patient had ARDS. She replied the ARDS had been caused by the heart failure. I had never seen a case or read in any journal or textbook that CHF can cause ARDS. I subsequently asked several of the other cardiologists if they thought CHF can cause ARDS, and they all said no. I tried to explain what I had learned at the Critical Care course I had attended in 1992. When I mentioned that Dr. Parillo, the course director, said the albumin should be maintained at a level of 2.7 to 2.9, Dr. C. started to yell at me: "Richard…!" I was not about to be yelled at and hung up. We had both been instructed to be collegial with each other. Apparently, she thought this applied to me and not to her.

I knew my diagnosis and treatment were correct, and I was desperately trying to save Mr. W.'s life. We had a close relationship. He was a toy distributor and had given both my young children toys at Christmas and other times. He was one of the nicest people I knew. The only thing I could think of to do was call Stan Wetschler at home and ask for his advice and instructions. Stan remembered the case of Mrs. N. when Laman refused to come in to do the thoracentesis, and he had instructed me to call the chest surgeon to do it. The boss on every case is the patient's attending physician, so Stan instructed me to call Tom Schaefer and ask him who he wanted to manage the patient's fluid status. I was nearly panic-stricken when I spoke to Tom, and I told him Stan had instructed me to call him. I was absolutely convinced that increasing Mr. W.'s fluids would lead to his death, and I told Tom exactly what I thought. The truth was imperative and I felt I had to be as blunt as possible; this was no time to be pussy-footing around. "I can't guarantee you that if you let me do the fluids he will survive," I told Tom, "but I can guarantee you that if they do it he will die." Tom knew me well, and he knew I wouldn't say something like that unless I thought it was absolutely true. I also knew he trusted my clinical judgment.

Before I made the decision to call Wetschler that morning, I went through the following analysis. Because of my experiences with Dr. C. on Mrs. L. and Mrs. K., I thought it was not possible that the problems I was experiencing with the pulmonary group could be limited to my patients. My practice was quite small at that time. If three of my patients were being mismanaged by the pulmonary group in only a few short months, a simple statistical extrapolation meant there must be a much larger number of other doctors' patients being treated the same way. Since Dr. C. had told me her group supported her care, I felt the problem was a general one with her group. I knew many people felt intimidated by fear of retribution if they spoke out against the pulmonary group. I knew Larry's group felt this way, as did many of the ICU nurses.

I was sitting in front of Mr. W.'s room. He was utterly helpless. He was barely conscious and had a breathing tube in his windpipe. I thought of the movie "A Few Good Men," in which one of the Marines repeats the purpose of his service: "We are here to protect those who cannot protect themselves." At that moment Mr. W. was clearly one of those people who could not protect themselves. Since I knew it was mathematically certain that other doctors' patients were being treated the same way by the pulmonary group, I felt I had to speak out. When I was in Larry's group I could not have spoken out because doing so would put my partners at risk of retribution. Now I was in solo practice. I was being supported by my disability insurance, not my practice. I knew I would survive, even if I were forced out of medicine. I knew if I made a fuss, the pulmonary group would be out for my blood.

The usual form of retribution in medicine is for the retaliating doctors to stop sending patient referrals to the target of their ire. Since the pulmonary group wasn't sending me patients anyway, I figured they couldn't harm me. I knew they might use their power to set the hospital against me, but Stan Wetschler was my friend and was to take over as

President of the Medical Staff on January 1, 2001. In addition, Mike Nathanson, the Chief of Medicine, was my friend. I thought they would both stick up for me. I felt I had no moral choice but to speak out for the patients because no one else was in a position to do so.

Tom told me to go ahead and manage Mr. W.'s fluids. Mr. W. was requiring 80% oxygen to stay alive. Dr. C. wrote in her note that this would damage his lungs and that we had to get him down to less than 60% oxygen. I pushed hard on the diuretics and restricted his fluid. I also added intravenous albumin because his capillary pressure was greater than his protein pressure. By Monday morning his capillary pressure was down to nine. His cardiac output and blood pressure were normal and his chest x-ray displayed clearing of the fluid in his lungs. Plus, his oxygen requirement was down to 35%. I felt he had turned the corner and was on the road to recovery.

This was not to last. Over the weekend, the political aspects of his care had taken a turn for the worse. I was told by the nurses that Dr. C. had spoken to Dr. Schaefer on Saturday evening and had talked Tom into getting a second cardiology opinion. Whether or not Tom's acquiescence had anything to do with the fact that Prime Medical, run by Laman and Chauhan, owed him money is something you would have to ask him. Tom had previously told me that, when he left Prime, that group owed him a large sum of money and that he needed to refer his patients to them in order to support them so they would have enough money to pay him what they owed him. That Sunday afternoon a second cardiology opinion was rendered on Mr. W. Tom had consulted a cardiologist whom I will call Dr. Politics. Dr. Politics had been with a large group from which he had been asked to leave. He told me he had gone to court against them and received a substantial monetary settlement. He had told me he wanted to build his own group. Since Laman controlled Prime, and they had many patients to refer, it made sense for Dr. Politics to play ball with them. He would have wanted to represent himself as a supporter of the pulmonary group.

Dr. Politics was off that Sunday and one of the cardiology fellows from one of the teaching hospitals was seeing his patients for him. I was somewhat thunderstruck when the ICU nurse caring for Mr. W. told me that the fellow had made the diagnosis of ARDS. I knew he had made a mistake and was determined to rectify it. I tried calling Dr. Politics at his home but couldn't reach him. Instead, I got hold of his covering fellow. I told him about Mr. W.'s medical history and recent hospital course. He told me he didn't know the details of the case, but now that he had heard them, he agreed totally that the diagnosis was CHF and pneumonia, not ARDS. I called Stanley to update him on the situation, and he told me that he subsequently spoke to the cardiology fellow. I thought and hoped that I had been able to straighten things out and save Mr. W.

When I arrived in the ICU that Monday morning, December 11, 2000, I found that Tom had thrown me off the case. Despite the fact that Mr. W. had shown x-ray and hemodynamic evidence of marked improvement with my treatment, Dr. Politics wrote on the patient's chart that Mr. W. had ARDS. Dr. Politics ordered the patient to have more fluids, 500 cc's of normal saline (salt water). I knew this was going to make his heart failure worse and thereby lead to his demise. There was absolutely no doubt in my mind that this was going to lead to his death. This is exactly what I had told Tom previously. But, as I was no longer on the case, I could not write a progress note or an order on the patient's chart. I also knew I would face allegations of being inappropriate if I tried to interfere in the patient's care. As I sat in the ICU at the entrance to Mr. W.'s room, I faced an ethical dilemma. I could just keep my mouth shut or do something to try to save him. I thought about telling his family, but I knew that would create the possibility of a malpractice suit, so I didn't. But I knew I couldn't live with myself if I didn't do everything I could to try to save Mr. W.

So, instead, I tracked down Tom and Dr. Politics and spoke to each one separately and in private. I pleaded with Tom to stop the extra fluids but he declined. He thanked me for not talking to Mr. W.'s family. Dr. Politics told me he would not change his treatment or diagnosis. I again pleaded with him, as I had with Tom, to no avail. He told me he would take care of Mr. W. and not to worry; he would keep me informed about the patient. I would never do a second opinion without talking to the cardiologist who had given the first opinion. Dr. Politics had done something similar to me on a previous occasion, when he assumed the emergency care of one of my patients one evening, in the ICU, without calling me to find out the patient's history. That patient died. I considered the possibility that he might have been asked to leave his previous group for similar behavior.

Mr. W. remained on the ventilator without any improvement over the next several days. By that Friday, I guess Dr. Politics admitted to himself that his diagnosis was wrong, and that Mr. W. did in fact have congestive heart failure and not ARDS. He manifested this by transferring the patient to a hospital in Pittsburgh for a cardiac catheterization. He told me the catheterization indicated that Mr. W. needed urgent heart surgery. (A patient with active ARDS would never be sent for heart surgery.) He consulted the cardiac surgeons at that hospital, who turned the patient down because he was too sick to tolerate open heart surgery. Dr. Politics told me that Mr. W. died at the other hospital four days later.

I kept Wetschler informed of these events in the hopes that he would use the information to understand why I was so concerned about the pulmonary group. I figured two dead bodies in less than a month would convince him that something was wrong. It didn't. I wondered to myself, *How many dead bodies does it take to convince these guys?* Instead I was called on the carpet again, in late December, 2000, and was forced to meet with Borrero, Wetschler, Payton, and Collins. I called Stanley to ask if I could have Joel Dresbold be a witness at the meeting. I didn't want Joel to negotiate, but I felt I needed a witness to prevent further lies being spread about me. They refused. At the meeting, in the medical staff conference room, I was excoriated for "talking down to the nurses." They wouldn't tell me what I had said or to whom I had said it. I was left to guess what I had supposedly done. Does this sound a little like what life is like in a dictatorship? It certainly seemed that way to me. I couldn't believe I was living in the United States of America.

Dr. C. was invited to the meeting for a few minutes. I had written to Stanley prior to the meeting, after I got the letter from Bill Maruca, the pulmonary group's attorney, accusing me of making defamatory comments about Dr. C. I asked him to ask Dr. C. what I had said about her and to whom I had said it. He never answered. At the meeting, he asked Dr. C. what I had done to harass her. She replied that I had told her I was going to report her to the Chief of Medicine. Reporting her was within my rights, and I believe, was normal procedure under the bylaws. So I was being castigated for exerting the rights granted to all the hospital's doctors in order to protect their patients. I was forced to write a letter of apology to Dr. C.

Six months later, I saw Wetschler in the Medical Office Building. I mentioned to him that the hospital had to obey the laws of the United States of America and the State of Pennsylvania. He disagreed and said, "I think we can do what we want, but I'll check it out." He really seemed to think that being President of the Medical Staff put him above the law. This was similar to Fingeret's sense of immunity from criticism in the case of Mr. J.B. in 1998. Power corrupts, and absolute power corrupts absolutely.

In order to determine what charge they had been talking about, I had to speak privately with individual nurses. I spoke to ten different nurses in various parts of the hospital. With one exception, all the nurses said that I had never talked down to them, nor had they ever heard any other nurse complain I had talked down to them. I had worked with some of these nurses for the entire 16 years I had been at Jefferson. The only exception to this was that Paula Gaffney had complained about me because of the one incident with Mrs. L. It was apparent that Wetschler and Payton were exaggerating and/or fabricating events in order to punish me for criticizing the pulmonary group. The events of 2000 were a harbinger of 2001, when I was driven out of medicine for good by some of these same individuals.

CHAPTER 66

2001

The fallout from the cases of Mrs. K. and Mr. W. continued into the New Year. After Mr. W died in December, 2000, I told Tom Schaefer I wanted to discuss the case with him, but that we should wait until after the holidays. Wetschler had told me that the consultants on Mr. W.'s case could not be held responsible for his outcome because it was the responsibility of the attending physician to understand the disease process well enough to choose his consultants wisely. I planned to talk to Tom about what Wetschler said and how that related to Mr. W.'s demise. He agreed to meet with me in January. When we met privately I explained in detail what had happened to Mr. W. I wasn't angry but I was disappointed in Tom's behavior. I felt he knew I was right and I resented that he had played a role in what happened. I told him I didn't want him to consult me anymore, but that, according to Wetschler, he had to be more careful in picking his consultants. Of course, he was in the same boat as the rest of us in having only one realistic choice of pulmonary consultants.

Later that spring, I got a letter from the peer review committee about Mr. W.'s case in response to the letter I wrote them asking them to review the case. It said there were no quality issues because the principles involved were controversial. (In my freshman physiology class at Michigan, the principles were *not* controversial!) The chairman of the peer review committee was Buzz Fingeret. On May 7, 2001, I wrote Buzz a letter, asking to make an appointment with him to discuss ARDS and congestive heart failure in general. He never replied.

In January, 2001, Sims was still behaving as if he wanted to make my life miserable. This manifested itself in his behavior regarding one of my own patients. Mr. U. was an elderly gentleman admitted in January directly to the ICU on my service. Because I was the attending doctor of record, I had the final say in his care. I was also responsible for communications with his family. Mr. U. had suffered a major heart attack at home and had gone into cardiac arrest prior to arriving at the hospital. As a result, he developed what is called "anoxic encephalopathy." This is the injury or death of brain cells due to lack of blood flow and oxygen delivery that result when the heart stops pumping blood to the brain. Rarely, the brain will recover from this injury. However, if there is no sign of improvement in 72 hours, the patient will usually not survive. Mr. U. showed no signs of improvement after three days. The neurological consultants evaluated him thoroughly and essentially concluded he was brain dead and had no hope of recovery. The pulmonary group was on the case because the patient was on a ventilator.

Mr. U.'s heart had suffered so much damage that he started to slip into heart failure. Because of this, I had to be very careful not to give him too much intravenous fluid. Even though I knew he would die, I didn't know for sure that he was completely immune to discomfort. Having one's lungs fill with fluid is *very* uncomfortable, so I did not want to take any chances this would occur. Once I came to the conclusion that he had no chance, I decided that he could go to a regular bed and be treated as a hospice patient. We would keep him as comfortable as possible with medications until the end. This decision can be very delicate and requires careful empathic discussion with the family members. It is the role and responsibility of the attending physician, in this case me, to talk to the patient's family and obtain their permission, as the family has the final say in any decisions.

So, when I arrived in the ICU on the morning the patient was to be transferred out of the ICU, I was surprised to learn from the nurses that Sims had taken it upon himself to talk to the family. I remarked to the nurses that Sims was trying to undermine me. I didn't learn until the discovery phase of my lawsuit against Sims that my conversation with the nurses had been put into my file. The nurses said that I showed no disrespect toward Sims and had not been inappropriate in any way. Nevertheless, the fact was that the Medical Staff leadership, which included Sims, Wetschler, and Fingeret, were secretly monitoring me to use anything they could against me to shut me up or get rid of me.

Sims seemed to be trying to show me that he could use his power as Vice President of the Medical Staff to abuse me and get away with it. He was certainly demonstrating his desire to make my "life miserable," but he didn't stop there. He took it upon himself to increase Mr. U.'s fluids from 25cc/hr to 80cc/hr., despite the fact that his chest x-ray that morning clearly showed excess fluid in his lungs. I decreased his fluids. The next day I saw Sims in the hallway by the patient-and staff-only elevators. There was no one around who could overhear the conversation. I took this as another opportunity to enlighten him about the necessity of limiting fluids in patients with heart failure. He took umbrage at my audacity that a cardiologist might know more about heart failure than a lung doctor and said, "Let me clue you in, Richard; I knew that."

I said, "Good," and that was the end of the conversation. Then I asked myself, *If he knew that, then why did he give so much fluid?* I found out later that he wrote a letter of complaint about me for having talked to him about the issue. He said he was just trying to make the patient comfortable. Well, if he knew that 80cc/hr was too much, then why did he give that much? Did he think filling Mr. U.'s lungs with fluid was going to make him more comfortable? I don't know. But what I did know was that he was using any excuse, even this minor episode, to put more letters into my file in his crusade to assassinate my character.

At the meeting with Borrero, Wetschler, Collins, and Payton in December, 2000, I was forced to sign a letter allowing Borrero, the Chief of Psychiatry, to communicate directly with Paul Scott. I signed the letter because it said the information had to be "mutually agreed" upon and conveyed in an "honest and accurate manner." So I was quite surprised when Paul Scott showed me a letter he got from Borrero, dated February 15, 2001 accusing me of three things, all of which were not "mutually agreed upon" and all of which were not "honest and accurate" concerning my relationships with other doctors in the hospital. I had had no similar problems with any other physicians at Jefferson, but the few doctors I had privately criticized for negligence—the pulmonary group and Fingeret—had gotten themselves into positions of power in the hospital and were using those positions to spread lies and exaggerations about me because I had the courage to stand up against them in my determination to protect my patients. I also had reason to believe that they were responsible for soliciting letters defaming me from Paula Gaffney and Tom Schaefer. I know for a fact that Borrero wrote what they told him to write in his letter to Dr. Scott. I know this because I asked him one day, in the hospital parking lot, why he had written the letter to Scott. He said, "I just wrote what they told me to write."

Not only were false letters being written about me, but Wetschler was continually refusing to ask me for my version of events. He just took the accusations as fact and kept repeating them. I was getting very frustrated. Bruce Payton subsequently told me, "In every hospital I have ever worked, doctors are always guilty until proven innocent." So I was guilty of all these unprofessional behaviors, even though they never occurred, and all I was trying to do was save my patients' lives.

Because I was still under the assumption that the 17 years I had known Stan Wetschler would cause him to give me some degree of credibility, I decided to call him at home one evening. He refused to talk to me in any other venue. He began by chastising me for criticizing the pulmonary group. He persisted in his insistence that I had done something wrong. I told him this was not about my complaints about other doctors; it was about the unnecessary deaths of Mrs. K. and Mr. W. Still, he kept defending them. Again I kept thinking to myself, *How many dead bodies does he need until he understands there is something terribly wrong going on here?* I thought two was more than enough. He asked me to give him permission to talk to Paul Scott directly. I thought this was better than nothing, so I agreed. I couldn't understand why he was hanging me out to dry after I had done so much for his patients and his family over the years. I may have finally found the answer in January, 2005.

I was attending a cardiology seminar at a hotel in downtown Pittsburgh. Connie, the nurse I had worked with in Adler's group and afterwards as one of their referring physicians, was at the seminar, and we got to catching up on each other. Connie told me that Wetschler had been angling for the job of Vice President for Medical Staff affairs at Jefferson. This was a salaried administrative position, not a voluntary clinical job like president. (The president did receive a small stipend from the hospital, however.) Stan was retiring from the active practice of medicine because of his health, but in our private conversations, he told me he had some money problems. He was in his mid-fifties and still wanted to work. Connie told me that, after I left, Wetschler had been turned down for the job. In retrospect, that would explain his behavior. Maybe he thought he had to show the hospital that he was tough enough to handle me. I can't think of any other reason he would have kowtowed to the pulmonary group; he needed their political support to get the job over his competition. Paul Scott told me later that he thought Wetschler and the others had no idea with whom they were dealing. I hope that my lawsuit was the reason the hospital didn't hire him.

Wetschler and Borrero spoke in a conference call to Dr. Scott on March 8, 2001. When Paul told me about the conversation, he said that they had made reference to my conversations with Tom Schaefer about Mr. W. and with Sims about Mr. U. I didn't know until then that Schaefer and Sims had written letters excoriating me for what I knew was just normal discourse among physicians. I knew instantly that Sims had instigated a letter writing campaign against me. I was furious. They were doing everything in their power to shut me up and prevent me from protecting my patients. If this wasn't creating a hostile work environment, I don't know what would be. I knew their behavior violated my protections under the Americans with Disabilities Act (ADA). They knew I had a legally recognized disability, bipolar disease, and they were putting me in a stressful situation to get me to crack. I was determined not to. These guys were using all their power to avoid any accountability for what they had done to my patients. I was going to fight back.

CHAPTER 67

FIGHTING FOR THE TRUTH

After getting nowhere trying to tell the truth about my patients to Wetschler, I looked for other avenues to fight for the patients. At most hospitals in which I have worked, conferences were held periodically to discuss difficult cases. At these conferences, which were closed to the public, doctors were supposed to be allowed to discuss their honest opinions without fear of retribution. Despite the fact that Wetschler told me he was mandating a conference on the use of albumin and fluids in heart failure patients, he told me that Laman and his group were refusing to attend any such conference. In response I set about to try to institute periodic conferences at the hospital. Barbara Juriga was another solo cardiologist at Jefferson who held the same opinions as I did concerning treatment and diagnosis of congestive heart failure in the ICU. Because we both feared that she would be subjected to retribution by the pulmonary group, we had to keep our attempts to orchestrate the development of these conferences secret.

Jefferson Hospital was going through a period of change in early 2001. Jan Jennings had just been appointed CEO. He was very energetic and proclaimed his desire to make Jefferson into "the best community hospital in the country." I had high hopes that his desire for quality care would help me institute the conferences, called M & M, for Morbidity and Mortality. Bruce Payton told me that when Jennings found out Jefferson did not have an M & M conference, he expressed disbelief. Jennings noted that all the hospitals he had worked in had had M & M conferences. I even think such conferences are mandated for every hospital in order to be accredited.

The other big change at Jefferson was the start of the open heart surgery program. The hospital was investing millions of dollars to start it. The medical directors of the program were going to be two prominent cardiac surgeons from teaching hospitals in Pittsburgh. Dr. Park headed a large group at St. Francis Hospital, and Dr. Machiraju was Chief of Cardiac Surgery at Shadyside Hospital. Both were outstanding surgeons. Barbara Juriga and I thought this presented an opportunity to get political support for M & M conferences, so we met with the surgeons. They too were surprised that Jefferson had no M & M conferences and felt that any hospital with a heart surgery program must have them. But Dr. Park expressed his concern that he had to advocate for the conferences gingerly to avoid political problems with the pulmonary group. I was satisfied and optimistic.

About the same time, Jan Jennings hired a consulting firm to evaluate the needs for other additional doctors at Jefferson. Most of the members of the medical staff were interviewed individually and in private for their opinions. During my interview, I was asked my opinion about which specialties at Jefferson needed additional doctors. I was assured repeatedly by the man who interviewed me that my opinions would be confidential. He told me this was to prevent those interviewed from fearing retribution from other doctors. I told him I was satisfied with the quality and choices in every specialty except pulmonary. At the conclusion of the interview he confided in me the concerns of the other doctors that had been interviewed by his firm. He said that at most, only five percent of the medical staff was dissatisfied with any one specialty at the hospital. He told me there was only one exception: pulmonary medicine. He said that fully 20 percent of the doctors interviewed had said the hospital needed more pulmonary physicians. Since probably only about 20 percent of the hospital staff spent much time practicing in the ICU, this was a remarkable result. I felt vindicated and optimistic that my concerns about the pulmonary group would be effectively addressed.

But Wetschler had escalated his assault on me in his and Borrero's conversation with Paul Scott in March, 2001. The allegations they made against me were quite serious, and I knew they could use them against me to threaten to have me thrown off the staff. I felt I had to document everything that had occurred, so I decided to write a letter directly to Wetschler detailing all the events. I wrote the letter so that any attorneys who read it would have a clear idea of what actually occurred, not the fantasies that had been written and said about me. Given the events of 1997, I knew I might have to defend myself in court. Contemporaneous documentation is always more credible than retrospective recollections. I spent a month writing the letter. It was dated April 12, 2001 and was 17 single-spaced pages (see appendix A). I included the names and comments of all ten nurses I had spoken with about my supposedly "talking down to the nurses" charge and asked Wetschler to speak with each of them to verify that the allegations against me were untrue. I sent copies of the letter to Chuck Cline, the Secretary Treasurer of the Medical Staff, Paul Scott, Gary Perecko, the Chief Operating Officer, Bruce Payton, and Paul Verardi, the hospital's attorney. I wanted to give them the sense that I was prepared and capable of defending myself legally if necessary, but that I wanted to avoid doing so. I told them I was not a litigious person, had never filed a lawsuit against anyone, and had no desire to sue the hospital or anyone else. I just wanted them to stop lying about me and let me take care of my patients.

The letter had a dramatic effect. Two or three days later, Laman and Sims spoke to me in the most deferential terms any doctors have ever spoken to me. From that point on, I had no more problems with their care of my patients. Obviously, someone had spoken to them about my letter. I saw Paula Gaffney in the ICU. I didn't talk to her, but she stared at me with fear and trepidation. The timing suggested to me that someone had spoken to her about her unprofessional behavior in her care of Mrs. L. I asked Wetschler if there had been anything wrong with the letter. He said: "Nothing." I spoke to Chuck Cline about everything that had transpired. "I didn't to anything wrong," I said.

"I know," he responded. I knew any objective observer would think I was the target of a big-time hatchet job. My "secret dossier" showed no evidence that Wetschler or anyone else had ever spoken to any of the ten nurses I asked him to speak with. To me this was a clear indication that Wetschler had a reckless disregard for the truth and was just out to intimidate me.

Nevertheless, I got a letter back from Stanley, dated April 27, 2001, telling me to keep my mouth shut in the future. If I had any complaints I was to put them in writing. I had no trouble with that. But I had no further complaints as I was now getting the type of care from the pulmonary group that my patients deserved. Stanley said he was going to treat me like every other member of the medical staff in the future. I felt the issues were resolved. But Wetschler was still out to get me, "big time."

By the spring of 2001, my practice was growing significantly. Several primary care physicians were referring their cardiac patients to me almost exclusively. The biggest referrer was Lee McCormick. Lee told me he had been forced out of Prime and said they had tried to destroy his career. Lee was in his sixties and told me he did not have enough financial resources to retire comfortably. Fortunately, he had managed to stay in practice. We then re-established the relationship we had had before he joined Prime a number of years prior. At the rate I was going, 2001 was shaping up to be the first year in which I would reach my goal of $60,000. I was planning to practice until age 65, the year 2012. I was next in line to be elected to the Medical Staff Leadership. I planned to use my position to reform the Medical Staff procedures so that other innocent doctors would not be subjected to potentially career-ending punishments, as I had been in 1997.

But I began to run into patient care problems again, this time in the cardiology department. Treadmill tests were done in the department in the morning. The hospital liked the fact that I didn't do these tests in my office, because they could bill for the technical component of tests I did on my patients using their facilities. I had been working in the department for 17 years and had excellent relationships with all the staff there. I was always on time. If I were stuck in an emergency, I would call them to put someone else's patient in front of mine, and I would come as soon as possible. Not all the other cardiologists were as considerate. Sometimes they would be an hour late and refuse to allow another cardiologist's patient to have their test done in the interim. At all the other hospitals in Pittsburgh in which I had practiced, doctors were expected to be on time for stress tests. If they were more than a few minutes late, their patients were disconnected from the machine and the next patient in line took their place.

Increasingly, in the summer of 2001, my patients were being delayed. Patients were being forced to lie on stretchers in the hallway for uncomfortably long periods of time. In addition, the women who worked in the department had been asking my assistance to help them rectify the poor working conditions in their department. They complained of poor staffing, lack of break time, and lack of lunch time, in addition to the unreasonable delays caused by the failure of some cardiologists to show up for their tests in a timely fashion.

On July 10, 2001, one of my patients was delayed for over an hour. I sat in the stress room for a while, commiserating with the staff. I felt the administration was wasting a lot of expensive employee time with their policies, and I commented to two of the technicians, "What do you guys do while you're waiting for the other cardiologists—twiddle your thumbs?" I was trying to be sympathetic to their concerns. I few minutes later I was told by one of the staff that Wanitta Anderson, one of the technicians, was in the bathroom crying because of what I had said. She said she thought I was criticizing her when I made my comments. I told her I didn't like people complaining about me behind my back for something that hadn't actually occurred. I thought that was the end of it. What I didn't know was that she had an ulterior motive.

Things were getting out of control in the cardiology department. I spoke to Terry Riffer, the administrator in charge of the department, about the problems with doctors not showing up for their tests. He told me he had met with the cardiologists about the issue and was told he could not institute a time limit. I was appalled that the doctor's convenience would take priority over patient care. I knew the only reason the doctors wanted to be able to be as late was they wanted was to keep up their work pace in the other areas of the hospital in order to maximize their income. If they were stuck with real patient care emergencies, there was no reason another doctor's patient could not be tested while they were tied up. Jefferson had always been a patient first hospital. I was quite concerned that greed was taking priority over patient welfare. I spoke to Pete Lemis, the cardiologist in charge of the department, a friend of mine to whom I referred half of my permanent pacemaker patients. He was sorry but said there was nothing he could do.

That Friday, July 13, 2001, things boiled over. I had two treadmill tests scheduled for that morning, and patients were due to arrive in the office starting at noon. Both my tests were scheduled with plenty of time to finish before I had to get to the office. Because one or two of the other cardiologists were more than an hour late, my patients had to wait. Both of them waited for two hours on stretchers in the hallway. The staff told me another patient had been forced to lie on a gurney for three hours waiting for her test. I just couldn't believe the hospital was tolerating patients being treated in such a callous manner. I was told by the staff which cardiologists had not shown up on time for their tests; both were members of large groups. I felt that my patients had every right to be treated equally with theirs, despite the fact that I only had a small practice at that point.

I went to the office to see patients at noon and awaited the call saying my patients were ready. It was almost 1 o'clock when my first patient was ready. I left the office and went back to the hospital. The first patient, Mr. Porter (not his real name), was complaining bitterly about having to wait so long. After I finished his test, I called Terry Riffer and left him a voice mail message about what had occurred, saying that something had to be done. I then called my office to see if I had time to do the second test before seeing the next patient in the office. The next patient was actually a patient of Wetschler's whom I had been taking care of for many years. My secretary told me he couldn't wait any longer. Wanitta was in the room with me. When I got off the phone, I was facing the desk by the wall. She approached me from behind and started arguing with me that I couldn't go back to the office without doing the next test. I knew Mr. Porter was sitting a few feet away from us and I didn't want to get into an argument in front of a patient. I turned around with the intention of gently brushing the tips of the fingers of my right hand across the upper part of her left arm as an indication that she should be quiet. She was a lot closer to me than I thought, and the back of my right hand accidentally made contact with the front of her left shoulder. I said I was sorry and put my right arm around her shoulders and practically whispered in her left ear: "Wanitta, give me a break. I'm under a lot of stress here." She didn't say anything and just stood there.

I told her I would go talk to the other patient before I went to the office and would be back as soon as possible.

The other patient, Mr. R., was in the next room. He told me he hadn't been given anything to eat since the previous evening (patients have to fast for a treadmill test.) He was starving and beside himself with frustration and anger. I totally agreed with his sentiments. I apologized profusely for the hospital and told him I would be back as soon as humanly possible. When I returned from the office, I was looking for Wanitta and Deb, the RN, to do Mr. R.'s test. Deb did the test with me. What I didn't know at the time was that Wanitta was again in the bathroom crying. She was also contemplating the fictitious story she was going to make up so she could try to sue me for $50,000 for assault and battery.

CHAPTER 68

FOOL ME ONCE, IT'S YOUR FAULT; FOOL ME TWICE, IT'S MY FAULT

The episode in the stress lab on Friday July 13, 2001 had left a bad taste in my mouth, and I was beginning to doubt that the hospital had the ability and the desire to care for my patients properly. By Monday morning I was talking to myself in frustration. I didn't know what else to do. It turned out that Wanitta was going to make the next move: She had complained that I had assaulted her. I was notified that Wetschler wanted to meet with me in the Medical Staff Office at noon. As soon as he walked into the room he said, "We all know what happened." He didn't tell me what he thought had happened and didn't ask me for my version of events. Instead he demanded that I take an immediate "voluntary medical leave of absence." He had a letter for me to sign typed up on hospital stationary. The letter even had my middle initial as "P" instead of "R."

I told Wetschler I wasn't sure I wanted to do this, but I was willing to take a three week leave to straighten things out. He left the room and returned five minutes later. I assumed he called the hospital attorney, Paul Verardi, to ask what he should do. He returned and said he would not allow me to do that. He also said that if I demanded due process I would surely be found guilty and thrown off the medical staff. This would result in a report to the National Practitioner Data Bank, and likely result in the end of my medical career. He told me that they had a statement from the patient in the room with me and Wanitta, confirming Wanitta's version of events. This was a bald-faced lie. He also subsequently wrote to the Pennsylvania Human Relations Commission that he had a statement from the patient. It is a crime to lie to a government agency in Pennsylvania. I didn't doubt he had a statement from Mr. Porter, but he refused to tell me what was said. Because of his lie about having a statement from Mr. Porter, corroborating Wanitta's story, I felt obliged to sign the letter and take a LOA.

Since I knew the problem had arisen in the context of a poorly-run stress lab, I asked if they could accommodate me in the future by doing my stress tests before noon each day. I knew that, under the Americans with Disabilities Act (ADA), the hospital was required to make reasonable accommodations for me because of my disability. Terry Riffer, who was at the meeting, told me that he could not accommodate me in any way. Wetschler had notified Tom Hobbs, the Director of the Physicians Health Program in Harrisburg, about what I had supposedly done. Hobbs told me I had to be in his office the next day, Tuesday July 17, 2001.

After I arrived at Hobb's office, Hobb's got Wetschler on the speaker phone. The meeting lasted at least an hour. When I asked Wetschler why he wanted me out of the hospital, he replied, "You are a perfectionist who expects other doctors to live up to his standards." This was clearly the honest reason for his behavior. The event with Wanitta was just an excuse. Instead, I was being punished for having the temerity to fight for my patients' lives against those in positions of power. Basically what he was saying was that I was too good a doctor and that Fingeret, Sims, and Laman resented what I believed to be heartfelt and scientifically accurate criticism. I asked him if any other doctors at Jefferson had ever complained about me. He refused to answer. The fact was that, in 17 years at Jefferson, to my knowledge, not one other single doctor (except for Dr. KIA, of course) had ever complained to the hospital about my behavior. When I pointed this out, he said it didn't matter. Does this remind you of the Queen of Hearts saying, "Sentence first, trial later"?

Hobbs made his living by getting referrals from hospitals and he couldn't afford to stand up to Wetschler and risk losing a referral source. Wetschler insisted that I be sent to some institution to correct my personality, someplace like the psychiatric hospitals the old Soviet Union used to imprison people who were "mentally ill" because they disagreed with the government. Wetschler preferred a place in California. Hobbs insisted I be sent to Alabama. I knew this meant that he would get the report he wanted. It seemed to me he was trying to avoid the possibility that he would get a contradictory report from any referral institution. This was similar to what had occurred at the Farley Center and the Menninger Clinic in 1997. It seemed to me that Hobbs had to make sure that the referral institution had its first loyalty to him as a referral source, not to me as a patient.

I was referred to Dr. Sandra Frazier, a psychiatrist, who ran a program called "Health for the Healer" at the University of Alabama at Birmingham. I had been through this play before. The most important thing for me to do was to get this Kafkaesque nightmare over with and get back to work as soon as possible. Unfortunately, no place in the program was available until the end of September. I was still able to practice in my office, but I didn't have enough work in the office to keep my practice financially solvent. I immediately stopped taking any salary. The practice had about $12,000 in cash. Between my office billings and the cash on hand, I would be able to keep the practice solvent for a few months. Overall, I was losing about a hundred dollars a day from that point on.

What I didn't find out until the discovery phase of my lawsuit was that Wetschler had gone to the CEO with his complaints on July 18, 2001. Jennings was quoted as saying that, because of my assault on Wanitta, my relationship with the hospital should be terminated. So the decision to get rid of me was made even though the hospital bylaws mandated that any doctor who takes a medical LOA had to be reinstated without humiliation or prejudice. Because I wasn't told of this decision, I complied with their request to go to Alabama. In the meantime, I repeatedly asked that I be allowed to go back to work before my trip. I was told no and continued to think that I would be allowed back if I completed the program and got Hobbs's approval.

My appointment in Alabama was for September 24th through the 28th. I called Dr. Frazier to discuss the situation with her in advance of my trip. I wanted to tell her the truth before she heard all the lies about me. She was very nice on the phone, and I had high hopes she could help me set the record straight. I sent her a copy of my April 12th letter to Wetschler and a letter I sent to Jan Jennings on September 16th (see appendix B) in which I pleaded for his help. I sent Jennings the letter informing him of the truth. I knew we might be heading for a lawsuit and I wanted to make sure that the hospital could not plead ignorance. I hoped that perhaps Frazier was a decent person who would have the courage to stand up for the truth.

At the beginning of August I knew my days at Jefferson might be numbered, so I immediately set out to look for another job in Pittsburgh. At that time Ben was in 10th grade and Sarah was in 7th. Since Barbara and I had joint legal custody, I had to stay in Pittsburgh in order to remain part of their lives. They came first, period. I put together an updated curriculum vitae and sent it out to hospitals I thought might need a half-time cardiologist. I put an advertisement in the newspaper and the medical society bulletin, offering my services. I called or spoke to other cardiology groups. I spoke to Alan Gradman, Chief of Cardiology at West Penn. He told me that there are no part-time jobs for cardiologists anywhere, so I also began to explore the possibility of starting a new career teaching high school physics. I researched programs in Pittsburgh that led to certification. I felt that the two most important things a person could do with his life was to work in medicine or education.

One day I got a call from Art Feldman, the Chief of Cardiology at the University of Pittsburgh Medical School. He said the CV I sent to their affiliated VA Hospital had come across his desk. I arranged a meeting at his office. The first thing he said to me was: "You're a great cardiologist. What are you doing here?" I was flattered. I told him I could only work part-time because of my bipolar disease. That was okay with him. He said they had a half-time position doing consultations at Magee Women's Hospital and reading echocardiograms at the University Hospital. I subsequently had four more interviews with other cardiologists and the administrator in the department. Everyone was enthusiastic except for John Gorcsan, the head of echocardiography. He told me he thought my bipolar disease was a problem, even as he complimented my honesty in revealing my illness. (I described my interview with him in a previous chapter.) I didn't get the job. I didn't even get a phone call. I guess they were too embarrassed to admit my illness was the reason they didn't give me the job. I thought the reason for this might be that discriminating against me because of a disability would be a violation of the ADA. Paul Scott told me that I might have been lucky not to get the job because the university had a bad reputation for abusing its employed doctors. I was also seriously concerned that my reservations about doing unnecessary catheterizations would get me in trouble with my bosses. If I were responsible for teaching, I wouldn't be able to teach something I believed was not in the patients' best interest.

With all this going on, I notified my disability insurance companies. They understood my situation, as they had probably seen similar issues with other policy holders. One company sent an investigative team to Pittsburgh to meet with me to confirm the facts of my case. Since leaving medicine was not my choice and I was doing everything I could to find a new job in medicine, they continued to meet their obligations to me.

CHAPTER 69

BACK TO WONDERLAND

After my experiences in Williamsburg and Topeka in 1997, I resolved to be more successful in Alabama, but I ran into the same problem. Sandy Frazier seemed really nice, but in the end she was more dedicated to her referral sources than to me as a patient, despite the fact that I paid two thousand dollars for her help. She neatly deflected all responsibility for herself by claiming that her workshop was not to be considered actual medical care. This made her immune from a malpractice suit. In my case, this was a wise decision on her part. In her final report she did not hesitant to criticize my personality, despite the fact that she knew me for only five days. She said my personality was hopelessly dysfunctional because I was continuing to play out my sense of victimization from my childhood. She also said I talked too much, but didn't even mention what I had talked about. Of course, when I asked how I could have accomplished so much in my life if I was so dysfunctional, I was treated with blank stares. She clearly didn't want reality to interfere with her preconceived notions. Wetschler told me she said her report was limited by her need to be "politically correct." Wetschler seemed to think that Sandy was trying to protect me. I think she meant that she was being "politically correct" in a medical sense, that is, protecting her referral sources from embarrassment. At the same time she made it clear to me personally that she supported me. What hypocrisy! If I could have sued her for malpractice I would have.

To start with, by the end of four days at her workshop, it became apparent that she didn't share the information I had given her prior to my visit with her two assistants, Paula and Mike. They had seemed to think I was a little crazy until the last day, a Friday morning, when they essentially apologized for not taking me seriously. Mike had even intimated to me during that week that he thought Linda was a figment of my imagination and secondary to my delusional state. That Friday morning, Mike told me he agreed with me and that "There are too many abuses." Paula, on the other hand, tried to ram her ideas down my throat. Her idea was correct, however. She said I should sue the people involved in what was done to me. Of course, Sandy did not include that in her summary letter to Tom Hobbs and Wetschler. My stay in Alabama was made immeasurably more difficult because Mike and Paula did not seem to have gotten copies of my letters to Jan Jennings and the April 12th letter to Wetschler. If in fact Frazier did withhold these letters from Mike and Paula, she was wrong to allow them to treat me during the week.

The one objective assessment I had in Alabama was a Karson Clinical report, done on Sept. 25th, which involved my answering a series of questions as to what I would do in various hypothetical situations. The result was a six-page report that clearly stated that I had no evidence of problems in psychological functioning. Is that why Sandy wrote in her final report that "his behavioral improvement process will be quite lengthy"? She knew nothing of my life and disregarded what I told her about my behavior and motivations, yet she felt qualified to make a life-altering judgment about me without even talking to Paul Scott for his opinion. She spoke to Wetschler while I was in Alabama, so I guess she was basing her assessment on Stanley's lies. She also told me that Stanley said he thought he was "doing me a favor" by allowing me to take a LOA instead of being reported to the data bank. She said I had "boundary problems." She had mentioned this to me in passing while I was still in Alabama. I don't think she was in any way competent to make this judgment. I had been through enormously extensive evaluations during the previous six years and was in continuous therapy with Paul Scott, reputed by many to be one of the finest psychotherapists in Pittsburgh, and no one had ever mentioned that I had boundary problems. In fact, my successful relationship with Linda and the fact that Sandy was still single at her age suggested to me that I had a lot more to teach her about personal boundaries and relationships than she had to teach me.

At my exit interview with her, she asked me if Dr. Scott supported me. When I told her that he did, she said he could then advocate for me. Clearly she meant that she couldn't advocate for me, and she didn't. I truly believe that the reason she didn't advocate for me was because she didn't want to embarrass Hobbs and Wetschler. She did say, however, in her letter to Hobbs on September 28, 2001, that I appeared "to be a dedicated, intelligent, compassionate physician." She said I was reported to be disruptive, not that she mentioned any instances of my supposedly disruptive behavior to me or asked me if any of the reports were true. We did discuss the episode with Cathy Davis and Wanitta Anderson. She dismissed Cathy's complaint because Cathy was black, and accepted my version of the events with Wanitta. This continued the pattern of accusation about my behavior and personality without ever actually saying what I had done other than to insult the pulmonary group and Fingeret because of their poor care of my patients. She criticized me for talking too much in the group sessions, but didn't explain why being loquacious was grounds for me being banished from the practice of medicine. Remarkably, her letter made no reference whatsoever to the fact that I had bipolar disorder. I wondered how anyone could take her opinions seriously.

Sandy also violated one of the rules of psychiatric evaluation. I was told by one of the psychiatry residents involved in her program that a therapist should never trust any evaluations that take place in the context of certain serious life events. This included a person undergoing forced retirement. I was talkative because I was desperately trying to save my career. As Paul Scott subsequently told me, these doctors in the so-called "therapeutic community" just seemed to project their own issues onto the people they were supposed to help. So much for me being a "victim" of malpractice. There was absolutely no accountability for these doctors. The only recourse was to sue for malpractice, which in Sandy's case was not possible. I didn't confront her with what she had done until 2006 when I gave her a call. I told her it was "wrong and unethical" for her to have deferred advocating for me to Dr. Scott. She seemed to be surprised that I said that. I think in her frame of reference, she may have actually believed that in some way she did advocate for me.

The stated purpose of the Physicians Health Program in Pennsylvania is to advocate for the physicians in the program. I guess that only applies if it's not personally inconvenient for people like Hobbs and Frazier. I told her she was partially responsible for me having to retire and how that adversely affected my patients. She didn't express anything that could possibly be construed as having any concern whatsoever for the patients who where counting on me to take care of them.

One thing from my exit interview with Sandy Frazier does stand out in my memory. We were discussing my relationship with Linda, and I offered that Linda was strong-willed and didn't have any trouble standing up to me. Sandy replied, "Oh, she's an intellectual like you." I have heard the term "New York Jewish intellectual" more than once in my life. Sandy also asked me if the fact that Linda was raised Lutheran created any problems in our relationship. I said "No," and chuckled to myself at how primitive these people were. I can't help but wonder if Sandy's thoughts about my dysfunctional personality were colored by a subconscious discrimination against New York Jews in the Deep South. I had even voiced my concern to Hobbs, during the July 17th meeting, about going to an institution in Alabama, because I feared the possibility of discrimination against me for this reason. He reassured me and told me not to worry about this. I had never really thought of myself as an "intellectual." Rather, I just thought I was a smart guy who tried to use his brains to do the right thing by people.

One of the great ironies about my trip to Birmingham was the city's role in the history of the Civil Rights Movement. I visited the Civil Rights Museum and the church where several small black girls had been blown up. Visiting these places just reinforced my determination to speak out for the rights of others, in this case my patients and other innocent doctors who were being unjustly punished by hospitals abusing their power.

Sandy did not offer an opinion as to whether or not I could continue to practice medicine. She said, appropriately, that that was up to Paul Scott. In 1997, the decision was left to Tom Hobbs, so I thought that the hospital was obliged to take his recommendation. Wetschler had clearly disregarded Paul's recommendations about me previously. After Sandy sent her letter, I called Hobbs to ask if I could go back to work in the hospital. He said I could. I asked him to call Wetschler and let him know. I even ran into Borrero in the office building and told him I was going to go back to work. He said he was glad I would be back. Except for the perfidy to which he had been coerced, he and I had had an excellent relationship over the years.

I tried to get in touch with Wetschler to let him know what Hobbs had said. He did not return my calls for more than two weeks. I had to write a letter asking him to call me. Finally, on the morning of Wednesday October 17, 2001 I spoke to him and Bruce Payton.

I was at home during the call. Bruce and Wetschler were on the speakerphone in Bruce's office. I guess Bruce was there to be a witness and to take notes for my file. I didn't get a copy of Bruce's note until the discovery phase of my lawsuit. He conveniently managed to only write down the parts of the conversation that would cover his ass. Because Wetschler had a witness to the conversation (Bruce), I made sure I had a word for word transcription of the entire 40-minute conversation (see appendix C). Wetschler made it clear that I could not come back to Jefferson, despite the fact that Hobbs had said I could. He said he expected me to go to work for an insurance company. Bruce said he thought I belonged at Columbia University Medical School. I know Bruce was sincere. Wetschler said I would certainly be convicted and thrown off the staff if I asked to come back to Jefferson.

Since I knew he was right, I couldn't directly ask to come back in writing because that would mean I would get reported to the NPDB (National Practitioner Data Bank), which would mean the end of my career. I certainly didn't want to be reported to the data bank because of a lie. Wetschler said I would have to go to "another county" to get a fair hearing. Bruce offered that he thought I could get a fair hearing at Jefferson, even though the previous week he had told me privately that he thought I couldn't. Wetschler said he thought I was "delusional." He said I was "dogmatic" in my conversations about medicine. No one else had ever said that to me. Then he said one of the reasons he wanted me out was because I had a "pattern of escalation." I guess he meant he resented the fact that I tried to defend myself by going over his head to Jan Jennings in my pleas for justice, when he categorically refused to discuss any of the issues with me directly. *If he thought I had been escalating in the past,* I thought to myself, *he hasn't seen anything yet.*

Wetschler said that even if I had done nothing else wrong, had I been a hospital employee, I would have been fired for what I had done to Wanitta. I told him in no uncertain terms that Wanitta had lied about what had occurred and had made her accusations for secondary gain. Then I saw an opening and asked him if Wanitta had not made her allegations, would he have still asked me to take a LOA. He said no, but he implied that he would have eventually gotten me on something else in the future. He wanted me to write him a letter showing my contrition. I asked him what I had done that I needed to admit to. He offered no answer other than Wanitta's allegations and his derogatory name-calling. Later that day, the records show, he spoke to Sandy Frazier and said that my "private conversations with members of the medical staff did involve elements of slander, and were therefore disruptive." Clearly Wetschler was the one out of touch with reality, not me.

I told Wetschler that I would send him a letter. I couldn't ask directly to come back, so I sent him a letter the next day in which I documented that he said he wouldn't have asked me to take a LOA if Wanitta had not made her allegations. I reiterated that she had lied and had done so for financial gain. I told him that I had written evidence of what Wanitta had said I did to her, and that it was all a lie. Because of this I asked him to rescind, retroactively, his request that I take the LOA. I knew this was a long shot, but I had to show that I was doing everything I could to get back to work. What I didn't tell Stan was that I had received a letter from Wanitta's lawyer demanding $50,000. In the letter the lawyer described how I had physically assaulted her client. The story was an utter fabrication, just as Cathy's had been in 1995. I guess some people will do anything for money.

I was determined to prove myself innocent. I had received the letter from Wanitta's lawyer about a week after I got back from Alabama. I knew the only way I could defend myself was to ask Mr. Porter what he had told the hospital about what had occurred on July 13. I had his address and phone number from my office records. Joel Dresbold, my lawyer, tried to get in touch with him by phone, but it was disconnected.

He then wrote the man a letter but got no reply. Finally, Joel said that, for five hundred dollars, he would drive out to Mr. Porter's home in the suburbs on a Sunday morning to take a statement from him personally. I thought that if the patient confirmed Wanitta's version of events, then I must be delusional. If that were the case, I definitely should not be practicing medicine. So regardless, I had to find out.

I spoke to Joel later in the day on Sunday October 29th, and what he said nearly caused me to fall out of my chair. He told me Mr. Porter said he had never spoken to or given a statement to anyone at the hospital about the events. Not only that, the written statement he gave to Joel said, "I never saw the doctor hit or touch anyone." He did say I seemed upset and had "barked" at Wanitta. He said, "It didn't seem like a big deal to me." Now I had proof that I was innocent and that Wetschler had lied to me when he said the patient had confirmed Wanitta's allegations. At that point I knew I had a case. I was determined to sue him. I was just completely fed up with all the dishonesty I had experienced in medicine. Since I was going to have to retire from medicine anyway, I didn't have to worry about the potential fallout from a lawsuit.

By then I was working with Ken Behrend and Dan Ernsberger, malpractice attorneys, as a consultant on a malpractice case, so I asked them for advice. I was told to write to Wetschler asking for a copy of Wanitta's and Mr. Porter's statements. He wrote me back with the final nail in his coffin. In his written reply, dated November 21, 2001, he stated: "…to date, South Hills [meaning Jefferson Hospital] has received no written statement from any 'Mr. Porter' [a pseudonym]." This was clearly an overt admission that he had lied. There was no point in informing Wetschler of Mr. Porter's statement. I had to present my evidence in a forum in which I could get objectivity, and that was not going to be in an institution controlled by the likes of these guys. As far as I was concerned, having Wetscher, Sims, and Fingeret in charge of the hospital medical staff was equivalent to having the fox in charge of the henhouse, and in this case the "hens" were the helpless patients.

CHAPTER 70

RESIGNATION

Despite the fact that I had been judged guilty without having an opportunity to defend myself, Wetschler did not even conduct an investigation into what had happened. According to the hospital bylaws, an investigation has to be done according to certain rules. Some of these rules are in place in order to protect doctors from false allegations. I guess that, because Wetschler felt he was "doing me a favor," he thought there was no need to do an investigation to try to discern the truth. He also told me he had done enough investigating and spoke to all the right people. I guess he didn't think it was important to talk to the only eyewitness, Mr. Porter.

After Wetschler told me, on October 17th, that I would most likely be reported to the data bank if I formally asked to come back from LOA, I set in motion the process of liquidating my corporation. Larry agreed to purchase my practice. The final cost to him was only about $10,000, which he easily recouped from billings on my patients. I sold what office furniture and equipment I could. I felt terrible that I had to tell Addie, my office assistant, that she was out of a job. She was in her seventies and needed the job to make ends meet. I wrote letters to all of my patients telling them I was retiring. Many of them told me they were worried about finding a new cardiologist and said, "No one's like you, Dr. Schneider." Unfortunately, they might have been correct in their assessment, and I was genuinely worried about them. I had wanted to close up as soon as possible, because every day I stayed in practice I lost money. I stayed for a few extra weeks because I was to testify as an expert witness in a malpractice case. I was told by the lawyers that, in

Pennsylvania, a doctor had to be in active practice in order to be recognized by the court as an expert.

I had never been an expert witness before. In southwestern Pennsylvania, testifying in a malpractice case as a witness for the plaintiff is not considered acceptable by the medical community. I decided to do it because I was outraged by what the cardiologist had done to his patient. I was originally asked to review the case by Ken Behrend, a lawyer I had originally spoken to as a reference for a woman who was applying for a job in my office. After I reviewed the case, he asked me if I would be willing to be their expert. Initially, I told him he probably didn't want me because my credibility could be impugned by the fact I had bipolar disease. He said that didn't matter.

The patient was a man in his early seventies who had had a stroke during a heart catheterization at the age of 66. The problem was the catheterization was not needed to diagnose or treat his condition, new onset atrial fibrillation and mild congestive heart failure. The American College of Cardiology guidelines for diagnostic cath clearly state that neither of these two conditions is a recognized indication for the procedure. Not only was the cath unnecessary, the cardiologist who did the procedure had not even told the patient about alternative diagnostic and therapeutic alternatives, as is required under Pennsylvania law. This cardiologist represented to me everything that is wrong with medicine in this country. This was my chance to speak out for another abused patient. I wasn't doing it for the money; I was testifying because of my moral outrage at what had been done to this poor man. After the stroke, his mental functioning was severely impaired and his life essentially ruined. In my mind, the reason this cath had been done was pure greed.

I testified in early December, delaying my retirement until after the trial. I testified for four hours as I explained to the jury why the catheterization had not been necessary. My understanding of the malpractice laws includes the fact that, if a patient has a serious complication arising from a procedure that is not medically necessary, that complication is considered to be malpractice. It is also malpractice not to get proper informed consent. I felt this was a textbook example of this type of malpractice. I hoped that by speaking out I could at least get this doctor to think about whether a cath was really necessary for his future patients. I had been trained at Mount Sinai to only do an invasive procedure when the information could not be obtained by non-invasive methods, and then only if the information gained would affect clinical decisions about the patient. There was nothing I could do to help this man regain his lost neurological function, but I hoped I could help this doctor's future patients avoid the same fate.

Unfortunately, the lawyers were not able to get the testimony of their second expert witness admitted to the case because of a technicality. The patient's family and lawyers both told me that my testimony had been "perfect." Nonetheless, I was terribly disappointed, although not surprised, that the patient lost his case. Even though the lawyers did not have enough money to pay me the agreed amount, I was proud of myself for having stood up for what was right. This was confirmed a couple of months later. I was at a gas station early one morning when I was approached by a man I didn't recognize, who said, "You don't recognize me, do you? You testified against me." He was looming over me menacingly as I sat in the driver's seat with the window open.

I replied, "I know a lot of people who trained at your institution. I know how you do things over there. The Harvard School of Public Health says that 40 percent of the caths done in this country are unnecessary. That patient should never have been cathed. You caused that stoke. Live with it, buddy." He walked away speechless. I was happy to be able to fight for his patients too. I thought it was fitting that I should go down fighting for what I believed in. I closed my office on December 14th. I officially resigned from the Jefferson Medical Staff on the 18th.

PART IV

THE LAWSUIT

CHAPTER 71

FIGHTING BACK

Dan Ernsberger had been advising me how to pursue legal redress against the hospital. However, once he found out Borrero was involved with the defendants, he said he had to withdraw from the case because of a conflict of interest. He seemed quite relieved to be off the hook, and I didn't blame him. I knew his firm did not have the resources to prosecute such a difficult case on a contingency basis. But he did advise me how to proceed, telling me to file a complaint with the Pennsylvania Human Relations Commission (HRC). Dan told me exactly where to go to do this and what I needed to say. He said I had to file the complaint before six months had elapsed after the incident. To be sure I got in under the deadline; I dated the occurrence to be July 13, 2001, the date of the incident with Wanitta. An equally good argument could be made that the date was December 18th, the day I resigned from Jefferson. So, I had to file my complaint with the HRC before January 13, 2002.

I went down to the HRC in downtown Pittsburgh personally to file the complaint during the last week in December, 2001. I wrote it out in longhand and had a personal interview as well. I was told that the complaint would automatically be filed with the federal agency, the Equal Employment Opportunity Commission (EEOC). The basis of the complaint was that I had a recognized disability, bipolar disease, and that I had been discriminated against because of this. Dan had explained to me that in Pennsylvania, one cannot sue for discrimination unless one first files a complaint with the HRC. The HRC is supposed to do an investigation and make a determination as to the validity of the complaint. After a year the HRC will then issue a letter allowing you to sue in court.

Dan explained to me that I should use the state courts because the wait for a trial would be much shorter than in federal court.

I was excited to learn from the HRC that they were going to hold a "fact-finding conference" because I thought I would finally be able to tell my story to an objective party. I was quite disappointed when the HRC decided it would not hold this conference, but I was not deterred. According to the law, the hospital had 30 days to answer my complaint. I thought they would write a short letter denying they had done anything wrong. Then I would have to wait for the year to be over before I could file my lawsuit. A month went by with no response. I called the HRC. They issued another letter to the hospital and were told by the hospital that they never received the first letter. A likely story. Another month went by with no response from the hospital, and again the HRC made another phone call. By law I was to receive a copy of the hospital's response. I finally got their reply on April 4, 2002, delivered to my home in a large cardboard box. The response was in a large loose-leaf binder. The sheaf of papers contained in the binder was more than *two inches thick*. I was dumfounded.

The papers included the entire medical staff bylaws and scores of documents supposedly documenting to the HRC why I was designated a "problem physician" after I got sick in 1997. It included a full multi-page table documenting my supposed misbehavior. It was only then that I realized that the hospital was maintaining a secret dossier on me. As part of my lawsuit, it was pointed out to the hospital that the bylaws required the physician to be notified if he is under investigation. Clearly keeping this secret dossier on me was a breach of contract under Pennsylvania law. The hospital response included letters and statements from the hospital employees who had been asked by the defendants to write letters about me. I had never seen them before, nor had I ever been told who wrote them or the substance of the allegations against me. They included the letters form Paula Gaffney and Wanitta Anderson. Oddly enough, they did not include the interview with Bonnie Andrews. One table, however, did include an entry of a complaint of sexual harassment made against me on April 7, 1997. I had no idea what this was. It was especially perplexing because I wasn't in the hospital at that time. In fact, I was not in the hospital from March 17, 1997 until September 15, 1997.

This was clearly a frame-up. When I read what Paula had said I had done I was appalled. She completely distorted what had occurred. The hospital had refused to tell me what she had alleged, let alone given me the opportunity to give my side of the story. These guys were behaving the same way as the dictators had behaved against their own citizens in Russia and Germany. I thought we had suffered through at least two major wars, WWII and the Cold War, to put and end to this kind of behavior by people in power. I couldn't believe people could behave this way in the United States of America, in which the basic principle is "liberty and justice for all." The Bill of Rights stipulates that citizens are not to be deprived of liberty or property without "due process of law." What country did Wetschler think he was living in? I guess he really meant it when he told me, in June, 2001, that he thought he and the hospital didn't have to obey the laws of the United States or the State of Pennsylvania.

After I read though most of the hospital's tome against me, I called Bruce Payton and told him their response to my HRC complaint was full of distortions and lies. I told him specifically that what Paula had said about the case of Mrs. L. was nonsense. I told him what Mrs. L. and her husband had subsequently told me about his being called in to the hospital in the middle of the night because the nurses expected her to die. As I mentioned before, when I reminded Bruce that I had been able to send her home in good condition, he responded, "You are a great doctor, who fights for his patients." I believe that he got it exactly right. I also told him that, even though I had always considered him a friend, we were now "adversaries." He seemed genuinely upset. He said what had been done to me was the fault of the Medical Staff leadership and not the hospital administration. But the documents I had been sent included papers that verified how he had allowed himself to be used by the hospital to get information from me in the guise of being my friend. I didn't sue Bruce because I think he actually tried to help me but had been forced to do what he did by Wetschler and his cronies, as had Borrero.

Up until I got the hospital's response, I thought I might be able to handle the situation on my own with the help of the HRC. When I saw all the bullshit in their “book,” I knew I needed help. At the time, I was a student teacher in physics at Fox Chapel High School, and I was scheduled for cervical spine surgery for my pinched nerves in early May. I resolved that after my surgery I was going to go lawyer shopping. This is a lot harder than it sounds. There are no major plaintiff’s law firms for this type of case in Pittsburgh, to the best of my knowledge.

I was fortunate to read an article in the March 23, 2002 edition of the Allegheny County Medical Society Bulletin by a lawyer named Sue Gunn. In it she said that doctors with disabilities were entitled to the same protection against discrimination under the law as were other citizens. She was the first person I called in my search. I went down to her office in May, toting the huge hospital binder with me. When she saw it she said, “Methinks they doth protest too much.” It was music to my ears. When I told her Wetschler had lied to me when he told me, on July 16, 2001, that Mr. Porter had given him a statement confirming Wanitta’s allegations, she said: “They lied?!” She immediately said that she wanted to take the case.

I told her that Bill Maruca, a lawyer in her firm, Kabala and Geeseman, represented Laman and Sims. Because I did not intend to sue them at that point in time, she thought she could still take the case, but she had to check with her boss. She thought the hospital would want to settle the case upfront and that would be the end of it. I was hoping I could get a settlement of about $75,000, but I wasn’t really interested in the money. I just wanted the hospital to know what these guys had done, so that other innocent doctors would not be subjected to the same type of abuse I had suffered at Jefferson. I felt that I had an absolute moral and ethical responsibility to speak out and be heard. I knew I had the financial resources to sue, whereas most other doctors probably wouldn’t. I felt I couldn’t live with myself if I didn’t use my wealth to stand up for those doctors who couldn’t stand up for themselves. This was exactly the same way I felt when I was sitting in front of the room in the ICU of the helpless Mr. W.

Sue told me I could get the complaint written up for about $20,000 to $30,000. I knew I couldn’t get any lawyer to take the case for a percentage, so I decided to risk it. I anxiously awaited the decision of Sue’s boss. A few days later she called and said that, try as she might, she could not get her boss's permission to take the case. He felt that the conflict of interest created by their representation of the pulmonary group precluded the firm representing me. Sue said she was sorry, but she also said she had spoken to a lawyer in another firm who would probably take the case. His name was Mike Cassidy, and Sue described him as a "bulldog." I thought that was exactly what I needed to go up against those lying, thieving bastards. I know that sounds vengeful and vituperative, but you'd feel the same way if they had done to you what they did to me. That's not even considering what they had done to my patients. I'm just talking about what might have happened to the ones who were still alive when I was forced to leave them. The dead ones are another issue. The other thing was that these guys only picked on me because they viewed me as weak, disabled, and powerless. This is the definition of a bully. I was determined to stand up to these cowards.

CHAPTER 72

FIGHTING FOR TRUTH AND JUSTICE

One of the biggest roadblocks to pursuing my lawsuit was the ability to obtain the evidence. Jeff Blum had once told me, "Everything is discoverable." This means that if you violate the law and are sued, the plaintiff has the right to subpoena documents and other evidence. The law firm of Horty and Springer tried to use the Peer Review Law to prevent aggrieved physicians from obtaining any such evidence. I anticipated a big fight in court just to get the "secret documents." Paul Verardi, a member of this law firm, put a warning on every document indicating that it was confidential under the Peer Review Act. This allowed their hospital clients to hide any misdeeds and to find doctors guilty without having any burden of proof. I'm sure they were paid quite handsomely by the hospitals. Of course, the Peer Review Law is designed to protect the hospital and the Medical Staff involved in the Peer Review Process from lawsuits arising from legitimate peer review involving patient care issues and professional misconduct. It is also designed to protect the doctors who are found guilty from discovery by malpractice attorneys. The Peer Review Law is not designed to protect hospitals and medical staff who are violating the law. The Peer Review Law only protects them if they act in good faith. In my case, the defendants in the lawsuit were clearly not acting in good faith they were just trying to use the protections to cover their tracks. I was going to reveal their behavior.

I was not interested in retribution. I had no desire to harm the hospital or any of the other defendants. My goal was not to get money, it was to expose the truth about what Adler, Kostrub, Fingeret, Sims,

Laman, and Wetschler had done. I wanted the hospital to know what they had done so that the medical staff procedures would be modified to prevent other innocent doctors from being victimized by other unscrupulous powerful physicians in the future. The metaphor I carried around in my head since 1997 was, "I'm going to turn over this rock and expose the maggots to the sunshine." I was going to use my lawsuit to get all the documents and put all the defendants and witnesses under oath to expose the truth. I was prepared to fight hard to prove that no one is above the law.

When I got a copy of their response to the HRC, I knew they had capitulated on the issue of secrecy. Paul Verardi had thought that the material in the loose-leaf binder was protected under the Peer Review Law. Guess what, Paul? Wrong! When I walked into Mike Cassidy's office with Sue Gunn, I knew Mike and I had already cleared our first hurdle without having to spend any time or money doing so. We were already on first base, thanks to the single I hit by filing my complaint with the HRC, thanks to Dan Ernsberger.

Mike Cassidy, who was in his early fifties, was the head of healthcare law at a large Pittsburgh law firm, Tucker Arensberg. Their offices were quite imposing, occupying two high floors in one of the tallest buildings in downtown Pittsburgh. Appearances can be very important in these things. I knew just having Mike represent me would increase my credibility. Mike was a powerful-appearing man with an unusually peaceful demeanor. He had been an All Ivy Center for the Brown University football team when he was in college. This had left him with the need for artificial knees in both legs. I met him before the second knee was replaced, so he walked with a slight limp. I liked him from the get-go. He wasn't perfect, and he did make some mistakes, but he was totally honest and very smart. Sue had described him as a bulldog, but to me he seemed more like a large, friendly teddy bear. What I didn't know at the time was that he was not a litigator, that is, he did not try his own cases in court. I had had enough experience with litigators to know that they were much more likely to be bulldogs, or more accurately, pit bulls.

After Sue left, Mike and I spoke for a couple of hours, and I explained the case to him as best I could. When he asked me what I wanted, I told him twelve million dollars. I knew this was ridiculous, but I had made the calculations about how much money I had lost because of the illegal actions of the defendants. I threw in triple damages for punitive damages because they had acted with malicious intent, which was obviously true. Dan Ernsberger told me the only reason to make such a demand would be to intimidate the other side. That's what I wanted to do. But I was also angry. Mike made it clear to me that I would look foolish if I asked for so much, and I would undermine my own credibility.

Where Mike and I shared motivation was on the issue of due process for physicians. He had been in the business of representing doctors for a long time; in fact, he said that 98% of his clients were doctors. He had been appalled by the gross injustices that doctors were exposed to in their dealing with hospitals. I also got the sense that he felt that Horty and Springer were at fault for a lot of what he saw. (Paul Scott had a similar opinion of hospitals because many of his patients had been exposed to the same type of hospital malfeasance that I had experienced.) So, Mike and I had a lot of common ground on which to base our relationship. We both knew that didn't mean we wouldn't have disagreements, as almost all clients seem to have with their attorneys at some point. I was ecstatic when Mike told me he would take the case. I felt that my long search was finally over. It was not uncomplicated, however. When I asked him if he would take the case on a contingency basis, he said he had never done a case on contingency. His fee was $275 per hour, at the very high end for attorneys in Pittsburgh at that time. Of course, only litigators take cases on a contingency basis, and, as I said, I didn't find out until a short time later that Mike was not a litigator.

I knew I had to pay upfront since I had been unsuccessful in my attempts to find a lawyer to take the case on contingency. Sue Gunn had offered to do a hybrid deal, part hourly, part contingency, but Mike said he couldn't do this. Still, I was determined to succeed. I hoped I could get results with an investment of less than $30,000, as Sue Gunn had indicated. All I really wanted to do was get a settlement that would at least allow me to break even after taxes.

It turned out it cost a lot more, and I'm not even allowed to tell you if I eventually broke even. What I can divulge is that I increased my budget to $100,000. That was as far as I could comfortably go without jeopardizing my own financial situation. I felt that I had been really blessed in my life and that I would be extremely ungrateful if I did not ante up to protect the doctors and patients who couldn't fight for themselves. I was just thankful that I had the resources to do what I felt must be done. I also knew that Horty and Springer had gotten away with their shenanigans because the other doctors their clients had abused were not left in a financial position to fight back. They were bullies too. Mike and I knew that.

The first thing Mike said we had to do was go to Harrisburg to meet with Tom Hobbs, the Medical Director of the Pennsylvania Physicians Health Program, to review my records there. Mike was going to Harrisburg for another case, so he said I could save money be splitting his travel expenses with his other client. We reviewed all the information on record going back to 1997. Remarkably, the only thing we found in the record relating to the 1997 episode was a notation saying "sexual innuendo." The only communication we found with the hospital at that time was from Fingeret, then President of the Medical Staff. So Buzz had mentioned sex to Hobbs, but he didn't say anything to me about it before he coerced me under threat of being reported to the NPDB (data bank) to take a medical LOA. Of course, this was his first violation of the bylaws and a breach of contract under Pennsylvania Law. Hobbs had already told me the hospital had accused me of sexual harassment in a telephone conversation I had with him a few years previously. I had documented this in my letter to Jan Jennings of September 16, 2001, in which I pleaded for his help to get justice.

I was amazed that, when I asked Hobbs, in Mike's presence, whether he had made any effort to find out if the allegations against me were true, he simply replied, "I just know the allegations. I have no way of knowing if they're true." I told him what had been said about me were all lies and that he needed to know that. He expressed no remorse or any indication that he would take steps to insure that other doctors were not referred to him under false pretenses. At that point I realized all this man was concerned about was keeping his census up in order to keep his donations flowing. He didn't seem to care a hoot about the actual human beings he was supposed to be helping, the doctors and their patients. Hobbs was a self-described alcoholic in recovery, and narcissism is a feature of the disease of alcoholism. I guess this was why he seemed to be putting his own welfare ahead of his "patients." I wanted to expose his organization to the sunlight as well, but suing him was not on the agenda for now. This book is the first time I have publicly told the story of my experiences with Hobbs's PHP. Unfortunately, when I called to speak to Hobbs about this book in 2006, I was told he had recently passed away at the age of 73.

Mike and I left without much evidence about 1997, but we knew that Fingeret had been the one to transmit the lies to the PHP, and my credibility with Mike was intact and reaffirmed. We already had the information about the events of 2001 that was in my file at the PHP.

At about the same time, Mike and I tried to get my records from the Farley Center. We were mainly interested in finding out who had given Hedberg and Zeigler the false information about the so-called allegations, *which were never actually made about me,* concerning sexual harassment of "colleagues, patients, and staff." As I explained in a previous chapter, only a few people were authorized to speak about me to the staff at the Farley Center; not surprisingly, the notes from these interviews were conveniently absent from my file.

CHAPTER 73

PURSUING THE LAWSUIT

Sometime after Mike and I returned from Harrisburg, Mike brought in the "litigators" (Mike's quotation marks): Brad Tupi, the partner, and Ken Scholtz, the associate. Mike had told me these lawyers charged less per hour, and that by utilizing their services I would spend less money because he would not have to do all the work himself. I remember Brad charged $220 and Ken $120/hr. I thought this was a good idea. Unfortunately, I ran into trouble with Brad even before I met him. After he had been briefed on the case by Mike, he took it upon himself to call me as if I had retained him and not Mike. He left a message on my cell phone voicemail. He said I didn't have a case and their firm would not be representing me. He said something to the effect: "You got squeezed out of the practice and that's too bad." It was clear to me he had no idea about how hospitals worked and what had actually occurred. I also thought it was totally unprofessional for him to call Mike's client, whom he had never met, and unilaterally withdraw his entire law firm from the case. At a minimum, if Mike agreed with him, he should have been the one to call me. I called a friend of mine who was a senior partner in a large law firm in New Jersey to ask him about Brad's behavior. He said that if an associate in his firm had behaved that way with a client he would have been fired.

Brad did throw me a bone, however. In his voicemail he said Tucker (the firm) would file what is called in Pennsylvania a "Praecipe for Writ of Summons," or Writ for short. As long as this was filed before the statute of limitations expired, I would preserve my right to sue beyond that time period indefinitely. Brad said this would allow me to hire another attorney. I wrote to Mike that, if he didn't take the case, I would have to let the whole thing drop. I told him he was the best, and I felt that if he couldn't prosecute the lawsuit for me, no one could. I wasn't going to waste any more time. Mike arranged for a meeting with Brad, Ken, me and himself. As we walked to the conference room in his office, Mike told me the purpose of the meeting was for Brad to try to convince me to drop the suit. Mike smiled and gave a little chuckle when he said this. My understanding was that I was the one to decide whether or not to pursue the suit, not Brad. Mike was clearly on my side.

Brad started off with a long discussion of why I couldn't win, and it was again obvious that he didn't understand the case. He admitted that he hadn't read all the documents I had given Mike. I don't know if he had read any of them, actually. I did not hesitate to tell Brad that his phone call to me was inappropriate and that at least one law firm in New Jersey thought that, had he been an associate and not a partner, he should have been fired for his behavior toward me. Mike and Ken and Brad almost jumped out of their chairs when I said this. Brad said then I should get the New Jersey firm to represent me. I told him I expected him and Mike to represent me and I wasn't going to change my mind, and I told him I expected him to do a good job. Mike supported me, and we went on to discuss our next moves. We decided the first order of business was to depose Wetschler because he was ill, and I didn't know if or when he might die.

When I got the revised agreement with Tucker Arensberg, they said they wanted $10,000 up front and $7,500 a month in advance to cover their fees for that month. If the bill was less than this, the remainder would be applied to the next month. I was just glad I had found someone who could do what I needed, so I acquiesced without comment. It was clear that Brad didn't trust me to pay him. I thought at the time that this guy must have had a lot of dishonest clients in the past. As the months went by, I paid every bill on time and eventually I only had to pay each month after I got the bill. I got a good chuckle when their billing clerk told me that I was one of the very few doctors who ever paid their bill on time. Maybe Brad had never met an honest man before!

The Writ against the hospital, Stanley Wetschler, and Wanitta Anderson was filed on July 11, 2002; two days shy of the one-year anniversary of the event in the treadmill lab. I felt very relieved that something had finally been done. A few weeks later, Mike told me that a new defense attorney had been hired by the hospital to replace Paul Verardi. Her name was Maria Greco Danaher, a lawyer with Dickie, McCamey, and Chilcote, perhaps the largest corporate defense firm in the city. I was flattered and encouraged that they seemed to be concerned enough about my complaint to bring out the big guns. It went along with their excessively-sized protestations to the HRC that Verardi had filed in April.

The first order of business was to compile a list of questions, called interrogatories, and request for documents to send to Maria. Mike had previously worked at Dickie, and he and Maria were friends. I thought this would help me, but I was a little concerned about Mike having mixed allegiances. He assured me he didn't. The interrogatories were served on Sept. 12, 2002. The defendants had thirty days to respond. They didn't. On October 15th, I emailed Ken Scholtz for an update. Ken responded on the 16th, telling me he spoke with Maria and that she had received a stack of documents from the hospital and would have their response within two weeks. The hospital continued to play games, however. They played a charade of maintaining that my records were protected by the Peer Review Act and would not give my records to Maria without a signed release from me. I thought they were grasping at straws, sort of flailing about in the wind, because they had never actually had to defend their behavior under the law, or so I assumed. In a letter dated November 6, 2002, Mike told me both he and Maria thought the hospital's request for a signed release from me was "slightly unusual." Mike wrote to me, stating that, "I think the hospital is just making a show of being highly protective of your PHP records while simultaneously showing (sic) down the process." I returned the signed consent to Mike and anxiously awaited the documents and the defendants' response to the interrogatories.

While this was going on, the HRC process was nearing its one year duration. Mike made contact with Gwendolyn M. Ormes, the person handling my complaint at the HRC, and sent her a letter dated November 15, 2002. In it he referred to several issues:

1. The letter from Wanitta's lawyer demanding $50,000 because I had assaulted Wanitta and the signed statement from Mr. Porter indicating he never saw me touch or hit anyone.
2. The contention in Paul Verardi's voluminous response to the HRC that I had never responded to Bruce Payton's letter to me of November 11, 2001. In fact, I had responded in a letter to Wetschler dated November 16th, in which I rebutted Bruce's contention that I had effectively resigned from the hospital and was going to retire from medicine. Bruce had called me on November 8, 2001, masquerading as my friend and asking me how I was doing. Up until then I did in fact think Bruce was my friend and was on my side.
3. Mike rebutted the hospital's statement to the HRC that they had attempted to accommodate me in accordance with the ADA, when, in fact, they absolutely refused the only request for accommodation I had made: the one I had made on July 16, 2001, in which I asked them to schedule my treadmill tests to be completed prior to noon so I could get to the office to see my patients as scheduled.
4. The fact that the hospital never developed the "strict code of conduct" it envisioned for me in Wetschler's letter to me of March 8, 2001. And the hospital never appointed the committee that letter indicated was to be appointed to develop that "code." (Sometimes hospitals will devise a specific "code of conduct" for a doctor who behaves poorly. I guess they had a hard time figuring out what I had done wrong, since I *hadn't* done anything wrong.)

On November 21st, Gwendolyn Ormes called me and said the HRC wanted to find in my favor but needed some more information. I spoke with her at length and asked her to speak with Mike. Ken had previously written to the HRC, notifying them that Tucker was representing me. They said they never received his letter and wanted another one. Paul Scott also sent a letter to Ms. Ormes, as she had requested, dated November 26th, explaining my situation.

Mike told me he felt optimistic about the HRC decision. I was less optimistic because I knew from my conversations with Dan Ernsberger that the HRC usually only works with people who cannot afford legal representation. They have limited resources, and I figured they felt obliged to use them to represent poor people, not rich doctors. So Mike seemed to be a little more surprised and disappointed when the HRC decided against me. Of course, Mrs. Ormes' decision letter said her decision was based on the fact that she was told verbally by the hospital that all I had needed to do to get back on staff was send a letter. The hospital told her this was just a routine clerical procedure. In the State of Pennsylvania, it is a crime to lie to a state agency. I think that some of the information Jefferson gave to the HRC were lies based on all of the above. Maybe what they said to the HRC was technically true but meant to mislead. A court of law would have to decide that issue, not me. But as Wetschler had signed the original response to the HRC, I thought he should be the one to face trial on this issue. A question I still don't know the answer to is if Stanley lied or was just out of touch with reality. He certainly lied about Mr. Porter. Maybe it was both. At least the HRC had issued me the letter allowing me to sue the hospital for discrimination.

CHAPTER 74

PROBLEMS WITH TUCKER

From the very beginning it seemed to me that Ken and Brad did not understand my case. This created a lot of psychological stress for me. I tried to put up with it the best I could because I didn't feel I had any choice and I didn't want to hurt my relationship with Mike. My lack of confidence was only exacerbated when I met with Ken one on one. We had met to discuss the case on November 26, 2002 as a way to get on the same page. Ken was very nice, but the details of the case seemed to be too much for him to assimilate adequately. This reached a head on December 2nd when he and I met alone from 4 to 6 p.m. to discuss what to say in the letter to Mrs. Ormes, giving her the additional information she requested. Ken was the one originally assigned by Mike to write the letter, and I didn't object. I did the best I could with Ken during those two hours. I was there to help him help me. Toward the end of the meeting, he actually started yelling at me, saying something to the effect that, "I'm the one who best understands your case. I'm the only one standing between you and defeat."

I couldn't have disagreed more. I couldn't believe he was actually yelling at a client. I didn't respond directly or disagree. I was shaking inside with despair and frustration but didn't want to let on how I really felt since I needed these guys. Instead I said, "I can't listen to this. Excuse me; I have to go to the men's room." After I composed myself, I went back to the conference room to finish up the meeting. Ken said he would revise the letter to the HRC and email it to me that evening. I received the revised letter at 7 p.m. It was ridiculously incomplete and, as far as I was concerned, grossly incompetent. I was distraught. I was paying a lot of money for what I thought would be the best representation available in Pittsburgh.

I was to correct and rewrite the letter. If memory serves me correctly, Ken actually asked me to do my corrections on the email and send it directly back to him so he wouldn't have to do the work himself. My God, what chutzpah! At the time I was working as a day-to-day substitute teacher. I took the next day off to work on the letter. The HRC had given us a deadline to submit the letter of December 4, 2002. I was panic-stricken. The letter had to be rewritten from scratch, and I didn't have the expertise to do it properly. I sent off a panicky email to Mike at 7:30 the morning of the 3rd, telling him that I needed his help to write the letter. I didn't even mention the difficulties I had had with Ken. (In fact, if Mike reads this, it will be the first time he learns what happened.) Mike decided to write the letter himself. Of course, I still had to pay the firm for Ken's wasted time. Doesn't seem quite fair, does it?

Jefferson continued to be recalcitrant in responding to the interrogatories we had sent them in September, 2002, but we finally received them in early January 2003. Maria refused to answer any but a few of the questions. One of the questions she did answer saved me some time and money. Mike and I thought we would have to prove that Mr. Porter was in fact the patient who had been present at the time of the alleged incident. In response to one of the questions, Maria said Mr. Porter was the patient present. I felt that was the last piece of the puzzle I needed to prove my case. From there on all we had to do was write up the complaint, file it, and start deposing witnesses. By this point I had given the firm about $25,000.

Mike was scheduled to have his other knee replaced in January, 2003. Of course I was concerned he might have a serious complication. That's one of the burdens of being a physician; you know all the bad things that can happen from orthopedic surgery. I knew I would be sunk without Mike. Fortunately, Mike had a great surgeon, came through with flying colors and was back to work in a few weeks or less. He then told me it was time to do the "rug cutting," his parlance for writing up the formal legal complaint, or lawsuit. Ken was assigned to write up the first draft of the complaint. On Friday February 28, 2003, Mike emailed me to say he had finished commenting on Ken's draft. He said, "I do not think he will be able to digest those and incorporate them in the 2nd draft by the end of the day. We will certainly finish the process on Monday, and will send the draft then." Mike was a gentlemen, as he went on to say, "Sorry about the delay. I had hoped to finish my comments yesterday, but it took longer than I planned."

Ken sent me a letter on the same day. He stated, "As Mike had indicated to you in his email on Friday, we are currently making some changes to the drafted Complaint that I had prepared for Brad and Mike to review. Once we can put together a final draft, we will get it to you; this should be no later than early next week. Thank you for you continued patience." I think this would be a good point to interject the fact that Tucker Arensberg never finished the complaint, and I had to hire another law firm, with Mike's approval, to work with him in order to get it done. The complaint wasn't completed for another year. How could this have happened?

Sometime in early March, 2003, I received a copy of the first draft of the complaint. Mike said he knew it was incomplete and needed more work. He was being generous. The complaint Ken had written up was completely ridiculous. Ken still had no idea what was going on with the case. My bills were piling up and I had nothing tangible to show for it. At this point, Mike and I decided to take a new tact. He thought we could short-circuit the whole process by sending a letter to Maria, asking for a settlement.

At about this time we also received another batch of documents from my hospital records. Many of these documents had not been given to the HRC by Verardi. Mike wrote in his April 22, 2003 letter to me that, after he had spoken to her several times, "Maria expressed some surprise at the number of documents that the hospital identified as having in its PHRC response, which it did not produce in this discovery. She said she is checking into that." The hospital seemed determined not to tell the whole truth. They clearly felt they had something to hide, perhaps even from their own defense attorney.

In mid March, Mike drafted a demand letter to Maria. In it he quoted a legal case, Clark v. Columbia/HCA (Nev. Sup. Ct. 2001), that concluded that conduct by a physician who complains about poor quality of care for his patients is protected. If the hospital pursued a doctor for these complaints, the hospital is not granted immunity from a complaint by the doctor. Obviously, the hospital was disciplining me because of my complaints about the care of the pulmonary group and Fingeret. He pointed out several other points to Maria that I have already discussed. My disagreement with Mike arose concerning the nature of the demand he was making. He asked for an amount of money, which I won't mention because of my agreement with the defendants. But he also asked that I be reinstated to the hospital staff. I called Mike and left a voice mail, saying that, since I no longer had any patients at Jefferson, going back on staff would be of no value to me. Also, by asking to go back on staff I was implying that the damage the hospital had done to me was theoretically reversible. This was ridiculous. I had spent half a lifetime building a practice at Jefferson. Once it was taken away from me, there was no possible way I could recreate it, especially now that I suffered from a disability. Even more importantly, I was not going to undermine my own credibility with a jury by making a disingenuous demand. I also wrote Mike a page-and-a-half email addressing this issue as part of my overall evaluation of the proposed demand letter.

Mike disagreed and wrote in an email on March 19, "Your asking for reinstatement does not undermine our argument that your practice has already been destroyed, but if they refuse it does allow us to argue that you made the attempt to mitigate your damages." He also wrote me a full page letter on March 18th, delineating my risks in the case and indicating why he wanted me to ask for reinstatement. The letter was written from what I thought was the perspective of a litigator. I suspected that it had resulted from a conversation with Brad and reflected his ideas. I felt that Brad was doing everything he could to put an end to this case as soon as possible, even if it meant I had to undermine my own self-respect. I'm not the kind of person who can be easily coerced into doing something I believe is ethically wrong, and I was determined to stand up to Brad. Besides, I had had enough conversations with Mike to believe that I didn't think he agreed with Brad in his heart.

Therefore, I was a little surprised when Mike called me on my cell phone one afternoon, when I was at the movies with Ben, my son. (I missed the end of the movie, but I didn't like it anyway.) Mike called to insist that I ask the hospital for reinstatement. Good Grief! Didn't Brad know any honest men? I tried to be as gentle with Mike as I could, but I stood my ground and forbade him to include a request for reinstatement in his demand letter to Maria. Since I was paying him and not the other way around, as long as I didn't ask him to do anything unethical, he was required to obey the wishes of his client. At least that's what my extensive experience with lawyers told me. Maybe he could have quit, but he knew that would be unethical because I had already paid them around $30,000.

Mike sent the letter with my full approval, without the request for reinstatement, to Maria on March 31, 2003. I was sick and tired of Brad and his interference with my relationship with Mike. It also seemed to me that he really did not understand what I was trying to accomplish with the lawsuit. If he did understand, then he clearly did not agree with me. It also seemed clear to me that he did not have a handle on the facts of the case. Since Ken had already told me that he did not read all the documents I had given Mike, I suspected that Brad hadn't either. Although I was paying Brad $220 an hour, he seemed to be working to undermine me instead of working with me to help me achieve my goals. I didn't say anything about this to Mike. Instead, I wrote Mike an email on April 6, 2003 in which I said, "Going forward, I would like to be present at your meetings about my case with Brad and/or Ken."

He wrote back, "Certainly can be present at 'significant' meetings—but all meetings would be impractical." I thought that the meeting in which they decided, in my absence, that I should destroy my own credibility was "significant."

CHAPTER 75

A GRINDING HALT

I didn't hear about Maria's response to Mike's demand letter until April 22, 2003, at which time Mike sent me an official letter. Mike said he had spoken to Maria several times and she had told him "that there are two factions at the hospital, one that wants to settle and one that does not." He also said that Maria had suggested mediation. I thought this was a reasonable alternative, even though Mike told me I would be unlikely to get a large settlement. I wasn't concerned about the size of the settlement. I just wanted to have the opportunity to tell my side of the story in a setting in which they would at least have to hear me out, something Wetschler and Verardi had done everything in their power to avoid.

My main desire was to depose Wetschler. I wanted to have the deposition videotaped in case Wetschler's illness prevented him from attending the trial. I knew Wetschler didn't have a leg to stand on, and I wanted to put him under oath. That way he had two choices. He could come clean and tell the truth, or he could repeat his lies under oath. If he told the truth, I would be exonerated; if he lied, he would be committing a felony. The choice would be up to him.

Mike said it was unlikely Maria would agree to Wetschler being deposed. Mike emailed me on May 19th, stating, "Frankly, I do not want to depose Dr. W. before the mediation, because all he can do is repudiate our position." I disagreed because I knew we had all the evidence we needed to prove Wetschler a liar with my documentation of the conversation with him and Payton on October 17, 2001. I sent Mike a long email on May 20th, explaining my reasoning. Mike didn't buy this, but I couldn't understand why. I started to suspect that Mike might have a conflict of interest, possibly in some way related to his friendship with Maria. I asked Mike specifically if he had any conflicts and he told me he didn't. I accepted this at face value because, in my estimation, Mike was an honest man.

Maria had suggested early to mid June for the mediation. In preparation for it, I met with Mike and Brad sometime in late May. The meeting was horrible. Brad spent the whole time trying to tell me I didn't have a case. He said the judge would dismiss my case and give a summary judgment in favor of the hospital. He said the case was worth a maximum of $7,500. He based this on my routine biannual reappointment application to Jefferson in October, 2001. The application stipulated that the applying physician would not sue the hospital if the application was turned down. I pointed out to Brad that I had withdrawn the application when I resigned from the staff in December of that year. I also pointed out that I was already on the staff and that I was therefore covered by the Medical Staff Bylaws, which, as I mentioned before, constitutes an enforceable contract under the laws of the State of Pennsylvania. My frustration, at the time, centered about the fact that Mike didn't voice an opinion supporting me. In fact, it wasn't until June of 2004, that Mike told me, "I'm not worried about that, because then what are the bylaws for?" So I had to go it alone against Brad. I did not hesitate to stand up for my beliefs. He was basically telling me to capitulate, and I told him I was going to go to trial and go down fighting, period. The meeting ended with an agreement to proceed with the mediation.

After the meeting, I had to re-evaluate what I was doing. My litigator, Brad, was at best unenthusiastic, and at worst, openly against me. Brad's negative comments to me about universal health insurance suggested to me he might be a conservative who did not share my sense of justice for the little guy. But a few years later, when I was interviewing writers to help me write my book, one person I interviewed expressed surprise that Tucker had represented me. She said Tucker had a reputation for representing big institutions. In retrospect, I cannot exclude the possibility that Brad was concerned that suing the hospital would have hurt his reputation with other existing or potential clients. If this were true, then he should not have taken my case in the first place. As it was, he had had a copy of my reappointment application for a year before bringing up the issue of whether or not I was prohibited from suing the hospital. It seemed to me that he had not read the documents I had paid him to read. I hadn't been keeping track of how much I had already paid Tucker. The reality was that I had paid Tucker $40,000 up to that point.

I wrote off the loss of my money to experience. I still had more than $50,000 in my budget. I met privately with Mike on Thursday June 5th and told him that I thought Brad was not a good person to represent me in this case. He did not disagree. He said he had met with Brad, and I got the impression that Brad had told Mike he was withdrawing from the case. Mike told me he had thought that employing Brad and Ken on my case would save me money, but that it had not worked out that way. (I'll say!) Mike said he would have to take over. He lowered his hourly fee from $275/hr. to $150/hr. Mike said he had never tried a case before, but that he didn't think it was very hard and offered to do it himself. I had been involved with too many litigators to think that this was a good idea, especially considering how much I was spending. I knew I needed a litigator. He suggested Ken; without going into all my problems with Ken, I said I didn't think that was a good idea. When I asked Mike if he could work with a litigator from a different firm, he said that would be no problem.

At this point I didn't have a litigator. I didn't even have a written complaint. I was in no position to negotiate with the hospital. I told Mike to tell Maria I decided not to go to mediation at that time. But I had a new litigator in mind. His name was Martin (not his real name.) I had known Martin from the gym I go to. He was a litigator in his early fifties with his own practice. He had asked me for advice about some of his medically involved cases, including malpractice and contract issues. He seemed smart and aggressive. I had discussed my lawsuit with him on a few occasions, and he seemed sympathetic. I told him what had happened with Brad. He couldn't believe how much money I had already paid Tucker and the situation I was now in. I asked him if he would be interested in being my litigator, and he said that he was.

Martin was a star basketball player in college. He told me his team had gotten to the round of eight in the NCAA tournament. He was a big man, 6'2", 270 lbs. Between him and Mike, they made an imposing duo. I assumed that Martin was an honest man, but I am just too naive and trusting. As it turned out, he had been incarcerated for four months in the mid nineties for income tax evasion. His law license had also been suspended for a period of time. I didn't discover this until early 2004. So when Mike and I met with Martin in Mike's office on July 2, 2003, to discuss the case, neither one of us knew what we were dealing with.

The meeting went well, and Martin agreed to take the case. We agreed, at my request, that Mike write up the complaint as the first order of business. Mike sent a letter to Martin the next day, including many of the relevant documents. I told Martin that it was important for him to read the documents. At first he refused, but then agreed when I continued to bug him about it. As it turned out, he subsequently told me he never read the documents. Instead, he delegated that to his associate, Michael Monseur (his real name). Michael was in his first year out of law school. He was in his mid thirties, having gone to law school later in life. Martin had never told me he had a junior associate. I had agreed to pay him $150 an hour, thinking he would do the work himself. So I was a little surprised at this turn of events. I had been paying Ken Scholtz $120 per hour; now I was paying Michael Monseur $150 per hour. I didn't complain; however, because I felt I just had to play the hand I had been dealt. In August, Martin insisted on changing our deal. He wanted a hybrid. I agreed to pay him $100 an hour, plus a percentage of any judgment or settlement.

Mike Cassidy completed the first draft of the complaint by August 20th. Martin and Michael reviewed it and made comments, as did I. Mike and Martin and I met again to discuss where we stood, but I don't remember the exact date. What I do remember vividly was Martin saying to Mike, "Where is the complaint?" Martin said what Mike had written was not in the form of a complaint. Now I was back to square one. We agreed that Martin would write up the complaint, or rather, Michael Monseur would write it up. I was definitely feeling frustrated at all the delays. I knew the longer it took to do the paperwork, the more witnesses I would lose if I had to go to trial. Time was on the defendant's side, not mine. At the same meeting, Mike started to make some noise about not pursuing the complaint because it might adversely affect my disability benefits. I knew it wouldn't and explained this to him. He seemed to want to wiggle out of the case.

However, on September 17, 2003 the whole situation took a turn for the better. Mike emailed me saying he had just gotten a call from a reporter at the *Pittsburgh Post-Gazette.* The reporter was doing a story on whistleblower physicians and the retribution foisted upon them by hospitals. As I mentioned in a previous chapter, the reporter, Steve Twedt, published a five-part series entitled, "The Cost of Courage." He wanted to know if Mike had any cases involving this issue. Mike recommended that I not talk to Mr. Twedt, and he never called me. The series specifically cited Horty and Springer as being involved in some of these cases. He described cases from around the United States in which doctors had been falsely convicted of being "disruptive" and reported to the NPDB after they complained of poor quality of care at their hospitals. I knew Maria had no choice but to read Twedt's series in its entirety. My credibility had just taken a quantum leap upward. My optimism soared.

By early September we had decided to add Dave Laman and Bill Sims to the complaint. I felt that if it weren't for them, the problems everyone on both sides was facing would never have come to be. Ken filed the Writ for Mike against Sims and Laman at that time. I was delighted to learn from Mike in October that Maria said that, although the hospital was covered by insurance, she did not know if that included Sims and Laman. She would not accept service of the Writ against them. The county sheriff's office had to serve the Writs to them directly. I don't know if they were served at their home or office. It was almost three years since they had threatened to sue me and announced that they intended to make my life miserable. Now they were being told that what they had done was against the law. They thought they could get away with it, but now they were getting a taste of their own medicine. Since they weren't covered by insurance for breaking the law, their personal fortunes were at risk.

When they had threatened to sue me, I wasn't afraid, just angry. I knew I was only trying to protect my patients. I knew I had done nothing wrong and had violated no laws. They knew they had and they had gotten caught, so therefore they had reason to be frightened. I knew I wasn't going to go after them personally. I was just trying to teach them a lesson. But they didn't know what I was thinking. They were bullies and cowards, and someone needed to stand up to them.

CHAPTER 76

PULLING TEETH

Getting Martin to finish the written complaint was like pulling teeth, to use an old expression. I also ran into some more resistance from Mike, which to this day I do not understand. We had agreed that it would be useful to address what had occurred in 1997 as part of the complaint. We just didn't know exactly how to do it. I asked Mike to ask Maria to send us a copy of the minutes of the March 10, 2000 committee meeting at the hospital. (If you recall, that was the meeting with Rick Collins and Bill Jennings, in which I detailed what Larry Adler and Terry Kostrub had done to me in 1997.) I thought this would just be a routine request, but for some reason Mike didn't want to ask Maria for it. I emailed him on the September 27th, reiterating my request. At our next face-to-face meeting with Martin present, I pushed Mike about getting these minutes from Maria. He didn't give me a reason why he wouldn't. When I pushed a little more, he flatly stated, "I'm not going to do it." I dropped the issue. Did Mike have some sort of conflict? I thought it was a reasonable request.

Finally, on October 21st, Mike completed his review of the first draft of the complaint completed by Michael Monseur and sent it to Martin with a cover letter. Mike said, "I think we are now in a position to meet, compare notes, and finalize the complaint so that we can present it to Maria Danaher." Then on October 28th Mike wrote a letter to me and Martin in which he stated, "We need to meet quickly so we can present the Complaint to Maria Danaher although there may be some additional pressure due to the recent newspaper articles." On December 8th Mike wrote another letter to Martin, stating, "This is just a reminder that I would like to get the Complaint finalized and sent to Maria Danaher as soon as possible. The Pittsburgh paper stories are still fresh. The CEO [Jan Jennings] of the Hospital has just resigned. I think this would be a good time to cause a little consternation." Mike meant to cause consternation at the hospital; what Martin did was to consternate Mike and me. I spoke to Martin on the 16th, telling him how important it was to get the complaint finished. He told me to "get a life." He also did not respond to any of Mike's letters.

On the other hand, Michael Monseur was a pleasure to work with, and we developed a good rapport. Unlike his boss, Michael actually read all the documents I gave him and understood what had occurred. He even tried to make excuses for Martin's procrastination. Michael got me the revised complaint on December 26th. Mike and I made a few revisions and awaited the finished document. Mike emailed me on January 8, 2004, asking if I had gotten the final revision. I spoke to Martin that morning and he said it would be ready by the 13th. This was getting really tedious, and I was becoming more and more concerned that the delays might ruin my chances of success. But Michael Monseur had made the suggestion that we include Fingeret and Kostrub in the complaint because of their behavior in 1997. We had evidence for their involvement in the documents Maria had sent us in 2003. Since the statute of limitations begins after the plaintiff learns of the defendants' behavior, it was now possible to go back to 1997. This made me feel better. Michael was really on my side. Martin agreed to include Buzz and Terry; now we had to convince Mike.

Martin, Michael, and I met on January 19, 2004. Martin asked me to ask Mike to file a Writ against Kostrub, Fingeret, Bonnie Andrews, Bob Werkin (the cath lab head nurse), and Terry Riffer (the cath lab administrator). I thought this was a little over the top. Mike said he wanted Martin to file the Writ since he had been the one to make the decision, but Martin refused to do it. He wanted me to do it myself. Martin did not want his name on any documents, and he refused to answer Mike's letters or return any of my phone calls. When I refused to file the Writs myself, Martin changed his mind and said they shouldn't be filed at all. Martin said that Fingeret had reported the accusations against me to the hospital's board of trustees; therefore it was a protected communication and he couldn't be sued for it. But Michael and I had told Martin that the case against Fingeret was based on the fact that he had spoken to outside agencies, including the PHP and the Farley Center. This was really getting ridiculous. As bad as the problems were in the practice of medicine, the legal profession seemed to have even worse problems. At least problems with one's attorney weren't literally fatal.

Things seemed to be spiraling out of control, so I called for a meeting with Mike and Martin. I told Martin I wanted Michael to attend as well, but he absolutely refused. At one point Martin told me in no uncertain terms, "If you think you are going to hire Michael Monseur to do your case, you're crazy." Mike, Martin and I met at Mike's office on January 28, 2004. I met alone with Mike for an hour first. I described Martin's bizarre behavior and that his reversal on the Writ against the new defendants made no sense. Mike realized he had to retake control. He also had some new information with which he could now support adding the new defendants. Amazingly and very ironically, Mike told me that he had just been personally sued by *Larry Adler*. Larry was suing him for "civil conspiracy" because he was representing doctors who were suing Larry. (I can't reveal who they were, but you can use your imagination.) Mike hadn't heard of "civil conspiracy" before. He went down to the firm's law library and came back with the written statute. Sure enough, we could use it to sue Kostrub and Fingeret for conspiring with Adler to get me off the staff at Jefferson in 1997 under false and secret accusations. Larry was now responsible for paving the way for me to expose the very person he had secretly employed in his little scheme. I was delighted. Larry's perfidy had finally caught up with him. He was just another one of the bullies and cowards I wanted to teach a lesson.

By the time Martin arrived at the meeting, Mike and I had already decided on a plan of action. We decided not to name Andrews and Werkin because they seemed to just be pawns of Adler. I agreed that they had probably been coerced by people in positions of power over them. I didn't want to name Riffer because I thought he was also coerced and was just trying to save his job and support his family. Mike felt that because his name was listed in the documents, we had to name him to be consistent. He was a hospital administrator and therefore in a position of responsibility. Mike agreed to file the Writ himself. He also insisted that he would write up the conspiracy count himself and add it to the complaint. I totally agreed. I wanted to get Martin out of the loop because he just seemed to be obstructing the entire process. Martin called Michael from Mike's office and told him, in our presence, that he wanted the complaint finished by February 5th.

I met with Michael at his office on Friday, February 6th, to review his work. It was great. He emailed me his final draft, sans conspiracy count, that evening, and I forwarded it to Mike, who was out of town for a few days in February. He reviewed the complaint, filed the Writ, and wrote the conspiracy count by the end of February. Everything was complete except for Martin's final approval. Martin had promised me the complaint would be finished by Thanksgiving, 2003; then Christmas, then early 2004. He said the project would cost $10,000 to $15,000. After Michael sent me his finished work in February, Martin sent me a bill for $21,000. I saw him at the gym and handed him a check for $15,000, and he agreed I could give him the balance the following month. Something told me I should make the check out to his law firm and not to him personally. Even though I didn't know about his criminal record at the time, I didn't want to take the chance he would cash it and not report it on his income tax. If that were to happen, I wouldn't be able to deduct the expense from any money I received from the defendants. It turned out to be prescient. When I handed him the check, I watched his eyes to see if he was checking not only for the amount but also to whom the check was made out to. To my eye he definitely checked both.

Then something truly astounding happened. On March 3rd, 2004, I emailed Mike to suggest that, since we already had the finished complaint and Martin was out of town, he just clean up the complaint to his satisfaction and send it directly to Maria. So when I spoke to Martin on March 5th, I assumed we were ready to go. I was completely blindsided when Martin said that he was now insisting that I had to ask the hospital for reinstatement. I explained to him that Mike and I had been through this in 2003, but he refused to listen and started to yell at me. I raised my voice in return, trying to talk some sense into him. He then said that he was quitting the case. I apologized for raising my voice, and he replied, "Apology not accepted." I had just given him a check for $15,000 and he was leaving me high and dry.

The next day at the gym, I did something I suppose I should have done before I hired Martin; I checked him out with some of my acquaintances. One of the guys told me with complete certainty that Martin was really bad news and should be avoided. I was told Martin had been in jail for some type of crime. I went home and checked the Internet. Sure enough, right there in front of me on the website for The Disciplinary Board of the Supreme Court of Pennsylvania was Disciplinary Board Docket No. 95 DB 2001, Supreme Court Docket No. 665 D. D. No. 3. "Respondent was suspended pursuant to his conviction of two counts of willful failure to file federal tax returns. He was sentenced to four months of incarceration followed by four months of house detention and one year of probation." Discipline Imposed: "One year suspension" due to aggravating factors of "one prior admonition and three private reprimands." Ohmygod!

I was at a loss. At least I had Mike to turn to for advice, and I met with him in his office. Mike said I should write Martin a letter accepting his withdrawal from the case and telling him that, because I was now going to have to incur the expense of finding a new attorney, I would not pay the balance of my bill. I sent the letter certified mail on March 11th. When I saw Martin at the gym a few days later, he said he wanted to get back on the case. He also said he would sue me for the money he thought I owed him. He seemed sincere about wanting to get reinstated, so I said okay. When I told Mike about this, he responded appropriately, "Richard, are you crazy? He threatened to sue you!" I didn't make any more contact with Martin. That didn't stop him from sending me another bill, this time for a total of $26,000. He billed me for 267 hours of work. All I had to show for this was a 25-page complaint. There was no way in hell a 25-page document should take 267 hours. I had paid him the upper limit of what he said the complaint would cost—$15,000—and I thought that was more than fair. I turned to Mike again. Mike said to let him handle it. He wrote Martin a letter telling him to leave me alone. That didn't seem to be enough for Martin.

During our conversation on March 5th, Martin told me that he would only treat me with respect if I was 6'5" and weighed over 300 pounds. I knew I was going to see him at the gym again, so I resolved to pretend he didn't exist. I'm pretty good at that. I saw him multiple times. I knew he couldn't start a conversation with me because that could be considered harassment, and Mike would step in. But every time I saw him either in the gym or in the parking lot, he made movements toward me, indicating he wanted to talk to me. I knew he was going to threaten me if I talked to him. I also knew that if I didn't start the conversation, he wouldn't be able to do it. Because I'm so loquacious and gregarious, people sometimes think I don't have much self control. Actually, the opposite is true. When you have strong emotions, such as I do, you have to develop a large degree of self-control to stay out of trouble. Martin's gestures toward me continued every time I saw him at the gym for at least the next six months. Then I think he just got bored with it. Mike seemed quite worried that Martin would take some action against me and continued to ask me if I had heard anything from him for at least a few months. I still see Martin occasionally at the gym, but we just ignore each other.

Do you get the idea that this lawsuit was not an easy thing to do? It was no wonder Verardi and Wetschler didn't take me seriously; maybe no one else had ever been able to do it. That was my assumption, and that's why I was so driven. I had to prove to these guys it could be done. Considering what a good life I had, I felt that I would have been ungrateful if I had not done my best to try to protect those innocent doctors Horty and Springer would try to attack in the future if they always felt it would be a free ride. They had to understand there were consequences for unethical, illegal behavior. Wetschler had to understand he was not above the law, as he had insisted to me in June of 2001.

CHAPTER 77

THE NEGOTIATIONS

My "amicable resolution" with Jefferson Hospital precludes me from discussing the details of our negotiations or the final agreement. I am not allowed to say whether or not I "won" or "lost." But, of course, implicit in the terms "amicable" and "resolution" or "agreement" is the fact that negotiations did, in fact, occur. But I can discuss my conversations and negotiations with my lawyers. In any lawsuit, the primary negotiations occur between the lawyers and their clients. I also want to make it clear that I do not think that Jefferson Hospital did anything to deliberately violate any laws or hurt me or my patients. While any hospital is legally responsible for certain behaviors on the part of their employees, employees sometimes violate not only hospital policies, but also state or federal laws. In my case, the individuals I named in my lawsuit were the ones who needed to be held responsible for their actions.

My purpose, though, was mainly to inform the hospital of what these people had done in the hospital's name. I wanted the hospital to employ more oversight and develop new procedures to prevent damage to their patients and their honest doctors. So when I spoke to my lawyers about my goals, I told them I was not suing for personal financial gain. I was suing to express my gratitude for the wonderful life my career in medicine had provided for me and my family. The lawyers didn't seem to be able to believe me. All of them at some point expressed the opinion that it's always about the money. Well, I guess that's what lawyers do; they argue about money. They also deal with human dishonesty on a routine basis. After a while they must come to see the human race as composed only of dishonest, greedy people. This is understandable, given the nature of their business. They are always arguing with other people, and that's what they're paid to do.

Physicians, on the other hand, have different enemies: death and disability, both physical and mental. I went into medicine to help people and earn a decent living for my family and myself, not to get rich or feed my ego with money. Of course, a lawsuit almost always involves money. So, of necessity, much of my negotiations with my attorneys revolved around money. As I mentioned before, when Sue Gunn told me she thought the hospital would want to settle with me, I was hoping to get around $75,000. I wanted to make sure the hospital would take the situation seriously enough to take the appropriate steps to prevent a recurrence of similar episodes in the future. I also wanted to at least break even financially. When Brad Tupi told me he thought my case was worth only $7,500 and his firm was charging me $7,500 a month to represent me, I refused to give up.

After Steve Twedt published his "Cost of Courage" series, I began to think I could get at least $300,000. Around that time a jury in California had awarded a doctor, similarly abused by his hospital, $4.3 million. In 2006, a jury in Texas awarded a doctor $366 million! This was lowered on appeal to *only $24 million!* Martin thought I might be able to get $500,000. Mike thought the most was $100,000. Having done a fair amount of negotiating in my life, I wanted to go in with a large number and negotiate downwards. So, I told Mike I wanted to ask for $4 million. He was appalled. At one point he admonished me, "Richard, come to your senses!"

Once Michael Monseur finished the complaint, Mike delivered it to Maria on March 18, 2004. I don't remember if it was before or after she got the complaint that Mike called me to tell me that the hospital was indicating I could come back on staff if I wanted to. Of course, going back on staff was useless because I no longer had any patients or referring doctors. Starting a practice like mine was a once-in-a-lifetime opportunity. It would be impossible for me to duplicate, especially since I now had a disability and could only work part-time. But that didn't stop me from getting enormous satisfaction from the hospital's statement. After all my attorneys' admonitions that "The hospital is never going to ask you back," I felt vindicated. I knew I had done nothing that justified throwing me off the staff. I had repeatedly told Mike and Martin that, of course, the hospital would ask me back. There was no reason for them not to. When I expressed my satisfaction to Mike, he said I shouldn't feel vindicated because the hospital was only doing it to avoid having to pay more money. My lawyers just didn't seem to understand that I was fighting for my honor.

The one contribution Martin did make to my case was to insist that the complaint include a partial list of the patients whose care I complained about. He asked me if any of the cases represented malpractice. I said that would be up to a jury to decide, but that in my opinion they did. I said I would definitely be an expert witness for any family that would decide to sue any of the defendants for malpractice. Martin's plan was to threaten the hospital by saying that, if the lawsuit were actually filed and went to trial, the patients' actual names would be revealed publicly. Because the statute of limitations for malpractice begins *after* the malpractice is discovered by the patient or family, the defendants would then be at risk. He hoped to use this as a negotiating position in any mediation or negotiation. So, when Michael Monseur wrote up the complaint, he included a brief summary of five cases: Mr. W., Mrs. K., Mr. U., Mrs. L., and Mrs. S. The patients' names were not used. Once Martin was off the case, this strategy was no longer operative, but I felt it was important for Maria to see the cases, because the whole issue of poor patient care might have been lost to her in the mountains of paper she had to wade though.

The final complaint as written by Michael Monseur (see appendix D) was absolutely brilliant, as far as I was concerned. I even told Mike his firm should hire Michael. (At the time I assumed that Tucker might represent other plaintiffs against large institutions.) The final complaint was 26 pages long and included 16 counts:

1. Defamation—Wanitta Anderson
2. Punitive Damages—Anderson
3. Defamation—Wetschler

4. Punitive Damages—Wetschler
5. Breach of Contract—Wetschler, Sims, and Laman
6. Punitive Damages—Wetschler, Sims, and Laman
7. Breach of Contract Promissory Estoppel—Wetschler, Sims, and Laman
8. Fraudulent Misrepresentation—Wetschler
9. Tortious Interference with Contract—Wetschler, Sims, and Laman
10. Intentional Infliction of Emotional Distress—Wetschler, Sims, and Laman
11. Breach of Contract—Wetschler, Sims, and Laman
12. Breach of Contract—Wetschler, Sims, and Laman
13. Unlawful Discrimination—Jefferson Regional Medical Center, Wetschler, Sims, and Laman
14. Unlawful Discrimination—Jefferson, Wetschler, Sims, and Laman
15. Breach of Contract—Jefferson, Wetschler, Sims, and Laman
16. Civil Conspiracy—Wetschler, Sims, Laman, Fingeret, Kostrub, and Riffer

I finally had the opportunity to defend myself, something I had never been afforded the opportunity to do. I had accomplished my purpose. At this point, Mike told me it would be counter-productive to actually file the suit. He thought my negotiating position would be weakened once the suit was made public. He said the hospital would not want the negative publicity and would be more inclined to settle prior to filing. Of course, what the hospital didn't know was that I didn't even have a litigator. So at that point I had already decided to settle the case. I didn't tell Mike that because I wanted him to fight as hard as possible. I still insisted he demand four million dollars.

We agreed to enter mediation with a federal mediator. The mediation was scheduled for Tuesday June 8, 2004 at the Federal Building in downtown Pittsburgh. Mike had prepared a beautiful, two-inch thick, loose-leaf presentation (see appendix E), which he had given to Maria the previous Friday. It mimicked the loose-leaf presentation Paul

Verardi and Wetschler had sent to the Pennsylvania Human Relations Commission more than two years prior.

A few weeks after the mediation, an agreement was reached. Most lawsuits are settled before going to trial. I had spent $75,000 in legal fees. They say a good outcome occurs when both sides feel they could have done better. My only disappointment was that I didn't get to put Wetschler, Payton, Kostrub, and Adler under oath and force them to tell the truth, or not. But one of the benefits I got was certainly not one I ever expected: the look of awe on Maria's face.

From my experience with the defense attorney from Dickie who had represented the cardiologists in the only malpractice case in which I had testified as an expert witness in December, 2001, I had expected Maria Danaher to be a hard-nosed, dishonest, win-at-any-cost lawyer. In my opinion, she wasn't. Mike had told me she was a nice person, and I concur. She was a small woman in her early fifties, about five feet tall and a hundred pounds. She left the mediation before Mike and I did, but we ran into her on the sidewalk immediately afterwards. I was very careful not to say anything she could use against me. Mike was standing beside me, so I felt protected. In an apologetic tone of voice, I told her I was sorry for all the mess, but that it was the only way I could defend myself from all the false allegations made against me.

The three of us stood on the sidewalk chatting for a minute or two. I don't remember her saying anything specific, but I will never forget the way she looked at me. She was looking up at me as I spoke. I can't remember anyone looking at me that way in my professional life. I can only describe her expression as a combination of reverence, respect, and admiration. I knew she was the only one who had had to read everything I had written to the hospital since 1997 (I don't think Mike was never given all the documents.) When I wrote those letters, I was writing to her, as the hospital attorney, even though she didn't exist yet as the hospital's attorney. I knew that she understood what had happened to me. She must have understood that I was courageous in my fight for justice for my patients and myself. Was this the reason that our final agreement did not include any prohibition against me writing this book? You'll have to ask her. Thank you, Maria; I will never forget you.

The last time I saw Mike he said to me: "Rich, I think they heard you."

I replied, "Yeah, Mike. I hope we did some good." I certainly hope so, not only for the sake of the people in the Jefferson area who trust their medical care to their hospital, but also for the sake of the hundreds of wonderful, dedicated people, including doctors, nurses, and staff, whom I had the honor and privilege to work with at that institution. These fine people have devoted themselves to truly helping the patients they are devoting their lives to serving. It is for these selfless people who place the well-being of their patients above their own that I have written this book. I hope that my efforts will benefit their lives and those of their patients in some small way.

PART V

PROBLEMS WITH AND SOLUTIONS FOR HEALTHCARE AND EDUCATION

CHAPTER 78

THE UNIVERSITY OF PITTSBURGH MEDICAL CENTER (UPMC)

After I retired from the active practice of medicine in December, 2001 I went back to school to get my Pennsylvania state certification to teach high school physics. I didn't have quite enough money to make ends meet and I still wanted to make a contribution to society. I learned a lot more than I taught during the two and a half years I worked in education. I stopped teaching in June, 2004. (In the interest of continuity, I will describe these experiences in later chapters.) Once I stopped teaching, I still didn't want to stop making a contribution. My finances were now in better shape, and I wanted to do some form of meaningful volunteer work that would employ my skills and education.

I was still on the honorary staff at the University of Pittsburgh Medical Center. Using my experience at Mount Sinai as a guide, I thought I could make a contribution teaching medical students and residents. I inquired and was told that my volunteer staff position allowed me to attend the Division of Cardiology conferences. At Sinai, the cardiology conferences were free-wheeling affairs where both full-time faculty and volunteer faculty (those in private practice) were encouraged to express all points of view without fear of recrimination. The volunteer faculty had a lot to contribute and was well respected.

The first conference I attended was a lecture given by James Shaver, MD. Jim had been Chief of Cardiology at Pitt when I arrived in Pittsburgh. He had recently retired from that position and was now a revered senior faculty member. He had also been a neighbor of mine when I lived in my big house. We spoke after the conference. He was quite enthusiastic about my attending the conferences. He had recently been put in charge of increasing the participation of the volunteer faculty in the cardiology division. Very few of the private practice cardiologists were involved with the division at that time. Jim made reference to Julian Levinson, a teacher of clinical cardiology at the medical school for many years, as well as being in private practice. I met Julian on a flight to one of the national cardiology meeting many years previously. I remembered quite vividly that he told me his main interest was in diagnosis. He thought that was the most challenging part of cardiology. Of course, he had an office based practice and didn't do procedures in the hospital. Jim Shaver, on the other hand, worked mostly in the hospital and had specialized in cardiac catheterization.

I was excited about the prospect of passing on the knowledge I had accumulated to the next generation of cardiologists. Jim also told me he wanted me to participate in teaching the second-year medical school students cardiac physiology. After my experience at Jefferson, where there were no conferences to discuss difficult cases, I was looking forward to being in an environment where people were anxious to learn and teach. While this was true to some extent, I was disappointed in the lack of intellectual honesty I found. I take no pleasure from relating my experiences at UPMC. I have nothing to gain from telling what I experienced. In fact, I am more concerned that I will be subject to retaliation and retribution from telling my story. But I feel that someone must tell the truth about what is going on in medicine today, even at the highest levels. What I saw reinforced the observation that the medical profession is being driven by money and the lust for power. This was further confirmed by a conversation I had with an associate professor of cardiology, who was a full time academic at Duke University, regarded as one of the top five cardiology centers in the country. He told me that in their cardiology faculty meetings, 85% of the time was spent discussing business, not medicine. I was and am deeply saddened by what had happened to the profession I love so much.

The most important thing to me in the practice of medicine was to admit one's mistakes, learn from them, and be determined not to repeat them. What I found at Presby (short for University Presbyterian Hospital, the main teaching hospital of the medical school) was more of an atmosphere of fear of retaliation. I can't remember a single time when a medical resident or cardiology fellow challenged or disputed an attending physician in one of the conferences. The main discourse seemed to me to be people falling all over each other to tell everyone who presented anything how wonderful they were. When I was a medical resident and cardiology fellow at Sinai, no one ever suggested to me that I shouldn't speak my mind in any cardiology conference. The conferences at Presby seemed more political than intellectual. This is not to suggest in any way that most of these people were anything less than brilliant; they weren't. But I think the environment was best summed up by Treasury Secretary Paul O'Neill, who was on the Board of Trustees at UPMC (University of Pittsburgh Medical Center) after he left the Bush administration. Mr. O'Neill was interested in improving the quality of patient care at the institution, and he tried to promote his ideas from his position on the board. When Mr. O'Neill quit the board in disgust, he was quoted in the local newspapers as saying something to the effect that "They're not interested in quality, they're interested in dominance."

As part of the process of publishing this book, I spoke on the phone with a Ms. Sharon McCartney in the medical staff office at Presby. I wanted to be sure that I was not violating any contractual obligations I had via the medical staff bylaws by discussing the cases I saw presented at the hospital. I had been told that Ms. McCartney was the expert in the bylaws. We spoke on December 12, 2006, at approximately 10:30 a.m.

Ms. McCartney informed me that once a case is presented at a conference in the hospital, it becomes public information. She assured me that, so long as I did not mention any patients' names, I was free to discuss the case with anyone outside the hospital. In the following pages I will discuss several of the cases I saw presented at conferences at UPMC between September 2004 and November 2005.

I was very excited to attend my first Morbidity and Mortality conference at Presby in the fall of 2004. I remember the full professor who ran the meeting started off by telling the fellows that the idea was to find mistakes so as to learn from them and not repeat them. He quit a few months later and moved back to New York, and after he left, the conferences stopped. They resumed a few months later. I was a little surprised to hear Jim Shaver tell me that only full-time faculty members were now allowed to attend the M&M conferences. He explained the new policy somewhat apologetically by saying, "We don't want to wash our dirty laundry in public."

At the time I wasn't planning on writing the story of the woman who had a stroke during an unnecessary catheterization that I related in a previous chapter. Since I was the only non-full-time faculty member who even bothered to attend the conferences, I took the new policy to mean they didn't want any independent thinkers who might rock the boat. I knew I would have problems if I had gotten the job there in 2001, because I knew I would be willing to say some procedures should not be done. Do you think this might have been related to the fact that unnecessary procedures generate the same amount of income as necessary ones?

I was still allowed to attend the weekly catheterization conferences, where interesting and difficult cases were presented. I never had to agree not to talk about these conferences outside the hospital in order to attend. I also never had any intention of discussing the cases in public. I was quite happy just to attend and feel that I was making a contribution. At the conferences, I tried to be careful not to say anything that I didn't think was important or educational. I thought very carefully about everything I said before saying it. I also tried to wait until everyone else was finished saying what they had to say. Frequently, I would not say anything during the conference, but rather talk privately to the presenter afterwards. I had one bad experience, in which I was excoriated for speaking out during a lecture given by a visiting professor who did not disclose the fact that he had a financial relationship with the drug company whose drug he was discussing, or the fact that the drug company representative was standing in the back of the room, listening to his every word. I pointed out to the audience, comprised mostly of medical students and doctors in training, that he was misleading them by drawing unfounded clinical recommendations from the statistics he presented. I felt that he must have been aware of the fact that his recommendations would lead to the over utilization of the drug, and thought he was being deliberately dishonest in return for any money he was getting from the drug company for himself or his department. Only after I made my comments did he admit to the group that the drug company was in fact giving money to his department. Of course, advocating for more utilization of the drug in question would result in more profits for the drug company and more cost to society. I felt that he was deliberately trying to dupe the young doctors in the audience and felt compelled to speak out. I simply believe that drug company propaganda has no legitimate place in any medical school. After being called on the carpet for this, I became even more careful to watch what I said. I even checked with Jim Shaver frequently to make sure I wasn't being inappropriate in my public comments during the cardiology conferences. He consistently reassured me that I wasn't.

My concern was with the quality of care I witnessed in some of the cases presented at the conferences. As I mentioned before, after I left academics in 1984 and went into private practice, I realized how little I knew and how much I had to learn about the care of patients in the real world. At Sinai, all the residents knew the best private guys were much better clinicians—read "doctors"—than the best-full time faculty. When I first went to Presby, I expected to find a high degree of clinical competence from the senior faculty. After all, UPMC is rated as one of the best medical centers in the United States. Unfortunately, some of the cases I saw indicated what I thought were serious errors in judgment and understanding. Quite frankly, I was more than a little appalled at what I witnessed on many occasions. I think it will be quite educational for the reader to review four cases that stand out in my mind. I don't think any of the good private clinical cardiologists I worked with in Pittsburgh could ever have made these kinds of mistakes. I don't know the names of any of the patients involved, and I won't mention any of the doctors' names. The purpose here is to demonstrate that even in the best medical centers, the quality of care can leave much to be desired.

The first case occurred in 1996 when I was still working full time in Adler's group. (This is not a case I heard about at a conference, but rather a patient I cared for myself.) I was on call for the group one night when I received a panicked phone call from one of the experienced general surgeons at Braddock General Hospital in a nearby suburb. He told me a patient of his had just had a precipitous fall in blood pressure to seventy systolic. The patient was a woman in her fifties who had been admitted to the hospital a few days before with multiple fractures from an automobile accident. I told him immediately that the most likely problem was blood clots in her lungs (pulmonary emboli). I had seen this many times, because the cardiologist is always called in these situations. He said I was definitely wrong. He maintained she was bleeding internally from the trauma of the accident. On the other hand, her blood count was not dropping and her abdominal CAT scan revealed no evidence of active bleeding. He thought this could be a false negative result, however. What usually happens in these types of situations is that blood clots form in the legs of patients who are at bed rest, especially if there has been trauma. Traumatized tissues release chemicals into the bloodstream to promote clotting to stop the bleeding from the trauma. But this promotes clotting throughout the body, not just at the site of the trauma. Clots typically form in the leg veins and then can break off and travel through the inferior vena cava, through the right ventricle of the heart and into the pulmonary artery, through which blood travels from the heart to the lungs. This wreaks havoc with the entire cardiovascular system via multiple mechanisms. The patient can go into cardiovascular collapse and die without warning. In her case, we at least had some warning. But she needed emergent treatment.

The doctor explained to me that there was a big problem: The patient was a Jehovah's Witness and refused any blood transfusion. I raced to the hospital and got there by 11 p.m. I found the patient alert and oriented, asked her a few questions and reviewed her chart. I knew her survival depended on my ability to make the correct diagnosis. In order to get some of the tests I needed in the middle of the night, I had to have a few ancillary staff awakened at home. This delayed things a little. I stayed at this woman's bedside for more than four hours, wracking my brain for any nuance I could use to differentiate between active bleeding and pulmonary emboli. If I got the wrong diagnosis, I could kill her. If I gave her blood thinners for the blood clots and she was in fact bleeding, she would bleed to death. If she were operated upon for abdominal bleeding and instead had pulmonary emboli, she would die in the operating room. Massive pulmonary emboli are usually an absolute contraindication to any type of major surgical procedure.

During my time with the patient, I had several conversations with her family and minister about the situation. By around 3 a.m. I felt confident that the correct diagnosis was pulmonary emboli and that there was no objective evidence for bleeding. I bit the bullet and ordered the heparin (blood thinner). I had used every bit of reasoning and clinical judgment I could muster. On my way home, I got a call from the minister. He wanted to know if I would approve of her being transferred to Presby. I didn't see any reason not to, and I thought the patient and family would feel more confident in a large, prestigious institution. When the minister asked me if they would do anything differently, I told him no.

Around 5 a.m. I got a call from the attending surgeon at Presby to give me an update on what they had found. He told me my diagnosis was wrong and that, in fact, the patient was bleeding internally. They were going to take her to the operating room immediately to open her abdomen, find the site of bleeding, and stop it. I was aghast. I thought I had almost killed the patient. I desperately asked him if he had stopped the heparin. I was relieved a little when he said he had. I wished him luck.

A few hours later I got another phone call from him. He told me the patient had gone into cardiac arrest and died almost immediately after the start of the operation. This is what one would have expected if she had had pulmonary emboli. I didn't say anything except to express my condolences. I was glad to hear that the family had agreed to an autopsy to determine the actual cause of death. Within 24 hours I got the preliminary verbal report: "Massive Pulmonary Emboli." I couldn't help but think that the surgeon at Presby was just an academic with little clinical experience and even less clinical judgment. He must have viewed me as some ignorant community clinical cardiologist whose judgment was best ignored. I was quite familiar with the whole "town vs. gown" sentiments present in most Ivory Towers. Of course, unless someone was sued for malpractice, there would be no accountability whatsoever for any doctor involved. No one ever seemed to pay any attention to these mistakes.

CHAPTER 79

WASHING THE DIRTY LAUNDRY IN PUBLIC

The second case involved a middle-aged man whose case was presented at a cardiology conference at Presby, which I attended after I retired. He had symptoms of congestive heart failure, and his echocardiogram revealed a small heart. The problem was not that his heart was big and baggy with poor contractions, but rather that the heart didn't seem to relax properly. Sometimes this type of problem is due to what is called "Restrictive Cardiomyopathy." In this condition, the heart muscle itself can be infiltrated with abnormal substances that make it very stiff. This can be due to one of several diseases. For example, the heart might be infiltrated with excess iron, hemochromatosis, which is a rare condition. Another example is amyloidosis. In this condition, a substance called "amyloid" infiltrates the heart muscle, restricting its contraction.

A similar type of heart failure occurs when the covering of the heart, the pericardium, becomes diseased and thickened and prevents the heart from expanding normally during relaxation. This condition is called "Constrictive Pericarditis." This condition can occur in several different kinds of diseases that affect the pericardium. The clinical presentation of "restriction" and "constriction" can be similar. The treatment for each condition, however, is quite different. If the pericardium is thickened and constricts the heart, the treatment is the surgical removal of the pericardium. Every cardiac surgeon I have talked to about this operation has told me it is very difficult and akin to removing the skin of an orange without removing any of the pulp, even though the skin is stuck to the pulp. The process of removing the pericardium from the heart muscle in this condition requires a tedious slicing away of the pericardium from the heart muscle. Because of this, the risk of serious complications is much higher than for, say, routine coronary bypass surgery, so it's important to make sure you have the correct diagnosis before you open the chest.

As a medical resident, one is taught that the diagnosis of amyloidosis can be made by a biopsy of the rectum or cheek. The diagnosis can also be made by a blood test called a "serum protein electrophoresis." Amyloid is a substance that comes from abnormal protein in the blood. The amyloid settles in the tissues of the body where it can cause dysfunction of that tissue. When it deposits in the heart muscle, the heart becomes stiff and cannot contract normally. The patient develops signs and symptoms of congestive heart failure. In Pittsburgh, this is a well-known diagnosis because, not many years ago, the mayor died from amyloid heart disease while in office.

In the case presented, the patient was sent to the operating room with the presumptive diagnosis of constrictive pericarditis. The diagnosis of restrictive cardiomyopathy was entertained, but the patient did not get any of the simple tests for amyloidosis before going to the operating room. The pericardium was removed from the patient's heart. I asked if the heart muscle had been biopsied during the operation and was told it was not. The diagnosis of amyloid heart disease, not constrictive pericarditis, was subsequently made. The patient died two days after the surgery. This is considered an operative death. When I asked if a rectal or cheek biopsy had been done prior to surgery, I was told that neither had been done. When I asked why, I was greeted with blank stares and incredulity. No one else at the conference commented on this fatal mistake. No one seemed to care. If they did, they didn't speak up. The impression I got was that I was considered to be rude for bringing up such a sensitive issue. At Sinai, when I was there, the room would have exploded with outrage. Would that still be the case today? I have no way of knowing, but I certainly hope so.

The third case occurred almost a year later. A man in his early sixties was admitted with symptoms of congestive heart failure. He had had an episode of acute pericarditis six years previously, due to a viral infection of the pericardium, a relatively common disease that usually heals spontaneously. If the patient has symptoms of heart failure due to the fluid in the pericardial sac, the fluid can be easily removed with a needle or small incision in the pericardium called a "pericardial window." In most cases, the patient does not suffer any long-term cardiac problems. Sometimes, the patient can develop thickening of the pericardium, which can cause constrictive pericarditis. Also, any patient with a history of viral pericarditis has an increased risk of a repeat episode.

This patient had thickening of the pericardium consistent with a diagnosis of constriction. But, in addition, the patient's echocardiogram also showed fluid in the pericardial sac, and the patient had a large amount of fluid in the pleural space around the lungs. This was similar to the fluid Mrs. N. had in 1998. The diagnosis of constrictive pericarditis can be established by cardiac catheterization by measuring the pressures in the various chambers of the heart. Jim Shaver was an expert in this area, having told me he published a treatise about it with P.S. Reddy, who had been the head of the catheterization laboratory at Presby for many years.

While this patient's pressure measurements were consistent with constriction, I knew from clinical experience that constrictive pericarditis was not usually associated with large pleural effusions, so I questioned the diagnosis. I said the pleural fluid should be removed first. Then, if the patient still had significant heart failure, the pressures should be measured again, because the presence of such a large amount of fluid could alter the pressures in the heart chambers and give the false impression of constriction. Also, I said that if the patient's symptoms resolved after the removal of the pleural fluid, he could be safely observed for a period of time to see if the symptoms recurred. In either case, the patient might avoid a dangerous operation, removal of the pericardium.

When I brought up my concerns, I was treated to abject ridicule. Jim Shaver looked at me pointedly and said, "I disagree with you."

One of the other professors in the room said, "The only time I would take out the pleural fluid would be on the way to the operating room." He meant on the way to have a pericardiectomy. I said there was absolutely nothing to lose by taking out the pleural fluid first.

When I brought up the fact that pericardiectomy was a dangerous operation, Jim said, "When Dr. Bahnson was here, I just sent my patients for pericardiectomy and never had a problem."

The only person in the room who supported me was a junior faculty member who was a cardiac surgeon. Jim had practiced cardiology for decades but didn't know pericardiectomy was a high-risk, difficult operation. I brought up the case of the patient who had died the previous year from an unnecessary pericardiectomy. The surgeon in the room volunteered that that patient had had a misdiagnosis. No one seemed to care. I felt enormous hostility from everyone else in the room. I left the conference feeling humiliated, but I knew I was correct and was appalled at the lack of clinical experience the full-time faculty demonstrated. As I left the building, I ran into one of the well-regarded cardiac surgeons and told him what had happened. He completely agreed with me.

Jim told me he would get me two articles proving his point. I read the articles and saw him at medical grand rounds a few weeks later. I told him one of the articles said recurrent viral pericarditis should not be treated with pericardiectomy initially. The other article concerned only eight patients who were operated on who had not had symptoms of congestive heart failure, and there was no non-surgically treated control group. He said that, since the patient had not had any complications from his pericardiectomy, he (Jim) had been correct.

"Jim, that's not true," I countered. "If an operation has a ten percent mortality, you're still going to get away with it nine times out of ten. That doesn't make it the right thing to do." He agreed with me. Then I said this patient most likely had recurrent pleuropeicarditis, a viral infection that would have caused the patient to have fluid in both the pericardial and pleural spaces. I said the patient had had a history of viral pericarditis six years previously, which would make my diagnosis most likely.

Jim sheepishly responded, "You have to excuse me, but I didn't know that. I came late to the conference and didn't hear the patient's history." That comment speaks volumes about my concerns about the clinical abilities of full time academic cardiologists. I should mention that a week after the cardiology conference about this patient, I received a phone call from one of the full-time cardiologists that the cardiology fellows had voted to ban any volunteer faculty from attending future cardiology conferences; so much for academic freedom of thought. I had had no definite plans to write this book at that time, but now that my desire to improve patient care by working within the system had been thwarted, I began to write as a last resort.

The last case I will discuss was the most saddening and disturbing; I believe it was presented in late winter or early spring of 2005. A four-year-old child (I don't remember if it was a boy or a girl) came from another city to UPMC Children's Hospital with evidence of congestive heart failure. The cause was thought to be due to a large hole in the wall separating the left ventricle from the right ventricle, a ventricular septal defect, or VSD. The patient had been in the hospital for some time, and the pediatric cardiologists were presenting the case at the adult cardiology conference. The patient was still sick and they wanted our input.

I was at first heartened to see the extraordinary technological abilities of the pediatric cardiologists. Initially, they used a catheter to place a device in the heart to actually close the hole. I even commented to the person sitting next to me how miraculous the procedure was. Then they showed the pictures of the patient's coronary arteries taken during the catheterization. They had interpreted the pictures as showing a heart attack in the front (anterior) of the patient's heart. A heart attack like this can result in a ventricular septal defect. They assumed this heart attack was caused by a blockage in the artery supplying blood to this part of the muscle, the left anterior descending (LAD) coronary artery. Because of this, the patient was taken to the operating room and a coronary bypass operation was performed on this coronary artery. Unfortunately, the patient continued to be in heart failure despite the operation.

A coronary bypass operation in a very sick patient is a risky operation. Any heart operation can result in complications that can cause the death of the patient. Therefore, one must be as sure as possible that the operation is needed before the decision to proceed is made. I don't know the actual mortality statistics of bypass surgery in four-year-old children with documented ventricular septal defects. In adults, however, the risks are quite high.

When I saw the coronary pictures, it was obvious to me that this patient did not have a heart attack caused by a blockage in the artery that was bypassed. The LAD was clearly moving normally during the cardiac cycle. I will say categorically that any experienced competent cardiologist who performs coronary angiography would have seen this immediately. I did. I couldn't believe these guys had made such a serious mistake. No one in the room understood what I was talking about. I had to go up to the front of the conference room and point out the obvious findings on the projection screen. There were a lot of blank stares in the room.

After I sat down and thought about the situation for a few minutes, I realized the patient had probably had a heart muscle infection called myocarditis. Actually, I remembered a case from the streptokinase study. That patient had died from a ruptured heart muscle near the same area as this child's VSD. He had not had a heart attack; rather, the autopsy showed a condition called "focal lymphocytic myocarditis." This is probably due to some form of viral infection of the heart muscle. I told those at the conference about this case, although no one had ever heard of this disease. That was totally understandable considering it is probably quite rare. But this in no way excused the gross misinterpretation of the coronary angiogram, because obviously heart attacks are quite common, and the angiographic features are common knowledge among invasive cardiologists.

The professors at the conference, both adult and pediatric cardiologists, ultimately agreed with me. We decided the patient needed a heart transplant. A couple of months later I ran into the senior adult cardiologist who had been in charge of the conference. He said the patient had had a heart transplant and was doing well. I breathed a sigh of relief. He told me I had been correct in my diagnosis. I asked him if the microscopic examination of the removed heart muscle had shown focal lymphocytic infiltration. He just said the patient had a "cardiomyopathy" and didn't know what the pathology report showed.

To my mind, the appalling nature of this case was the utter inability of those responsible for this patient's care to correctly interpret simple angiographic findings. This misdiagnosis caused the patient to undergo a needless and risky heart bypass operation. The fact that the patient survived does not excuse this lack of competence. One would never expect to find this level of care in one of the foremost pediatric hospitals in the country. It just reinforced my belief that academics in prestigious medical centers are sorely lacking in clinical experience and judgment. What this brings home is the need to hold all physicians, regardless of reputation and credentials, accountable for the quality of their care. In the next two chapters, I will briefly outline my prescription to rectify these failings in the American healthcare system.

CHAPTER 80

THE ONLY SOLUTION

The only solution to the healthcare morass is to embrace the American reliance on free markets. Capitalism works because people are free to spend their money in ways that give them the best value for their dollar. The automobile market is a useful analogy. When people buy a car, they look at two things: the price and the quality of the vehicle. They do not purchase a "plan" that they hope will allow them to get the car or truck they want and need. They compare a vehicle's features with others in their price range. They talk to other people for recommendations. They can read consumer magazines that publish reliability data on all models and makes. The decision generally comes down to price and quality. The result is "value": How much are they getting for their money? Two reports published by the Rand Corporation in the *New England Journal of Medicine* in the past four years indicate that the chances of any patient getting the proper diagnosis and treatment in any given medial encounter are only about 55%. This is simply no longer tolerable.

The healthcare "market" simply does not exist in the traditional sense. (I should mention here that I got straight A's in twelve credits of economics courses I took in college.) Patients generally are reduced to buying "a pig in a poke." First, it is simply not possible to determine the quality of care rendered by each of the physicians in one's geographic area. Second, the patient does not pay for the care himself; fees are determined by the person's insurance company. Since the fees paid to the physician are generally the same for all doctors on contract to that insurance company, be it private or public sector insurance, shopping by price is not possible.

In order to establish a marketplace for physician's services, it is mandatory that the quality of care for each physician be known to the public. The second part of the equation is to know the "cost" of each physician. Clearly, both of these are not something that *Consumer Reports* has the resources or expertise to determine. Determining cost and quality of physicians is conceptually simple but extremely difficult to determine accurately in the real world. Nonetheless, society has no choice but to do so if we are to solve the problem. There is simply no other economically rational solution. While this solution may be difficult to put into practice, the failure to do so is resulting in the loss of many thousands of lives and hundreds of billions of dollars annually.

The Institute of Medicine (IOM) published a position paper a few years ago stipulating that the most important thing to accomplish in American medicine over the next two to three *decades* is to generate "report cards" for every provider in the country. In 2006, the IOM advocated that doctors and hospitals be paid depending on the quality of care provided. Within the past three years, Medicare, under Mark McClellan, started a pilot program with twelve large clinics around the country. Under this program, simple measures of quality were made for each clinic for each of several diagnoses. The measures of quality used are what I refer to as "process" quality indicators. Examples include how well blood sugars are controlled in diabetic patients, or if patients are given the recommended medications after a heart attack. The clinics with good adherence to the recommended care receive a slight—I believe 3%—increase in reimbursement for each service provided. Preliminary published results have shown an increase in the use of desirable practices in these select institutions, but not necessarily a corresponding improvement in patient outcomes.

Ultimately, process indicators do not give a true picture of the quality of care. True quality can only be determined by measuring "outcomes." In New York and Pennsylvania, outcomes for all cardiac surgeons in the state have been measured and published for many years. These outcomes include the death rates for surgery by an individual surgeon for different types of heart operations. So, the precedent has been set, but there is a serious problem with these published data. They do not accurately measure how sick a given surgeon's patients are *prior to* their surgery. Obviously, if one surgeon operates on patients who are much sicker to begin with, the death rate will be higher than another surgeon's whose patients' condition is not as bad to begin with.

Because of this, a surgeon who is willing to operate on sicker patients will be unfairly penalized if his outcome data are not adjusted for the severity of illness of his patients. This same principle applies to doctors in all specialties. Adjusting outcome data is not an easy task to accomplish, but we simply have no choice if the measured outcomes are to be a true reflection of the quality of care provided by a doctor. Fortunately, we have the mathematical and scientific tools to accomplish this difficult task.

Over the past several decades, the medical community has developed the tools to accurately measure severity of illness in patients. All one has to do is pick up any respected medical journal and peruse any of the scientific articles. In each article, the characteristics describing the group of patients being studied is listed in meticulous detail. These include the basics of age, sex, and conditions such as high blood pressure or diabetes. In articles describing the results of a particular form of treatment for a cardiac condition, all relevant aspects of the patients' disease are quantitated. For example, if heart failure patients are being treated, the severity of symptoms and the basic measure of heart function, left ventricular ejection fraction, will be summarized for each patient group being treated with a certain drug or operation. Careful statistical analysis of the data allows scientists to determine whether or not a given drug or operation will actually improve symptoms or prognosis for any given condition.

These same methods can be applied to an individual physician's patients. If we know the severity of illness for a cardiologist's heart failure patients, then we can measure how well those patients do over a period of time as an accurate measure of that doctor's outcomes for heart failure patients. Say, for example, a cardiologist has a thousand patients with heart failure in his practice. It is a simple matter to follow those patients over the course of a year. The number of hospitalizations those patients require during that year can easily be counted; so can the number of deaths or total days spent in the hospital. In addition, it is vital that a method be devised to calculate the percentage of diagnoses made by each individual physician or group of physicians which subsequently proves to be in error. The public needs to know and has a right to know which doctors are poor diagnosticians. In the final analysis getting the correct diagnosis for any patient is a precondition for quality medical care.

Is it too big a job to measure outcomes for the tens of thousands of cardiologists in the United States? Heart failure patients in the country number in the millions. While it may not have been possible to do this in the past, computer technology has changed that. The methods used in medical research are scalable and can be applied to entire populations. The adoption of digital medical records will result in a system in which data can be easily obtained and analyzed. But even using the information available with the current medical record system is adequate to get started measuring quality in a meaningful and accurate way. The longer we wait to get started, the more Americans will die unnecessarily from poor quality medical care.

The next part of the solution requires measuring costs. Let's use the example of congestive heart failure again. We can measure Dr. Schneider's outcomes, but if he spends a million dollars per patient per year, his care will certainly not reduce the cost of healthcare in this country. So we have to measure Dr. Schneider's average cost per patient per year for all one thousand heart failure patients in his care. Clearly, hospitalizations are very expensive. Most procedures, such as heart catheterizations, open heart surgery, cardiac MRIs and echocardiograms, are also very expensive. Adding up all the costs to the healthcare system for Dr. Schneider's 1,000 heart failure patients for each year is a simple matter of arithmetic. Once we know Dr. Schneider's outcomes and cost per patient, it can be determined if he is a low-cost, high-quality provider or a high-cost, low-quality provider, or somewhere in between. It then becomes a simple matter to give Dr. Schneider a "report card" for congestive heart failure each year.

The next part of the solution is to pay doctors with better grades more for each service provided. Under the current system, doctors are paid for quantity, not quality or cost effectiveness. This results in a massive over-utilization of resources. As illustrated by the numerous anecdotes in this book, there is enormous economic pressure on good doctors to order unnecessary tests. There is also enormous reward for greedy doctors to do as many tests and procedures as they can get away with. I think human nature is such that, if society wants high-quality, low-cost care, the only way to get it is to pay for it. It's not possible to pay for something that is not measured. Q.E.D. *(Quod erat demonstratum.)*

Exactly the same basic economic principles apply to other health care providers such as hospitals and nursing homes. This data must be openly available to the public in the same way that cardiac surgeons' data is available today. This will allow all patients to make informed decisions when choosing a doctor and hospital. Of course, patients will not be motivated by cost data as much as outcome data, because patients don't pay fee for service; insurance companies do. By law, doctors must charge every patient the same for the same service. However, we must develop a system in which insurance companies reward doctors financially for keeping costs down and quality up. Will they do it? If not, and I don't believe private insurance companies will, then the system must be changed. Don't forget private insurance companies and HMOs have as their primary fiduciary responsibility the financial well being of their stockholders, not the patients. Of course, the executives who run these companies are not at all interested in the amount of money they make every year. Not! The next chapter addresses this issue.

CHAPTER 81

MEDICARE FOR ALL

The United States spends about 2.2 trillion dollars per year on health care. Given a population of 300 million, this is more than $7,000 per year for every man, woman, and child in the country, including, I believe, illegal immigrants. The most any other country spends is less than $3,500 per year, per person. All the other developed countries cover all their citizens with government-sponsored health insurance. More than 45 million people in the U.S. are without insurance at any given moment. Throughout the course of a year, more than 75 million people are without health insurance for some period of time. This is despite the fact that all people over 65 are covered by Medicare and all the poor are covered by Medicaid. The system of employer-sponsored health insurance, developed during World War II, is covering a smaller and smaller percentage of working Americans with every passing year. Where is all this money going?

The answer is that it is going to the middlemen, the people who are sitting with you in the exam, operating or hospital room with you and your doctor. If your doctor is in his own private practice, the money goes to the private insurance companies and HMOs with whom he contracts. If your doctor is in academic medicine, the money goes to the medical school he works for. If your doctor is an employee of another doctor or group practice, the money goes to the senior members of the group. We must eliminate all these people who take a cut off the top from every dollar that is supposed to go to the doctor taking care of you.

Additional money goes to all the employees who must be paid to work their way through all the red tape needed to collect fees from third-party payers. A recent article in the *New England Journal of Medicine* reported that overhead expenses account for 31% of all health care expenditures, despite the fact that Medicare has overhead costs of only 2-3%. A direct comparison of the cost to Medicare of those covered by traditional fee-for-service Medicare is actually lower than for Medicare patients enrolled in Medicare HMOs. The economic realities all point to the fact that the system of private health insurers is a high-cost, low-quality system, period. Society should base its economic decisions on economic efficiency, not ideology.

From a macro-economic point of view, the current system leads to the massive misallocation of capital. Employers are forced to make hiring decisions based on the cost of health insurance for a prospective employee, not just on their economic productivity. This leads to decisions to hire younger, healthier employees who may not actually be able to do as good a job as an older, more experienced person. It also forces employees to stay in jobs in order to keep their health insurance, even if they could produce more for the overall economy by making a job or career switch.

But why should we make health insurance universal? Won't that be too expensive? The answer is "Expensive, compared to what?" What is the cost to the economy in terms of poor health for so many millions of people? This is difficult to quantitate accurately, so it is never included in the cost calculations. What is the cost to American industry as it loses market share to countries where employers do not have to factor the cost of health insurance into their prices? The executives of the U.S. auto companies recently met with the President to ask for government help in paying for their health insurance costs. A recent estimate is that health insurance costs add $1,400 to the cost of every vehicle produced in the United States by American car manufacturers.

From my perspective, the human reasons for universal health insurance are even more compelling. Let's go back to basics. The Declaration of Independence states that all men are created equal and are endowed with inalienable rights, which include the "right to life." When these words were written, there was no such thing as health insurance. In fact, doctors could do very little to improve or extend the life of anyone, no matter how wealthy. Today, with all the advances in medicine over the past fifty years, it is safe to say that one's "right to life" is severely impaired if one does not have ready access to health care. Notwithstanding some who say that people without health insurance can get care at the local emergency room, all studies have shown a much higher death rate for individuals without health insurance. So, the present system is just un-American, period. I also believe it is grossly immoral.

The present push to use digital medical records is due to the fact that people are constantly forced to switch doctors. When I was in training, it was drummed into our heads that the continuity of patient care was absolutely essential to maintain high quality. The reason for this is obvious. The doctor's brain is the best record-storing device we have. No written record can fully describe all the particulars of a given patient's history as can be stored in a physician's brain over years or decades. Of course, written records are essential to help the doctor remember every detail, but no written record can substitute for the direct, ongoing patient-doctor relationship. My best care was always delivered when I knew the patient directly. This was especially true when I was called by the emergency room or the patient during off hours. Knowing the patient could actually make a difference in saving a patient's life. It could also make a difference in knowing when a patient did not need to be admitted to the hospital. The latter could save the system tens of thousands of dollars.

The current system does not ensure that the patient-doctor relationship will survive for years, let alone the decades that I feel are in the best interest of everyone. Under the current system, the power brokers have the right to fire a doctor and send him packing to another city or town, regardless of the negative effect it may have on that doctor's patients. This is unconscionable. The patients' welfare must take precedence over the economic interests of the doctor's employers. No doctor should be "sold" to the public and then removed involuntarily from the market after patients have formed a relationship with that physician. The idea of "restrictive covenants" or "non-compete" clauses in physicians' employment contracts must be strictly outlawed. Other forms of compensation for aggrieved employers can be easily substituted.

The last part of the triad of health care, after doctors and hospitals, is the pharmaceutical industry. Medicare must include affordable access to needed medications. Drug prices must be negotiated, as they presently are for the Veterans Administration Hospitals. The other constraint on drug cost will be doctors' decisions to use the most cost-effective, not the newest, most expensive drugs, to treat their patients. Doctors will do this as a natural response to the fact that their outcomes and costs per patient will be measured and reported.

I am convinced on a purely mathematical and economic basis that if this plan is adopted, the overall cost of care will go down, the quality will improve astronomically, and the economic growth of our country will improve dramatically. And we will be able to cover all Americans. And, if the plan is carried out properly, the incomes of most doctors and nurses will actually increase. Former Treasury Secretary Paul O'Neill has estimated that total health care expenditures could be reduced to 700 billion dollars. This was a few years ago, so his estimate would probably be higher now. But I do think a cost savings of 30%, or more than 600 billion dollars out of over two trillion, is completely realistic.

How do we pay for this? Presently, the Medicare tax is a payroll tax of 1.5%. Congress would have to decide to increase this tax to the percentage necessary. I think the tax should be progressive, with the higher income brackets paying a higher percentage of their income. The increased profits to all companies would insure that the incomes of the wealthy would increase in such a way as to offset this increased tax on high-income citizens. The money saved in reduced healthcare spending would be redirected to increased investment and development of new products and industries that would raise the overall standard of living. Even more importantly, the working people and middle class in this country would no longer have to live in constant fear and anxiety about the loss of health insurance for themselves and their families.

CHAPTER 82

EDUCATION

I have always considered myself an educator. As a high school student, I earned a little money by tutoring underclassmen in math. I remember being president of the tutorial society for a year in college. As a teaching fellow in physics at the University of Michigan, I taught sophomore-level physics lab in electromagnetism for a year. In medical school at Michigan, I was the medical student representative to the Committee on Research in Medical Education. As a medical resident and cardiology fellow at Mount Sinai, I taught medical students and residents on a daily basis. As a full-time faculty member at Sinai, I extended my teaching to cardiology fellows. Most importantly, in private practice, I educated my patients about their diseases and about what they needed to do to help me achieve the best possible outcomes for their conditions. So, it seemed natural to me to consider a new career in education after I was forced to retire from medical practice.

I hoped to continue to contribute to society as a high school physics teacher. I didn't think I was qualified to teach anything else. I thought that, as a high school physics teacher, I could contribute in several ways. First, I could actually teach physics and the basic principles of scientific inquiry, subjects that I consider very important to the understanding of all aspects of life. Second, I would have the opportunity to influence the character development of young people. Third, as a physician, I would be able to recognize symptoms of mental illness in students who were struggling to learn, and refer them to the appropriate school authorities for help with their difficulties.

In August, 2001, when it became clear to me that my career in medicine might be over, I researched what would be necessary for me to obtain state certification as a high school physics teacher. The University of Pittsburgh School of Education had a program called "The Professional Year." The program allowed professionals in other fields, such as law or medicine, to use some of their original course work as undergraduate or graduate students toward their teacher certification. After my October 17, 2001 speaker phone conversation with Wetschler and Payton, I knew my career in medicine was over. I signed up for the university's program in December. I was to start course work and student teaching in January, 2002. With hard work I would have my certification in time to start teaching by the following August.

As I had done when looking for an internship after medical school, I wanted to do my student teaching at a school that was committed to excellence. I aggressively pursued a student teaching position at a high school that was widely considered one of the finest in the Pittsburgh area, Fox Chapel High School. Fox Chapel, located in one of the wealthiest Pittsburgh suburbs, had won designation as a national "Blue Ribbon" school. I had to interview with the senior physics teacher, a man whom I will call Don, and the other physics teacher at the school before they would take me on. When Don subsequently asked me why I had chosen Fox Chapel, I gave him the same one word answer I had given Mel Kahn during my Sinai internship interview almost thirty years previously: "Excellence."

Don was renowned as a superb teacher. He and his wife, a physics teacher at one of the finest private schools in the Pittsburgh area, gave seminars for other physics teachers about the best methods for teaching physics. Don and I got along fine, and he ended up giving me a grade of "honors" as a student teacher. But my experiences as a student teacher opened my eyes to some of the country's serious problems in education today. This was only a prelude to many more such experiences over the course of my two and a half years as a public school teacher.

After I gave my first lesson, Don gave me a list of things I had done wrong. He didn't even give me lip service by saying I had done a good job. Don did not have a degree in physics and certainly did not have my level of education in the field. I felt he was just trying to put me in my place because he felt intimidated. I told him I thought I had done a great job. I said I was open to legitimate criticism, but I should also get positive reinforcement for things I did well. I told him that's how I felt all students deserved to be treated, and I expected him to treat me in the same way. I certainly was not trying to intimidate him; I just wanted to be treated with respect. Nonetheless, he responded, "I am not easily intimidated."

I was a little annoyed by his attitude, so I made him a proposition. He told me I was going to teach half of his students. He would teach the other half. I challenged him to a contest. After we taught each chapter, both groups of students would be tested with the same test at the same time. I said, "Let's see if your students do better than mine on the tests." He declined and treated me with the respect I deserved from that point on.

Don put me in charge of grading all the students' "portfolios." A portfolio consisted of all the homework assignments and laboratory reports done by each student in the class. The portfolio evaluations I did would count as a major portion of the students' final grades. The portfolios were to be evaluated every two to three weeks. My student teaching was to last 14 weeks. Don told me he would spend no more than five to ten minutes reviewing a portfolio. I found that it took me at least 30 to 40 minutes to do an accurate assessment of a portfolio. Given a total of 22 students, his group and mine combined, this amounted to a lot of work. I felt honored to be entrusted with such an important assignment.

As I started the task, it soon became apparent to me that the students were being shortchanged. I found myself grading homework assignments done weeks previously. I thought students should have their homework graded within a few days at most. How else would they be able to learn from what they had worked so hard to do? Physics problems and laboratory experiments can require a great deal of thought. To evaluate a student's performance requires a teacher to review a student's work in detail. How anyone could review 20 pages of such complex work in five or ten minutes was beyond me. I was reminded of Dr. Gorcsan during my job interview at UPMC, when he told me that I needed to do each echocardiogram report in only five minutes. I discussed my concerns with Don. He just said that was the way he did it. I continued to do it my way. I just didn't feel right shortchanging my students any more than I felt right shortchanging my patients. These were human beings. I was entrusted with their lives or with their education. They deserved my best. I needed to know I gave them my best in order to maintain my own self-respect.

I believe there are three levels of understanding for a physics student. The first level is an understanding of the basic principle involved. This understanding is expressed in words. For example, "momentum is conserved." The second level of understanding is being able to express the principle in mathematical terms, e.g., "M1V1 + M2V2 = M1V3 + M2V4," where M is mass and V is velocity (no need to explain this further here.) The third level of understanding is represented by the ability to use the mathematical understanding to solve a physics problem. An example, in this case, would be whether or not a 200-pound running back would have enough momentum to score a touchdown from the two yard line after being hit by a 250-pound linebacker at the one yard line.

When I studied physics, even in high school, we were expected to be able to solve problems. Physics homework usually consists of problems to solve. Every chapter in the physics textbook we used at Fox Chapel ended with a number of problems grouped by the level of difficulty. I thought it very important to teach the students how to do the problems. So did Don, and that's why he assigned these problems for homework. So when I graded the student's homework, I wanted to use the feedback I gave the students to help them grasp what they needed to learn. I didn't think I, or any one else for that matter, could do a very good job of this in only five or ten minutes two weeks after the fact. I instituted a lesson plan in which I would ask students to do the homework problems in the front of the whole class on the board in the front of the room. I reassured them that they would not be graded on their ability to do the problems in such a public way and that they would not be subject to any humiliation by anyone in the classroom, including me. Don did not object to my methods; after all, he did give me "honors," the highest grade.

Don and I spent a full month teaching the chapter on conservation of momentum. I was deeply concerned that the students were not expected to be able to solve physics problems. My standards were such that to get an "A" in high school physics, a student had to demonstrate the ability to do basic homework problems. Lesser levels of understanding would still receive a passing grade, just not an "A." Don did not seem to agree with this. I call this "grade inflation." As a teacher, my entire time seemed to be permeated with pressure by the school administrators to give higher grades than the students earned. I didn't consider this to be any more ethical than a doctor billing Medicare for a higher level of service than was actually provided. Fortunately for me, as a student teacher I was not responsible for handing out report card grades to my students.

I was allowed, however, to state my concerns to Don, and he was willing to listen. I wanted to prove my point to him. One day he told me he was going to be away on business for a day a few weeks hence. He said I could use the day to give the students any exercise I wanted, including a quiz the students could take for extra credit toward their final grade. This quiz would be optional at the individual student's discretion. I told the students the quiz would consist of two problems from the chapter on conservation of momentum, one of easy difficulty and one of medium difficulty. I didn't tell them which problems I would choose. The quiz would be "open book," so they wouldn't have to memorize any of the equations. The only rule was that they could not work the problems together during the quiz. Any cheating would result in disqualification for the extra points. Each problem was worth a maximum of three points, with partial credit for partial understanding. A correct final answer was required to gain the full three points for each problem.

During the quiz I walked around the room. Some students actually seemed taken aback when I stopped them from copying from the papers of other students. I watched them all like a hawk; I wanted an accurate evaluation of these students' abilities and what they had actually learned, and I was determined to get it. Don and I had spent a full month trying to impart to these students an understanding of one of the basic principles in physics. I had every reason to expect these very bright students, from mostly affluent families, in the finest of high schools, would be able to learn their lessons.

I remember that 20 of the 22 students elected to take the quiz. I graded the papers that evening. To my utter dismay and astonishment, only three students, all girls, achieved the full six points. This was not a difficult test. When Don gave more than half of the class an "A" for the grading period that mostly included the chapter on conservation of momentum, I knew there was something seriously amiss in American education.

While I was at Fox Chapel, I enjoyed talking to the students and tried to impart to them some of the life lessons I had learned. I had fun getting to know the kids, but I don't think I had much of an impact on anyone. Student teachers don't have much prestige or credibility with students in general. I also didn't see much in the way of symptoms of mental illness in the students in this upscale community. I did, however, have a very enlightening conversation with a woman in the faculty lunchroom one day. She was the representative from one of the biggest drug rehabilitation centers for adolescents in Pittsburgh. My hypothesis at the time was that many teenagers used recreational drugs as a means to treat symptoms of undiagnosed and/or untreated mental illness. I thought perhaps as many as 50 percent of teenage drug addiction was caused by this phenomenon. So, when I asked her what percent of the kids in her program were using drugs to self-medicate for mental illness, I was quite surprised to hear her say, "One hundred percent." When I subsequently taught at less affluent schools, I saw a much higher incidence of what I thought were obvious symptoms of significant mental illness in my students. I soon realized that students who were not mentally and physically healthy could not learn.

Recently published studies have shown a much higher prevalence of mental illness in teenagers than ever previously imagined. Also, newspaper articles have indicated a severe shortage of child psychiatrists in the United States. This is probably related to the fact that insurance reimbursements for children's mental health care are so low. Also, many children do not have any mental health insurance whatsoever. I simply think it will be impossible to cure what ails American education without universal mental health insurance for all children. To make matters worse, it is my impression that mental health problems are more prevalent in the children least likely to have access to affordable psychiatric and psychological services.

CHAPTER 83

THE SCHOOL OF EDUCATION

My program at Pitt included two required courses, Education and Society, and Introduction to Teaching Science. I was looking forward to being back in an institution of higher learning where ideas were paramount and could be actively debated in an atmosphere of academic freedom. What I experienced was more than just a little disappointing. What I found instead was a politically driven agenda that violated all my concepts of free thought. The agenda was driven by a rigid adherence to a concept of the human condition, which all my experience and education in life had led me to believe was utterly false and misguided. This lack of connection to reality, I quickly came to realize, was, and is, one of the root causes for the dysfunctional state of the educational community.

My section of the course, Education and Society, was taught by a kindly African-American full professor in his early sixties. I will call him Dr. T. The only assigned reading in Dr. T.'s course was a small volume written by Dr. T. with the help of a journalist. The book recounted the struggles of a nearby Pittsburgh suburb to save its failing schools from gross under-funding in the 1990's. This "text" had absolutely no bibliography or footnotes. I found this unique in all the college level courses I had ever taken. Dr. T. told the class of about thirty upperclassmen that our grade would be determined mostly by the term paper due before the end of the semester. The term paper had to be 14 pages long, and the topic was the same for everyone. We were to contact teachers and administrators from the high school from which we had graduated, and then describe the ways in which our high school experience was privileged compared to that of the disadvantaged students of the present day.

To me, the subtext was to prove that the reason each of us had been successful enough in life to get to the college level was because we had had an unfair advantage over those children who were less successful.

When I pointed out to Dr. T. that I had graduated from high school in 1964 and therefore it would be highly likely that many of the people he insisted I contact would be dead, or at the very least difficult to find, he scoffed at me. He began the course by teaching the class that all the problems with minority education in the United States were due to the evils of capitalism. He said that when he was younger he was a communist, but now he had become a capitalist. He said he converted to capitalism because he went to a professional football game once and was able to sit in one of the luxury boxes reserved for the wealthy businessmen. I thought this was intellectually dishonest at best, and totally insane at worse.

At one point, I couldn't stand it any more and asked to address the class. He allowed me to go to the blackboard to present an opposing point of view. I gave an extemporaneous 10-minute discourse in which I presented evidence to the fact that the United States of America was not inherently economically evil. I refuted each of his points one by one, based on my knowledge of history and economics. When I finished, he smiled and continued on his merry way. I knew his course was nothing more than demagoguery. I also knew there was no way I would be able to write the term paper. I certainly didn't think that my success in life was due to the advantages of birth. I felt personally insulted that all the enormous hard work and dedication I had exhibited to achieve success in life was being denigrated by this ignorant person. I had never dropped a course in my life, but I dropped his course and ran for my life. I had to beg the director of the program to allow me to switch into another section of the same course. When I told her I thought Dr. T. was a communist, she replied: "So, what's wrong with that?" I didn't say that, while I thought he had every right to his personal political beliefs, the school had no right to take my money in return for teaching me about the evils of capitalism. I was paying to learn about education.

The full professor teaching the section I transferred into was Richard Altenbaugh, Ph.D., whom I'll refer to as Dr. A. He told me his section was already full, but when I told him I was desperate, he relented. His required reading was extensive. Since I had already read Dr. T.'s book, I asked him if he would give me some credit for doing so. He practically laughed in my face. I assumed Dr. T.'s reputation was widespread. I recall that Dr. A.'s Ph.D. was in the history of education. I enjoyed the course very much and learned a great deal about the history of education going back to the Puritans. Dr. A. rewarded my interest and enthusiasm with an A+ on the final paper. Nevertheless, his historical perspective was one of deliberate oppression of the common people by the rich and powerful. He seemed to totally ignore the economic realities at any given point in history. When I told him and the class that I had taken a course in college entitled "The Economic History of the United States," he allowed me to share a somewhat different perspective on the economic reasons for the educational practices at different times in history. When I pointed out to him that the entire School of Education seemed to be preaching Socialism, he responded: "Yes, that's done deliberately. What's wrong with it?"

The course in science education was taught by a graduate student thought to be one of the best in the school. Her name was Michelle. (I don't remember her last name.) She was in her mid thirties and studying for her Ph.D. She told us she had taught seventh grade science for about 12 years. She did a good job, but I had a major intellectual conflict with her teachings. In medicine, as I mentioned before, a treatment is evaluated by using it on some patients in a scientific study, comparing it to a matched control group that does not get the treatment. Education and medicine both inherently represent an intervention on a human being. Whether or not that intervention achieves the desired purpose determines the efficacy of the tested procedure. In medicine, the intervention is usually a drug or an operation. The outcome is the patient's health. In education, the intervention is a curriculum or teaching method. The outcome is learning.

Michelle taught us what she considered the "proper" way of teaching science. I was naturally curious as to how she knew this was the proper way. In education, a common phrase is: "Research tells us…." I asked her to refer me to the academic articles describing the research supporting her contentions. After reviewing a few of the articles, I was absolutely appalled to see that control groups had not been used. When I tried to discuss this with her in class, she always responded the same way. "That's not the way we do things in education." Omigod! She was teaching science and seemed to have absolutely no insight into the need for control groups in scientific research on human beings.

I had spent my whole life dissecting scientific research on human beings, and Michelle dismissed me as being crazy and overly opinionated. I again felt like Galileo, trying to convince one of his contemporaries that the earth orbits the sun. At one point, I brought in the newspaper articles about the use of hormone replacement therapy (HRT) to treat menopause in women. For many years, this treatment had been advocated, despite the fact that there were no controlled trials showing its safety and efficacy. When the results of the first controlled trials showed HRT resulted in more women's deaths than did placebos, uproar occurred in the media. I thought this was an excellent example to use to teach the class about the importance of control groups in human research. Even though Michelle encouraged us to display initiative in class, she categorically refused to allow me to present my finding to the class. It seemed to me that she felt her career was threatened by the idea that her research was useless without a control group. Well, Michelle, just because the educational community doesn't believe in control groups doesn't mean the results of that uncontrolled research is true just because you say so.

The point of this story goes to the essence of one of the major problems in education today. Namely, no one has any idea what actually works and what doesn't. So, we end up trying different curricula, teaching methods, and school types while thrashing about in a sea of ignorance, just because the educational community is totally ignorant of the scientific need for control groups in educational research. I have been told that using control groups is much too difficult to do. That doesn't make the results of uncontrolled research any truer. Besides, I think doing research while using a control group to study the dripping of streptokinase into the heart of a patient having a heart attack in the middle of the night is a lot more difficult than using a control group of students when evaluating a new math curriculum. It's important to understand that control groups must be contemporaneous. Using historical control groups is simply inaccurate and can be extremely misleading.

I think one of the causes of the education community's resistance to using control groups is that they find it repugnant to categorize students. In their socialist worldview, everyone is the same. Categorizing human beings, to them, is nothing less than overt prejudice. This attitude represents a reckless disregard for the truth. Science attempts to find truth; it does not promote a political ideology. Categorizing students using mathematically and scientifically accurate methods is not prejudice; it is the pursuit of truth, and without truth one cannot pursue justice. In this case, the goal is the justice of an equal educational opportunity for everyone, irrespective of politically-driven, preconceived notions of right and wrong.

One area in which I generally agreed with the faculty of the school was in the funding of education. There is no doubt in my mind that the present methods of funding public education leave much to be desired. Presently, most school districts fund education through real estate taxes. This is grossly unfair to poor communities. In my final paper in Dr. A.'s course, I posited a method of funding schools that would be economically just and much more effective than the present methods. I drew a parallel with the method used by health insurance to fund medical care. Reimbursements are determined by the amount of care a particular patient needs. For example, if a patient with coronary disease can be best treated with medication, the insurance company pays the price (or a percentage of the price) of the medication. This usually amounts to several hundred dollars per year. If, on the other hand, the patient requires a coronary bypass operation, the insurance company pays the hospital and doctors tens of thousands of dollars for the operation. The worse the illness and the more expensive the treatment, the more the insurance company pays. We need a system that is predicated on the same basic economic principles in education. The system must be based on the basic principles of free market capitalism. The government still pays the bills, but the amount paid to the school is predicated on the amount of service a particular student needs to obtain a good education. This requires a scientifically and mathematically accurate way of assessing the educational needs of a particular child.

My plan is predicated on a basic premise similar to the one we use in medicine. The more services a patient needs, the more money his insurance company gives him to pay for that care. This is not rocket science or advanced economic theory; it is just common sense. Of course, every student, like every patient, is unique by definition, but we categorize patients according to diagnosis and severity of illness. For argument's sake, I will categorize students into three groups, using the terminology many teachers use to categorize the students in their classes: low, average, and high capability students. My premise is based on the simple assumption that low students need more resources to be educated than average or high students. (Duh! Of course this is true.)

The problem is that the students who need the most resources, those from disadvantaged socioeconomic backgrounds, have the least ability to pay for the resources they require. The only legal way for them to get the money they need for their education is from charity or government. Since private charity can only provide for some students, government must bear the ultimate responsibility to educate all children. Education is very expensive. For example, Fox Chapel School District, when I was there, spent around $15,000 per student, per year. Pittsburgh Public Schools, at that time, spent around $13,000. The disadvantaged communities described in Dr. T.'s book, and in Jonathan Kozol's book, *Savage Inequalities*, could muster only one third to one half that amount per student per year. (Remember: The students in these communities are the ones that actually require the most money. They also require the smallest classes and are the least likely to have access to mental health care.) The current system of educating students is simply stupid and ridiculous. It is akin to saying that poor people with coronary disease only get treated with one aspirin a day (a good treatment), even if their doctor thinks they need heart surgery.

When my children were in private school, the cost of their education in today's dollars was about $20,000 per year. This represents a reasonable estimate of the cost of education, and I will use it as a frame of reference. I believe that educational standards should be the same for all locations in the United States. A child in Mississippi has a right to the same level of learning as a child in California or New York or Fox Chapel or Pittsburgh. Of course, the cost of living is lower in Mississippi than in New York, and so are the costs of educational resources. So a child in a low cost of living area can have the same level of education as a child in an affluent area for less money. For example, to pay teachers' salaries, building maintenance costs and other educational costs in Mississippi requires a lot less money than in Manhattan, for the same quality of education. But the standards must be the same if we are to approach anything resembling social justice. This difference in cost is true in medical care as well. Medicare uses a formula, developed by Harvard University in the early 1990's, called Resource Based Relative Value Scale (RBRVS), to set reimbursement rates for doctors in different parts of the country based upon the cost of the resources required to provide care in those parts of the country. This system provides a model to use in education.

Health insurance is really a voucher system that pays according to the patient's needs. We can extrapolate the system to education using the same basic principles. Let's say an average student needs $15,000 per year to pay for his education. My premise is that lower capability students need more money for an adequate education than other, more capable students. They require more individual assistance, that is, smaller class sizes. This requires more teachers and therefore is more expensive. Many low-capability students have mental illnesses that require more in school psychological support, which is very expensive. These students require more money to pay for their education, perhaps $20,000 per year. The lowest students, those with the most obstacles to learning, might require $30,000 per year. Socio-economically disadvantaged communities simply do not have the resources to pay for this. Government must pick up the tab. Period. On the other hand, high-achieving students, like I was, can flourish in larger classes with fewer resources.

Simply put, they do not need as much money to learn because they need less assistance or incentive to learn. This is exactly the same economic principle that gives sicker patients more money for their care than less sick ones.

I believe that the only solution to the country's current educational mess is a system of vouchers that pays the actual cost of education. These vouchers must provide for the same quality of education in every state and therefore must come from the Federal Government. In addition, only the Federal Government can guarantee access to mental health care for all students according to need, not the ability to pay. Students who are not mentally healthy have far more obstacles to learning than those who have no mental impairment. In this plan, students will need to be categorized to determine how much money they receive for their education per year. Low-ability students, for example, could receive a voucher for $25,000 per year, while high-ability students might receive $15,000 and average students $20,000. Schools would then be set up for different levels of students. As in medicine, schools and teachers, both public and private, would be held accountable by measuring the outcomes for their students. The outcome, as in medicine, would be adjusted for the initial ability of the students in that classroom or school. These results must be mathematically and scientifically accurate, and they must be published. Parents would then be free to use their voucher money to send their children where they receive the most value for their educational dollar. This is how capitalism is supposed to work, and it's the reason it does, in fact, work. I think this plan will work. In fact, I can't think of any other plan that will work, logically.

CHAPTER 84

PUBLIC SCHOOLS

Before I could be certified to teach in the public schools in Pennsylvania I had to pass the Praxis examinations in math, reading, writing, principles of learning and teaching, and physics. Having not taken all the course work of education majors, I was forced to study using published guides for the principles test. For physics I used the study guides for the Advanced Placement B high school physics course. (This is physics without calculus. Physics with calculus is college level physics, and I had no intention to teach college physics again as I had at the University of Michigan as a graduate student in 1968-69). I studied very hard and was pleased that I passed with high scores in all the tests. The woman in charge of the program at Pitt told me she had never seen such high scores, especially in math and reading. Therefore, when I applied for teaching jobs, I was confident I could find a position in the Pittsburgh area.

In August, 2002, while Linda and I were in Europe on vacation, I was called with a job offer at the Woodland Hills School District just east of Pittsburgh. Because I couldn't be reached, someone else got the job, but I decided to work there as a substitute teacher until I could find a job I wanted. In November, the high school principle asked me to be a long-term substitute in ninth grade algebra because the teacher had quit abruptly. It was a half-time job with two classes. One of the classes, as I later found out, consisted of all the behavior problems in the ninth grade. My "classroom management" skills were being tested in a very difficult situation.

I soon found out that in my class of about 30 students, some were brilliant and some were very low-functioning. The class was racially very diverse. The ability of the individual students was not in any way related to race or ethnicity. In the same class, I had to teach students whose test scores literally ranged from zero to one hundred percent. Because I only had two classes, I was able to devote a lot of time to preparation and individual attention.

By the middle of December, the district offered to hire me as a full-time math teacher. I had a brief interview with one of the administrators, and during the interview I expressed my concern with grade inflation. I had done careful statistical analysis of the grading in my classes. I had done everything I could think of to help the students achieve higher grades, including make up quizzes and extra credit exercises. But I refused to compromise my ethics and give the students grades that they didn't earn. I found that the average grade in my difficult class was only 34%, and that only a similar percentage of students were able to achieve a passing grade of 65%. When I told the interviewer that I would take the job with the understanding that I could guarantee only one third of my students would get a passing grade, he responded: "The judge wouldn't like that."

"The judge!" I exclaimed. "What judge?!"

It was only then that he disclosed to me that the school was under Federal Court order in its math teaching. Now I understood why I had no textbooks or curriculum from which to teach: The judge had not yet approved a curriculum for my students. The school district had to show a much higher percentage of passing grades than I thought reality would allow for. What a mess! I certainly wasn't going to take a job in which I was expected to be dishonest, so I turned it down. Shortly thereafter I went back to day-to-day subbing. The school found another teacher for the job. I still talked to my previous students in the school cafeteria, however. One of my students, a boy who had gotten a grade of 34% in my class, proudly showed me that his new teacher had given him a grade of 75%. I told him the 34% I gave him was one he could be proud of actually earning and not to be ashamed of. A couple of months later I was physically assaulted by a younger male teacher in the school because he accused me of being "negative" for expressing my concerns to him about grade inflation. I promptly quit the job after reporting the assault to the assistant superintendent.

In May 2003, I got a job as a substitute teacher in the Pittsburgh Public Schools. By then I had come to realize that being a full-time physics teacher would require almost the same amount of effort as being a full-time cardiologist. Given my age and disability, I knew I couldn't do that. Linda told me that occasionally school districts would hire half-time teachers, so I limited my search to half-time positions. I was never able to find such a position and continued to work as a sub. I was called to teach at every public high school in Pittsburgh and most of the middle schools. I certainly learned a lot more about education than I taught the students about any of the various subjects I was asked to teach. One of my observations was that symptoms of mental illness were rampant in high school students. This is totally consistent with recent studies in the medical literature indicating a much higher prevalence of mental illness in American teenagers than previously thought.

My observations were not limited to the students, however. I found the same wide disparity in dedication among teachers that I had found among physicians. This was exemplified by my experience in one school considered by many to be the best public high school in Pittsburgh, Taylor Allderdice. In December, 2003, I received a phone call informing me that the senior physics teacher at Allderdice, a Mr. W., had taken ill and was to have coronary bypass surgery. He was teaching two physics classes, standard high school physics and a college level physics course given under the auspices of the University of Pittsburgh Physics Department. The students in the latter course would receive actual college credit for successful completion of the course. I knew I was not qualified to teach college-level physics with calculus. I was asked to teach both courses. I took the job after speaking directly with Mr. W. He assured me he would work with me on a daily basis from his home on the college-level course. He would assign and grade all the homework and quizzes and give me the lessons to teach as best I could. I received a phone call from one of the physics professors at Pitt to discuss the situation. He wanted assurances that the course would be taught well enough for the students to get the college credit they had been promised. I told him of my limitations but we were both satisfied with Mr. W.'s promises to help me out.

I took the job with the understanding that Mr. W. would return to the classroom as soon as he recovered from his surgery. I knew without any equivocation that men with jobs that did not require physical labor could safely return to work six weeks after an uncomplicated bypass operation. I told the high school principle that I would do the job for a maximum of two months. My main concern was that the students not be short-changed. Things started off well enough; this did not last long however. It was soon apparent that Mr. W. was not living up to his promises to me. I didn't have any trouble teaching the standard physics course. The principle had told me his main concern was that the students be educated properly. I told him that if I thought that was not happening I would tell him immediately. I did.

I told Mr. W. that I expected him to come back to work by the beginning of February. He was not going to pull the wool over my eyes. He didn't give me any legitimate medical reason for not coming back to work. It seemed to me he was just milking the situation to get an extended paid vacation, the students be damned. Of course, he claimed that he was not well enough to come back to work. I knew better. The students' course came to a grinding halt. I told the principle in early January that I thought he had to get a teacher in that classroom who could actually teach the subject matter. I told myself I was not going to be party to a fraud. I gave him notice that I was quitting at the end of January. He was not happy with me, but he did manage to get a teacher qualified to teach college physics to come out of retirement to take over for me.

Mr. W. came back to work by the middle of March. I stopped in to talk to him one day when I was subbing at Allderdice. He seemed to regard me as some sort of bad guy who had given him a hard time. I didn't tell him I was appalled at his lack of dedication to his students. Unfortunately, once the physics department at Pitt found out what had gone on, his students didn't get any college credit for the course. I felt bad for them, but I knew I had tried to do the right thing for them.

I continued to sub in the Pittsburgh Public Schools until the end of the school year, but I realized I wasn't accomplishing much as a school teacher and resigned my position in June, 2004. After taking the summer off, I decided to go to Presby to see if I could make a difference there.

PART VI

FINAL REFLECTIONS

CHAPTER 85

REFLECTIONS ON MY PROFESSIONAL LIFE

My professional life seems to have been a series of crises interspersed with periods of stability. I have been told that the Chinese symbol for "crisis" is the same as for "opportunity." With each crisis I have faced I have had to dig deep to find the courage to move on and survive. Each crisis seems to have resulted in my being better off than I had been before it occurred. I attribute this to focusing on "doing the right thing" in each instance. This has always required a dedication to the truth and a careful analysis to determine "right" from "wrong." I feel that the reason things turned out well for me after each crisis was a direct result of my commitment to honesty and respect for other human beings. In my professional life, this meant respect for my patients' welfare above all else, but also a commitment to treat my partners honestly and with an understanding of their needs. Unfortunately, this honesty and respect for my partners had not always been reciprocated. The events surrounding my relationships with Dr. Money, Mark Geller, Larry Adler, and Stan Wetschler defined the various crises I have had to deal with.

Dr. Money lied to me to get me to move to Pittsburgh in 1984. He told me I would become a full partner after a few years, a promise he never had any intention of keeping. I can't know the inner workings of his mind, but a few things seem apparent to me. He didn't seem to be able to tolerate being in an equal relationship with anyone. He said: "Everyone has to know their own worth." He had to be the one in the group who was "more equal" than anyone else. He had to structure the group to make certain the deck was stacked in such a way that he would always have the most money and power. I think he felt that the absence of dominance would represent an existential threat to his existence as a human being. In the process of trying to manipulate the situation to his benefit, he destroyed his relationships with at least five other cardiologists in little more than a decade.

Had Dr. Money been able to trust his partners and have enough self-respect and esteem, he would have been able to create a huge practice at Jefferson Hospital. Instead, by the early 1990's, as one of his intimates told me, he was consumed with worry that our group would surpass his dominance in the hospital. In addition, by the late 1990's, I was told by a member of his group that Dr. Money was no longer the doctor who brought the most money into his group. To me it seemed that this might have been his worst nightmare.

I would be very surprised if Dr. Money's net worth today is less than ten million dollars. I wonder if the money has made him as happy as he thought it would. Or, has he finally learned that, while money is an important part of human relationships, there is so much more? How does he feel working with another doctor whose "worth" is greater than his? If money is his gauge of self-worth, then how can he respect himself knowing he lied to and cheated his partners to acquire some of that money? As a competitive person, does he truly believe that winning by cheating is really winning? Isn't money supposed to represent the good you have done for others? Doesn't he want to wake up in the morning knowing the money he has in the bank was earned and not stolen? Does philanthropy truly compensate for the fact that the money one gives away was ill gotten? Will Dr. Money ever understand that money and power are ultimately poor substitutes for love and trust? I don't know; you'd have to ask him. Personally, I hope he has seen the light in his mature years.

Mark Geller also seemed unable to trust anyone. Our practice could have grown into one of the biggest and best in Pittsburgh had Mark not been so distraught over the possibility that a third cardiologist in our group would have conspired with me against him. I had no desire to hurt Mark; I only wanted to provide the best medical care to our patients. He told me repeatedly in 1989 that he was going to steal my practice from me after we broke up. Of course, I knew that was impossible, but he certainly tried. Again, it was a lack of the ability to trust that caused so much pain and disruption. Last I heard, as of this day, Mark remains in solo practice.

Larry Adler displayed great courage in acquiescing to Seymour's desire to bring me into the group. Without Larry, my financial situation today might not be so fortunate, so I hold no bitterness toward him. However, I will always resent the lies he told about me in an effort to destroy my professional career. Had I not been insured, his antics might have led to my suicide. I truly appreciated what Larry had done for me, and I had no interest or desire to take over his position as the leader of the group. Had he trusted me and enlarged the group with Steve Heilbrunn and John George, instead of being consumed with fear and distrust, I am convinced he would be the head of the largest private cardiology group in Pittsburgh today. Instead, he has been relegated to solo cardiology practice, a very taxing enterprise for a 75-year-old man.

Larry just didn't seem to be able to trust anyone. Lori, his office manager, told me at the time his group was suffering severe internal stress that he had said to her: "Everyone is out to get me." Of course, I wasn't one of the people out to get him anymore because he had kicked me out of the group at least five years earlier. Larry sowed the seeds of his own destruction when he refused to honor the contracts he had negotiated and signed with all of his partners in the early 1990's. No one was "out to get" Larry. Why did his brain not allow him to trust anyone? Does he really have "paranoid personality disorder"? I don't know. But I do know he never seemed able to trust anyone.

I think people who are unable to trust feel that way because of a deep-seated lack of self-worth. They must think that they have so little to offer that other people will naturally want to treat them badly. Ultimately, if you can't trust others, you come to fear others. It is this fear that drives these people to protect themselves by gaining power and control over others. It is this drive for power and control that causes people to lie and to cheat others. They justify this to themselves by saying they must lie in order to achieve their financial goals and/or to protect themselves from the perceived threats of others. They enter a self-perpetuating vicious cycle of mistrust leading to more lies, which leads to bullying behavior and finally the destruction of the relationship.

While lies and distrust will not be eradicated from the human condition anytime soon, it is only love and trust that have led to the advancement of civilization. I may not have always been able to verbalize these ideas, but I have always tried to treat my partners honestly and with an understanding of their own individual personal and professional needs. I guess that's why Stu Tauberg told me valued my friendship so much because he just thought I was an honest person.

That's more than I can say about Stan Wetschler. I always considered him a close friend. He trusted me to care for his father and other family members, and I always gave them 110%. He and others told me that he always said he was my friend. Why then did he turn on me and destroy my career? My only answer is that he wanted the job as Vice President for Medical Staff Affairs at Jefferson Hospital. He was scared because he had to retire from medicine for health reasons and needed the money. As Stanley Milavec told me, that may be an explanation, but it is not an excuse. He must have thought he needed the support of the pulmonary group to get the job. He displayed utter cowardice in throwing his friend to the wolves for his own personal gain. Even worse, in doing so, he told me he thought he was above the law. That's probably why he seemed to feel comfortable breaking so many of them. He was so scared that he forgot the difference between right and wrong. He didn't seem to understand that his job as President of the Medical Staff was to protect the patients, not the doctors. He never got the job he wanted, and I wonder if he actually has money problems today. I doubt it. Ironically, if he had done the right thing and protected his friend and stood up for my patients, he might actually have gotten the job. I know I would have supported him for it. But I guess I just wasn't bringing much money into the hospital at that time and didn't have as much clout as the pulmonary group.

My final comments are directed at Horty and Springer, the law firm that represents hospitals. Paul Verardi, their attorney in charge of my case, told me on the phone personally one day that doctors should never bring their lawyers into the hospital proceedings because that only results in escalation. This firm seemed to predicate its advice on the premise that due process for doctors should be avoided at all costs. This resulted in what Bruce Payton told me: "In every hospital I have ever worked, doctors are always guilty until proven innocent." Horty and Springer need to understand that, if one systematically avoids due process, innocent people will inevitably be punished. When an innocent doctor is punished, it is not only the doctor and his family that suffers, it is also his patients. If even one of my patients died because I was driven out of medicine, that is blood on the hands of Horty and Springer. No law firm should base a large segment of its entire practice on the denial of the basic premise of American jurisprudence: "Innocent until proven guilty." Money earned by denying doctors justice is nothing more than "blood money" if even one patient dies as a result. I believe this from the bottom of my heart, and I would consider myself a coward if I did not say it in no uncertain terms. I hope they feel I burned them, because I feel they desperately need to change their ways. A lawyer can certainly make an honest living in hospital law without having to violate the basic principle of due process of law.

A recent change in national regulations will now require all hospitals to apply the term "disruptive" to all physicians equally, not just to describe doctors whom the politically powerful want to punish for fighting for their patients lives. Perhaps this will force these miscreant lawyers to finally get their act together. But I'm sure they'll continue to make lots of money selling their loopholes to hospitals bent on using the "rules" for their own political and financial benefit.

While I know it would be Pollyannaish to think we can create honesty in every doctor as a way to improve medical care in this country, I do feel that if we start to pay doctors based on the quality and cost of the care they provide, we can remove a lot of the incentives for doctors to misbehave. I know the vast majority of doctors are honest and truly care about their patients; that's why they went into medicine in the first place. It is these doctors and their patients who ultimately suffer at the hands of the greedy and dishonest ones among us. I know I have the support of honest doctors everywhere in trying to contain the greed and power-lust that are causing so much pain to the American people due to our dysfunctional healthcare system.

CHAPTER 86

HEAVEN ON EARTH

My friend Hunter is a black man in his early thirties and a devout evangelical Christian. He tells me about how wonderful Heaven is. I tell him, only half jokingly, that I am already in heaven and have no desire to leave. To me, Heaven is a metaphor for an Earth upon which one lives forever and is always mentally and physically healthy. But there's a little more to it. A couple of years ago, National Public Radio broadcast random interviews with passersby in Grand Central Station in New York City. A 93-year-old man was asked to comment on what he thought was the most important thing in life. He responded: "That's easy. Love. Without love, there is no life." Of course, he was correct. So, my concept of "Heaven" also includes always being in love.

On thing Hunter and I agree upon completely is that the purpose of the human species is to seek truth and justice. He believes truth comes from religion; I believe it can only come through science. Regardless, we both believe that a commitment to truth is essential for human survival. That is why honesty is so important. Without honesty there can be no trust; and without trust there can be no love. While my professional life has been fraught with crises, my personal life has endured only one real crisis: my divorce. But even that was the result of honesty. Barbara came to realize that the truth was that we were just not compatible sexually. We were always honest with each other, and that's why I think everything turned out well for both of us.

I love my wife and my children. Both my children have turned into great adults. I consider myself extremely blessed to have two other people in my life whom I trust implicitly, Linda Rose and Paul Scott. It's not important whether or not this is absolutely true. What's important is that I feel it is true. Linda and Paul are impeccably guileless and totally honest. I aspire to be the same. Of course, no human being is perfect. Certainly, I'm not. But I can say that I believe I have never deliberately hurt another human being for my own benefit at any time in my adult life. Judaism teaches that one is rewarded for "good works" in the present life, not afterwards. So, I feel I have been rewarded in this life for simply trying to be the best person I could be.

In a material sense, I have everything I ever wanted. We live in a lovely, moderate-sized house (2,400 sq. ft.) in a nice neighborhood. We have a good degree of financial security and a nice lifestyle. Having always been a car nut, I drive a car (a BMW 650i) I would not trade for any other car in the world, at any price. I have a wonderful sound system and home theater (Sony 65" high definition TV and Thiel loudspeakers). I can go out to dinner and the movies any time I want, at least once a week. Linda and I can go anywhere we want to go on vacations.

But even in Heaven, the human condition is not complete without having goals and aspirations, regardless of age. Even though I am no longer able to practice medicine, I hope my writing will help transform the practice of medicine. Someday, after Linda's son follows his sister to college, we hope to move to Manhattan. It's natural for someone to want to go home. Pittsburgh has been good to me. I raised a family, had a fairy tale cardiology practice, and, above all, met my sexual sole mate. But my love for New York, and my longing for it, simply grows year after year. The thing I love most about New York is the people. I find them to be the most friendly, tolerant, intelligent, considerate, interesting people in the world. I would consider it an absolute privilege to be able to live among them again. I also dream of someday going back to Mount Sinai and teaching there on a volunteer basis.

To me life is a voyage of self-discovery, and success is a journey, not a destination. I have learned a lot about myself during my first 60 years. I hope to learn just as much, if not more, during the next 60. Writing this book has been a lot of fun. I hope to have as much fun writing about the next 60 years, in retrospect. If there is one final thought I wish to leave you with, it is this (to paraphrase the Beatles): In the final analysis, the love you receive during your life is, without question, equivalent to the love you give to others.

APPENDIX A

RICHARD R. SCHNEIDER, MD, FACP, FACC
Cardiovascular Specialist

April 12, 2001

Stanley Wetschler, M.D.
President, Medical Staff
South Hills Health System
Jefferson Hills, PA 15025

Dear Stan:

I want to thank you for your letter dated March 8, 2001. I also want to express my personal regret that these events have required you to take time out of your busy schedule. I want you to know that I believe that all of my behavior has been totally in accordance with all of your instructions, and in accordance with the rules and regulations and bylaws of the medical staff of Jefferson Hospital. Dr. Scott and I have had the opportunity to discuss the circumstances that you related to him and that were related to him in Dr. Borrero's letter of February 15, 2001. With the information you provided and other information I have been able to obtain, I have drawn the conclusion that Dr. Laman's pulmonary group has engaged upon a campaign of character assassination. This campaign began on November 27, 2000. On that date in the afternoon I was called by Dr. _____. Dr. _____ informed me that Dr. Laman had called him and told him that his group was going to "make his life miserable," referring to me. Dr. _____ has given me express permission to inform you about this conversation. However, this was done with the caveat that it remain strictly confidential and only be shared with the other recipients of this letter. Dr. _____ is willing to confirm this with you verbally. The campaign carried out by the pulmonary group has consisted, in part, of letters written to you by Paula Gafney and _____, both nurses in the intensive care unit, Dr. Thomas Schaefer, and Dr. William Sims. I have been able to arrive at this inescapable conclusion because of the falsehoods which these letters have promulgated. I will explain the reasons for my conclusions by reviewing the particulars of the events which you have discussed with Dr. Scott. Because of the serious nature of the allegations made against me, I must respond in detail and of necessity sacrifice brevity in the interest of thoroughness.

1. The Nurses

I wish to address the issue of the nurses first because this is the most glaring example of the falsehoods perpetrated against me. At our meeting on December 21, 2000 with Dr. Borrero, Dr. Collins, President of the Medical Staff, and Mr. Bruce Payton, Vice President in charge of clinical services, I was told by Mr. Payton that the "nurses" had informed him that I routinely "talk down" to them. At that time I was very surprised to hear this as I have been working at Jefferson Hospital for 17 years and no one has ever voiced this opinion to me in the past. During this discussion, Dr. Borrero chastised me for not using the information constructively to modify my behavior in the future. I had said no such thing and informed everyone that I had every intention of using this information to modify my behavior and improve my relationship with the nurses.

After the meeting, in my endeavor to modify my behavior, I wanted to get more information as to what I had been doing. In this regard, I asked Ms. Teresa Fowler, who has been a nurse on the step down unit for approximately 13 years, whether or not I had ever talked down to her. Ms. Fowler informed me that no, I had not ever talked down to her and that she was not aware of me talking down to any of the other nurses. In fact, she told me that I was one of the few doctors who never talked down to the nurses. I subsequently informed Mr. Payton and Dr. Borrero of this conversation without using Ms. Fowler's name. Nonetheless, I endeavored to be extremely careful in my conversations with the nurses so as not to be construed as talking down to them. However, after your conversation with Dr. Scott on March 8, 2001, I felt it was important for me to get further information about this because I felt it was certainly possible that Ms. Fowler was mistaken and this was just her limited perspective. In this regard, I initially spoke to Ms. Harriett Galeza, who has been a nurse at Jefferson Hospital for approximately 20 years. Harriett was head nurse on the step down unit for 10 of those years. Harriett informed me that she too had never heard of anybody complaining that I had talked down to any of the nurses. In fact, as I told you at the December 21st meeting, Ms. Galeza has told me in the past, without prompting, that the nurses on step down fully appreciated the fact that I was the only doctor who would never yell at them when they would call one of us at 2 o'clock in the morning. I then felt that perhaps the problem was limited to the intensive care unit. In this regard, I spoke to Ms. India Kunkel, a staff nurse in the ICU. Ms. Kunkel told me that while I had never talked down to her, there were other nurses who did complain that I had talked down to them. I did not ask her who these nurses were. I wanted to get more information, so I then spoke to Louise Urban, who until very recently was the nurse manager in the ICU and step down unit. Ms. Urban informed me that she had never heard any complaints about me talking down to any of the nurses. To confirm this I then spoke to Brenda Veschio, who has been a head nurse in the ICU for several years now. Ms. Veschio told me that she too had never heard of anyone complaining of me talking down to the nurses. I then suspected that perhaps this was a very limited problem and I approached India Kunkel again. I asked her that, other than _____ and Paula Gafney, had anyone else ever complained about me talking down to them. She said no, no one else had.

Again looking for further data, I asked Nancy Hodson, the head nurse on step down at the present time and she too confirmed that no one ever complained of me talking down to them. I then spoke to Carole Lewis and Sue Muha, also staff nurses on the SDU, and they also said I had never spoken down to them or knew of anyone who had complained of this. To increase my sample size and further document that this was not a general problem of my behavior, I spoke to Mr. Steven Grossman and Ms. Valerie Schaefer, also staff nurses in the ICU with the same response. In fact, Ms. Schaefer said "you are always nice, Dr. Schneider. You are a very nice man." At this point I felt that I had enough information.

For obvious reasons, I was extremely cautious in all of my conversations with the nurses to be brief and not intimidating. I wanted to convey the genuine impression that I was truly interested in being informed of any problems with my behavior so that I could improve my relations with the nurses. I believe I was successful in doing this and that the responses they gave me were honest and complete. Nonetheless, I may be mistaken. For this reason, I urge you or your representative to talk with the above mentioned ten nurses. If I am mistaken, would you please let me know?

I have been forced to come to the conclusion that these complaints were solely restricted to _____ and Ms. Gafney. Apparently in their letters they gave Mr. Payton a false impression as to my behavior. I believe they deliberately cast me in the worst possible light. _____ has always disliked me for the many years that I have known her. In addition, Paula Gafney holds a grudge against me because of an occurrence on August 21, 2000. On that date I was caring for Mrs. L, a patient in the intensive care unit to whom Paula was assigned. Mrs. L was 71-years-old and had an abdominal aortic aneurysm repair by Dr. Phitayakorn on approximately August 17, 2000. Postoperatively Mrs. L was in respiratory failure and was encephalopathic. She developed severe hypertension postoperatively to a level of 260 systolic. Initial treatment with intravenous nitroprusside resulted in an allergic reaction with further increase in her blood pressure and this had to be discontinued. Subsequently it was necessary for me to treat Mrs. L with intravenous nitroglycerin, intravenous Aldomet, intravenous Vasotec, intravenous

Lopressor, and intravenous Lasix simultaneously in an attempt to bring her blood pressure down. Despite this aggressive treatment it was extremely difficult to control her blood pressure. She remained on the ventilator for several days. On August 2 l, 2001 her wedge pressure varied between 16 and 22, and her serum albumin was 2.4. Despite aggressive diuresis, I could not lower her wedge pressure effectively and because of this I had to administer salt poor albumin to increase her serum oncotic pressure above her pulmonary capillary wedge pressure so that she would not develop pulmonary edema. I felt that if she did develop pulmonary edema, we would not be able to get her off the ventilator and that she would be at very high risk for pneumonia, and this could result in her death. On the morning of August 21st, Ms. Gafney approached me and told me that shc thought that was my treatment was incorrect. I took her aside and explained in detail what I was trying to do. Later that morning I saw Mrs. L again, and again Ms. Gafney disputed my care. She said I was "over-diuresing" the patient. I again took her aside and spent some time trying to explain exactly what I was doing and why. Sometime between noon and 1 p.m. that day Mrs. L's blood pressure increased while getting salt poor albumin. At that time Dr. C took it upon herself to discontinue my order for albumin. Dr. C did not call me to discuss this first. Ms. Gafney further did not call me to tell me about the patient's increased blood pressure or the fact that Dr. C had cancelled one of my orders. I made my third visit of the day to Mrs. L's bedside at approximately 2:30 that afternoon at which time I discovered what had occurred. I informed Ms. Gafney that it was inappropriate for her not to have called me to notify me about Mrs. L's change in condition. I then called Dr. C and told her that it was inappropriate for her to cancel one of my orders without speaking with me first. I told her that if she changed one of my orders in the future without speaking with me first, I would report her to the Chief of Medicine. Then Ms. Gafney again questioned my care and told me again that I was "over-diuresing" the patient and that the wedge pressure of 15 was normal. Having already had two conversations with Ms. Gafney about Mrs. L's care, I felt that further one-on-one conversations would be fruitless and that Ms. Gafney had now put herself in a position where she was obstructing my care of Mrs. L. For this reason, I asked Brenda Veschio to meet privately with Paula and myself in her office. At that time I again tried to explain what was occurring with Mrs. L's pathophysiology. Ms. Gafney took the position that she knew as well as I did what was best for Mrs. L. She told me it was presumptuous of me to think that my education was better than hers. Despite the fact that I informed her that I had graduated Summa Cum Laude in physics from one of the top physics programs in the country (University of Rochester), I graduated from one of the top ten medical schools in the country (University of Michigan), and had done all of my training and spent five additional years on the full-time academic faculty at one of the top cardiology programs in the country (Mt. Sinai Hospital and School of Medicine in New York City), she was not impressed and continued to insist that her education was the equal of mine. I do not believe that this level of arrogance serves our patients well. The conversation with Paula and Brenda lasted approximately 30 to 40-minutes and I returned to care for Mrs. L. By the following day, Mrs. Love's blood pressure was markedly improved. She had diuresed eleven liters. She was extubated and out of bed sitting in a chair. Her medications were being discontinued one at a time. She was subsequently discharged from the hospital in good condition.

Subsequent to this, I copied several book chapters from Guyton's Textbook of Physiology and obtained copies of Professor Guyton's original articles concerning plasma proteins and the development of congestive heart failure. I was going to give these articles to Paula. Louise Urban, however, informed me that Paula felt singled out and that I should not give these articles directly to Paula, but rather leave them in the nurse's lounge in the appropriate place for all of the nurses to review. I complied with her wishes. I also gave these articles and book chapters to Dr. C in hopes of opening a productive dialog concerning this disagreement with her. To the best of my knowledge, Paula never read these articles. In addition, Dr. C refused to discuss them with me. Instead, Dr. C, several weeks later, gave me several articles concerning the use of albumin. I read her articles and they clearly supported my position. However, Dr. C again refused to discuss these with me as you know. You were present at one of these conversations when she stomped off when I mentioned the use of albumin in congestive heart failure.

I believe that in this circumstance I conducted myself professionally and in the best interest of the hospital and the patient. I believe by spending so much time with Ms. Gafney, I was providing a significant service to the hospital in the interest of improving not only Mrs. L's care, but the care of subsequent patients that Paula would be engaged in.

Considering the fact that the conversation with Paula occurred on August 21, 2000 and it was not brought to my attention by Mr. Payton until December 21, 2000, I came to the conclusion that Paula had written her letter after Dr. Laman had told Dr. ____ that he was going to make my life miserable on November 27, 2000. This seems to me to be a logical conclusion that both Paula and ____, who are closely allied with the pulmonary group and have personal resentments against me would respond positively when the pulmonary group requested that they write letters of complaint against me. I am sure that it was with some degree of relish that ____ and Paula cast me in the worst possible light. Nonetheless, their accusations that I talk down to the nurses is clearly untrue.

In addition, you told Dr. Scott that I lecture to the nurses incessantly. I believe that this is untrue. In fact, as you know, I do lecture to the nurses twice per year in the critical care course. My most recent lecture was about the relationship of plasma proteins and congestive heart failure. This was greeted with a great degree of appreciation as you can see from a copy of the enclosed letter sent to me by Nancy Keller, who is in charge of nurse education. As a matter of fact, I was informed by Ms. Keller and the nurses in the class that the nurses are not taught in nursing school about this physiology. I believe that all nurses working in the intensive care unit need to understand the relationship between congestive heart failure and plasma proteins. I discussed this with Louise Urban, and she confirmed that none of the nurses are taught this in nursing school, although Paula Gafney says that she was taught this. Nonetheless, I think that my desire to educate the other nurses about this very important concept is totally in the best interest of the hospital and our patients, and should in no way be discouraged.

2. Dr. Schaefer

Concerning my conversation with Dr. Schaefer, I would like to elaborate on the circumstances surrounding this. On Saturday, December 9, 2000, in the morning, I was seeing Mr. W in the ICU. On the previous Thursday, Dr. Sims had informed me after putting in the Swan-Ganz catheter and finding an opening wedge pressure of 24 that he thought Mr. W had congestive heart failure and pneumonia. On Friday, December 8, 2000, I spoke, as you had instructed me, collegially with Dr. C as to her thoughts about Mr. W's diagnosis. She informed me that she also felt that Mr. W had congestive heart failure and pneumonia. I had reviewed the chest CT scan with Dr. Arevalo, chief of radiology, and we had agreed it was consistent with congestive heart failure and pneumonia. When I arrived in the ICU to round on Mr. W on Saturday morning there was a note in the chart from Dr. C that she now thought Mr. W had ARDS. I was again faced with a similar situation to Mrs. L in August, as Mr. W's wedge pressure was high and his serum albumin was low. As you instructed, I called Dr. C in a collegial manner to ask her why she now had changed her diagnosis and thought that Mr. W had ARDS. She said that she thought that the ARDS had been caused by the congestive heart failure. To the best of my knowledge, this does not occur. I have asked other cardiologists about this and they have told me that they have never heard of this either. I told Dr. C that I felt I needed to give Mr. W albumin in addition to diuresing him. She became irate and started to yell at me at which time I ended the telephone conversation and immediately called you at home. You instructed me to call Dr. Schaefer and explain the situation to him. You instructed me to ask Dr. Schaefer to make a choice between allowing myself or Dr. C to manage the patient's congestive heart failure. I did this and Dr. Schaefer asked me to do it, which I did. I aggressively diuresed Mr. W and gave him albumin as needed. At that time Mr. W was requiring an inspired oxygen percentage of 80%. Dr. C noted on the chart that this would be toxic to the lungs and that we needed to get the percentage of inspired oxygen to below 60%.

Under my care, by Monday morning, December 11, 2000, Mr. W's wedge pressure had decreased to 9 and his inspired oxygen percentage had decreased to 35%. His chest x-ray as documented on the chart had shown a significant clearing. On December 10, 2000 I was informed that Dr. Schaefer's covering physician had ordered a second opinion with Dr. Politics and that I was off the case. I believe this was a result of a conversation that Dr. C had had either with Dr. Schaefer or his covering physician on the evening of December 9, 2000. Nonetheless, when I was informed of this, I again called you and elicited your assistance. You intervened by calling Dr. Schaefer's covering physician. I spoke with Dr. Schaefer at home later that day. He informed me that he resented the fact that I had called him and asked him to make a choice. Of course I had done this at your explicit direction and I had informed him at the time that you had told me to call him. On the evening of December 10, 2000 I was informed that Dr. Politics' covering cardiology fellow had made the diagnosis of ARDS. I attempted to call Dr. Politics, but he was not home. I subsequently was able to contact the covering fellow and explained to him the particulars of Mr. W's case. He then told me that he agreed with me that this was not ARDS but rather congestive heart failure. As you know, after you spoke with Dr. Schaefer's covering physician on Sunday evening, December 10, 2000, I was informed that I was still on the case. On Monday morning December 11, 2000 I went to the ICU to sign my verbal orders. I discovered that Dr. Schaefer had by then removed me from the case. I noted that Dr. Politics had ordered 500 cc of intravenous normal saline to be given to Mr. W. This is the exact opposite of what one would do in someone in congestive heart failure and would certainly make the patient worse. I was very concerned and was in an ethical dilemma at that time. I could have just let the situation ride and let nature take its inevitable course. However, I felt that I couldn't live with myself if I did that and I had a moral responsibility to Mr. W. Mr. W had been my patient for 10 years. I had done his cardiac catheterization. I had had him see Dr. O'Toole for a second opinion, which turned out to be a concurring one related to his coronary artery disease and aortic stenosis. Mr. W had previously been a toy distributor and had given many presents at Christmas and other times to my children over the years. I therefore spoke with Dr. Politics and Dr. Schaefer in person and in private and beseeched them not to give Mr. W the saline solution. Dr. Politics informed me that he intended to do so despite my entreaties. Over the next four days Mr. W's condition did not improve. He remained on the ventilator and could not be weaned. By this time, apparently Dr. Politics realized his mistake and felt that Mr. W was in fact in congestive heart failure and took him to St. Francis for cardiac catheterization and referred him for open heart surgery. Unfortunately Mr. W was still on the ventilator with pulmonary infiltrates and the surgeons felt that he was too sick to operate upon. He died several days later at St. Francis Hospital. I was deeply saddened by Mr. W's death, as I felt that he did have a better than 50-50 chance for survival, had Dr. Politics not changed his treatment. Dr. Politics voluntarily informed me of all the details of Mr. W's care and the occurrences at St. Francis Hospital. I did not in any way criticize Dr. Politics about that, but merely asked a few questions. After Mr. W died, I saw Dr. Schaefer in the doctor's lounge and I told him that I didn't care if he ever sent me another patient again. I told him that I needed to talk to him about Mr. W's case. I said that this was not the time to do so. He agreed and said that we should talk about it after the holidays.

Prior to my subsequent conversation with Dr. Schaefer, you had informed me that you no longer felt that it was the consulting physician's primary responsibility as to patient outcome, but that the primary care physician was the one responsible for the patient's outcome. You felt that the primary care physician needed to know enough medicine to be able to make the appropriate decisions regarding the care of his patients and choosing his consultants. In addition to that, as you know, at the meeting in early December with Dr. Collins, yourself, Mr. Payton, and Dr. Laman, I was explicitly informed that it was always appropriate to discuss the case with the patient's attending physician. At that time there was no mention made that this was not appropriate if the patient had been subjected to peer review. I have confirmed this with Ms. Donna Klaas, who was present at the meeting. I did meet privately with Dr. Schaefer in January. I in no way coerced Dr. Schaefer to meet with me. He agreed fully to do so and this meeting was done by our prior arrangement. I told Dr. Schaefer that you had informed me that it was the primary care physician's responsibility for the outcome of his patient and that the primary care physician needed to understand the medical situation well enough to affect appropriate utilization of consultations. In this regard, I explained to Dr. Schaefer the pathophysiology of Mr. W's case and how Dr. Politics and the pulmonary group had misdiagnosed and mistreated him based upon the scientific knowledge and the data available at the time of his care. I told Dr. Schaefer that I understand this pathophysiology well. I said that apparently some other doctors may not understand this that well, meaning Dr. Politics and the pulmonary group, but there were doctors who did understand it as well as I did. I expressed the opinion that I felt that nobody understood it better than I did. Dr. Schaefer subsequently wrote a letter complaining that I had told him that I was the only one who could take care of difficult cardiology consultations in the ICU. This was not true.

In Dr. Borrero's letter to Dr. Scott, dated February 15, 2001, I was accused of making comments concerning all cardiologists. This is absolutely not true. My comments were solely implied to refer to Dr. Politics. In addition, Dr. Politics and I continue to have a cordial relationship despite this occurrence. In addition, I have excellent relationships with most of the cardiologists on staff. This includes all of Dr. Money's group and all of Dr. Adler's group, and Dr. Juriga. In fact, as you know, Dr. Money's group and Dr. Adler's group cover my practice for me for vacations and for every other weekend. I maintain cordial relationships with all of Dr. Pinto's group and with Dr. Lipman.

Also, in Dr. Borrero's letter to Dr. Scott dated February 15, 2001, he told Dr. Scott that I had been specifically instructed not to talk to Dr. Schaefer, especially as Mr. W's case had been submitted for peer review. This was false on two accounts. Number one, I had been specifically instructed by yourself and Dr. Collins in the meeting in early December that it was always appropriate to talk to the patient's attending physician regardless of whether or not the patient was subjected to peer review. In addition, Mr. W at the time of my conversation with Dr. Schaefer had never been submitted for peer review, despite my multiple requests that it be done. In fact, the peer review nurses had informed me that it was not possible for Mr. W's case to be submitted for peer review because he was transferred to another hospital prior to his death. As you may know, in the last several weeks I have made additional requests that Mr. W's case be submitted for peer review. This was finally done on March 15, 2001. In summary, concerning my conversation with Dr. Schaefer, it was done totally in accordance with your instructions and in a professional way and in a mutually agreed upon conversation.

I have known Dr. Schaefer since he started his practice in the late 1980's. In fact, until the formation of Prime Medical Group, in approximately 1993, I did virtually all of Dr. Schaefer's cardiology consultations, both in the office and in the hospital. However, at the time that Prime Medical Group was formed, Dr. Schaefer voted against having my group participating with Prime. He told Dr. Marsha Modery, who subsequently told me, that he held a grudge against me. This grudge was based upon the fact that when I invited him to dinner at my home with Dr. Myers and Mr. Mark Cohen, he resented that Mr. Cohen and Dr. Myers had homes in Colorado and the fact that he himself would never be able to achieve such a lifestyle. He also resented the fact that I had such a nice home and that he would never be able to live in such a home. He also resented a business dealing that I had had with Dr. Brooks in 1985. Dr. Schaefer was irate with Dr. Modery for telling me about this. At the time I did discuss this with Dr. Schaefer in the open and he confirmed what he had said. I also believe that Dr. Schaefer has carried a grudge since a lawsuit in the early 1990s concerning a heart attack suffered by one of his patients prior to my being consulted in her care. I was dismissed from the lawsuit, but Dr. Schaefer was forced to pay a settlement of $_____. I believe that he may have resented the fact that I was let off the case. Nonetheless, since the formation of Prime Medical Group, I cannot remember a single time that Dr. Schaefer has sent me a new patient. Knowing Dr. Schaefer, I do not think he is the kind of person who would write you a letter about my conversation with him. I think that when the pulmonary group approached Dr. Schaefer and asked him to write a letter, he agreed to do this because of the grudge factor. The letter that Dr. Schaefer wrote to you was deliberately designed to cast me in the worst possible light and was clearly part of the campaign of character assassination. The letter was untrue based upon the reasons I have explained.

3. Dr. Sims

Concerning my conversation with Dr. Sims at the end of January, I would like to make the following comments. Mr. U was an elderly gentleman admitted to my service at Jefferson Hospital in late January after suffering an acute myocardial infarction at home resulting in cardiac arrest and anoxic encephalopathy. In the intensive care unit he was maintained on a ventilator and had no signs of improving mental functioning. An echocardiogram on January 22, 2001 revealed a left ventricular ejection fraction of only 10% to 15%. I had been managing his fluids judiciously with small quantities of D5/half normal saline at 25 cc an hour. On January 24, 2001 he was transferred to the general floor on hospice. At that time Dr. Sims ordered his I.V. fluids to be increased to 80 cc an hour and then signed off the case. Mr. U's chest x-ray on January 24, 2001 indicated mild pulmonary congestion. I felt that 80 cc an hour, given his ejection fraction, was excessive and would result in worsening congestive heart failure. On January 25, 2001 I had a private conversation with Dr. Sims indicating that I thought 80cc an hour was too much fluid and would result in congestive heart failure. I had decreased the fluid to 30 cc an hour and informed Dr. Sims of this. I explained my reasoning to Dr. Sims and he agreed with me. In fact, he said "let me clue you in, Richard. I knew that." I said, "good" and that was the end of the conversation. As you have told Dr. Scott, Dr. Sims said that he was just trying to keep Mr. U comfortable. If this was the case and he knew that 80 cc of fluid an hour was too much, then why did he order that much? If he felt that Mr. U's level of consciousness was so impaired that his comfort did not need to be addressed, then why did he say to you that he was trying to keep Mr. U comfortable? Certainly I think we can all agree that even in Mr. U's condition, if we were going to try to keep him comfortable, filling his lungs with fluid would not be the way to do this. The issue here is not whether or not the amount of fluid that Dr. Sims gave was too much, but that he has said contradictory things. Given his contradictory statements, and the fact that he agreed with me about the amount of fluid that would be appropriate, I think that my conversation with him was not in any way disruptive. In fact, as Mr. U was on my service and I had consulted Dr. Sims' group to manage the ventilator, I not only had a right to question his fluid orders, I also had a responsibility to do so. My intention was not to chastise Dr. Sims, but only to enlighten. The fact that Dr. Sims wrote you a letter about such a trivial matter only indicates to me that he was intent upon adding another letter to the letter writing campaign instigated by his group. I maintain that this type of conversation is totally within the normal discourse engaged upon by members of the medical staff and that it is totally within the rules and regulations of the hospital, and as it was conducted in private, it was in no way disruptive.

4. Personal Animosity

The pulmonary group has a long history of animosity towards myself. I will relate only some of the history related to this. This animosity has always been related to my criticisms of their care of patients with congestive heart failure and the differential diagnosis of congestive heart failure vs. ARDS.

In the early 1990s surrounding similar disputes, I had consulted Dr. Joel Weinberg, a pulmonologist and the director of the medical intensive care unit at Shadyside Hospital. I asked Dr. Weinberg his opinion about these issues and found that he agreed with me on every one. I have known Dr. Weinberg since 1975 when he began his residency at Mt. Sinai Hospital in New York and I was his senior resident at that time. Dr. Weinberg graduated first in his class at the University of Pittsburgh School of Medicine and did his training at Mt. Sinai Hospital in New York. He is still the director of the medical intensive care unit at Shadyside Hospital and has served as the president of the medical staff. At that time Dr. Weinberg gave me multiple articles concerning these issues. I made copies of these for the pulmonary group and gave the copies to them. They refused to discuss them with me in any way. Instead, Dr. Deliere instigated Dr. Adler and Dr. Brooks to take me out to breakfast at Denny's one morning to berate my personality and chastise me for thinking that I might be right and the pulmonary group was wrong. I explained to both of them the fact that I had gotten these articles and had received no reply. Nonetheless, they would not accept my point of view. I did not know that Dr. Deliere had instigated this meeting at the time. However, in 1999 Dr. Brooks told me that it was in fact Dr. Deliere who instigated that meeting and not Dr. Laman. Dr. Brooks apologized to me for what he had done realizing that he had now come to agree with my position. When I asked Dr. Adler in 2000 about this meeting, he did not remember it. However, he did tell me that his opinion had changed and that he was very concerned about the success of the Jefferson cardiac surgery program because of what he perceived to be the inadequacies of care of the pulmonary group at Jefferson. Dr. Adler was in a position to make this assessment because he was able to do direct comparisons of care between Dr. Laman's group and Dr. Weinberg's group at Braddock Hospital and Shadyside Hospital, where both groups were on staff. In fact, subsequent to our meeting with Dr. Collins in early December, Dr. Collins told me that he spoke to Dr. Adler about participating in the group discussions which you had recommended. He said that Dr. Adler "feels very strongly" about this issue and the potential difficulties with the pulmonary group's care. I believe that this episode is another indication that the pulmonary group resorts to third parties to berate and intimidate their critics and does so in an anonymous way.

In 1997 and 1998 when Dr. Sims was Chief of the Department of Medicine, he voluntarily recused himself from all matters dealing with myself. I had not requested this at the time. The fact that he did recuse himself was an indication of the fact that he had personal animosity towards me.

In early 2000 I was taking care of a patient in the ICU, whose name I cannot recall. She was an elderly woman with congestive heart failure, renal dysfunction, and bilateral pleural effusions. The patient was in the intensive care unit bed 1302. On my weekend off, I called Dr. Sims, who was covering the pulmonary group to suggest to him that the patient needed therapeutic thoracentesis. Dr. Sims told me that the patient did not need thoracentesis, but needed emergency dialysis. He said that he would watch the patient closely over the weekend. When I made rounds that Monday morning, I found that the patient had not received dialysis because the nephrologist felt that it was not indicated at that time. I made a note in the chart documenting my conversation with Dr. Sims.

Subsequent to that Dr. Sims wrote an angry note in the margin of the progress note on the patient's chart that this was absolutely untrue and he had never said that the patient did not need a thoracentesis. When I saw this on the chart I was certainly concerned that the patient still needed a thoracentesis. At this point Dr. Laman and Dr. Sims approached me as I was sitting at the desk in front of the patient's room. In loud voices they began to berate me and say the patient did not need a thoracentesis. I responded that I disagreed with them, but that it was not appropriate to discuss this in front of the patient's room and in front of all of the nurses. I asked Dr. Sims to step out into the hall to continue the conversation. He said that he did not want to step out into the hall but preferred to go out and "settle this in the parking lot." I took this as a threat of physical violence and told him that it was unnecessary and we should discuss it in the hall. He again refused, reiterated his desire to settle it in the parking lot, and left. The fact that Dr. Laman and Dr. Sims felt that they could behave in such a way in the ICU and get away with it is an indication of the arrogance with which they conduct themselves. Shortly thereafter Dr. Deliere did perform a thoracentesis on the patient. She was immediately able to be taken off a 100% rebreathing mask and put on 4-liter nasal cannula. Her blood gases simultaneously improved dramatically.

In December of 2000 I received a letter dated November 30, 2000 from William H. Maruca, the pulmonary group's attorney (see enclosure). He threatened to take legal action against me because I had made false and defamatory statements about Dr. C. This was completely untrue. It was based upon circumstances surrounding the case of Mrs. K. Mrs. K had been admitted to Jefferson Hospital on November 4, 2000 with congestive heart failure. She had a history of congestive heart failure secondary to left ventricular diastolic dysfunction with normal left ventricular systolic function. She also had a history of renal failure having had a short course of dialysis previously. Mrs. K was diuresed and her pulmonary edema cleared. However, she had progressive renal dysfunction and the nephrologists were consulted. She continued to be short of breath despite clear lungs, and for this reason, I consulted Dr. Deliere to ascertain the reason for this. He felt that these were due to mechanical problems with Mrs. K's respirations. These had to do with Mrs. K's advanced age. On November 14, 2000, despite the fact that there was a nephrologist and a cardiologist on the case, Dr. C ordered intravenous fluids of D5 normal saline to run at 70 cc an hour for a total of 1500 cc. I wrote a note in the chart that this could potentially lead to recurrent congestive heart failure because it was such a large volume and high concentration of sodium. Within 24 hours Mrs. K went into florid pulmonary edema and suffered respiratory arrest. She had to be transferred to the intensive care unit and placed on a ventilator. I felt that there was an absolute cause-and-effect relationship between the excessive fluid that Dr. C had ordered and Mrs. K's recurrent congestive heart failure. I still maintain that given her history of congestive heart failure and renal dysfunction no astute physician would ever have ordered such a large amount of fluid. I did not discuss this with Dr. C or any other member of the pulmonary group as Dr. C had shown an intense aversion to discussing any cases with me considering the events of the previous August concerning Mrs. L. Instead I discussed this with Dr. Nathanson, the Chief of Medicine, and he advised me to submit the case for peer review. This I did in writing several days after the event.

The patient remained on the ventilator in the intensive care unit for some time. Dr. Mitro was caring for her renal disease and I was caring for her congestive heart failure. The pulmonary group was caring for her ventilator management. On November 25, 2000 Dr. Mitro ordered salt poor albumin for Mrs. K. On November 26, 2000 Dr. C discontinued this order without consulting Dr. Mitro. When I made rounds I saw this and called Dr. Mitro. I asked him whether or not he wanted his order for albumin discontinued and whether or not Dr. C had spoken to him. He responded that Dr. C had not called him and that he did want Mrs. K to receive the albumin. I documented this in the chart and reordered the albumin. I then called Dr. C. I asked India Kunkle to witness the conversation on the phone. I told Dr. C that I thought it was inappropriate to cancel Dr. Mitro's orders without talking to him first. This was similar behavior to what she had done in August with Mrs. L. I told her that I was going to report her to yourself and Dr. Nathanson. She told me that her group supported her on this. I told her that this had nothing to do with her group; it had only to do with her. As it was a Sunday when this occurred, I did not call Dr. Nathanson or yourself until the next day. At the time I called I was informed that Dr. Laman had threatened a lawsuit. That afternoon was when Dr. ____ called me to tell me that Dr. Laman had told him that they were going to "make his life miserable." As you, Dr. Collins, and I agreed at that time, changing another doctor's orders without talking to them first presupposes that it is not possible that the other doctor knows something you don't. This is especially unlikely if the other doctor is a subspecialist in another field. Therefore, changing an order without prior discussion can have potentially grave consequences for the patient. As you know, Mrs. K was never able to be taken off the ventilator. She subsequently died from a Mallory-Weiss tear of her esophagus and bled to death on November 30, 2000.

Shortly thereafter at the beginning of December we had the meeting with Dr. Collins, yourself, Mr. Payton, Dr. Laman and Donna Klaas. Mr. Payton told me that I had harassed Dr. C and should have used official hospital channels about my concerns about Mrs. K's care. I asked Mr. Payton what Dr. C had said concerning how I had harassed her. He said that he did not know, but only that she had perceived this. As you know, I wrote to you on December 4, 2000 asking you to ask Dr. C how I had harassed her (see enclosure). At the subsequent meeting with Dr. C, Dr. Collins and yourself you did ask Dr. C how I harassed her. She said that I had threatened her by telling her I was going to report her to Dr. Nathanson and yourself. Clearly this was not a threat, but an indication that I was going to use appropriate hospital channels. I have been told that this was the correct way to handle this issue. At no time did I make any false statements about Dr. C. However, on the day after the first meeting, I did receive the letter from Mr. Maruca, the pulmonary groups' attorney telling me that I had made false and defamatory statements. This was completely untrue and indicated to me that the pulmonary group had made false statements to their attorney in order to induce him to write me this letter and intimidate me from making any further criticisms of their care. This was a significant manifestation of the pulmonary groups' personal animosity towards me.

Another indication of their personal animosity occurred shortly after Dr. Borrero wrote his letter to Dr. Scott dated February 15, 2001. After Dr. Scott showed me that letter it was apparent to me that this had been influenced by Dr. Sims, as it contained many false statements. Dr. Borrero told me he only put in the letter what he had been told to write. I did not tell Dr. Sims about this but I did ask him to recuse himself from all matters concerning me. He said that he would recuse himself from matters concerning his group, but not from other matters concerning my relationship with the medical staff. I took exception to this and insisted that he recuse himself from all matters. He said that he would have to receive permission to do this. I subsequently spoke to Mr. Payton concerning this and he confirmed the fact that Dr. Sims was recused from any and all matters dealing with myself. His agreement to recuse himself is a clear indication of his personal animosity towards me.

While I cannot prove conclusively that the pulmonary group orchestrated the letter writing campaign against me, I believe the circumstantial evidence is overwhelming. This circumstantial evidence includes: 1) they had the motive including personal animosity towards me and a desire to silence my criticism in an effort to maintain their monopoly at a time when another pulmonary group (Dr. Chaudhry's) was seeking to establish themselves at the hospital; 2) they had the opportunity to engage in this letter writing campaign with the willing cooperation of Ms. Gaffney, Ms. ______, and Dr. Schaefer; 3) they used the same modus operandi of employing third parties anonymously to attack me, as they had done with Dr. Brooks and Dr. Adler; 4) they had the stated intention of trying to make my life miserable; and 5) they thought they could get away with it.

5. Peer Review

I would also like to comment upon the peer review process. In your letter to me dated March 8, 2001, you indicated that I thought that my speech was protected by the peer review law. This is not the case. In actuality, when I told the pulmonary group's attorney that as long as I spoke the truth my speech was protected, I meant that it was protected by the First Amendment to the Constitution of the United States. I wish to bring your attention to the recent decision by the United States Court of Appeals for the Third Circuit of February 14, 2001, in the case of David Warren Saxe vs. State College Area School District. The court found that even such clearly disruptive and repugnant speech as racial harassment was protected by the First Amendment. My conversations with Dr. Schaefer and Dr. Sims were not only not disruptive, but even if they could have been construed as such, would still have been protected under the law. In another recent case a jury found that an employee of the Pittsburgh Public Schools had had his First Amendment right to free speech violated when he had been dismissed for making complaints. The jury awarded him one-quarter million dollars. I have enclosed the newspaper articles from the *Post-Gazette* dated February 16, 2001 and March 11, 2001 respectively for your perusal.

Of course, Dr. Laman would be free to sue me in court if he felt that I had libeled him. However, at the time his attorney threatened to sue me for making false statements about Dr. C, the only statement that I had made concerning Dr. C was that she had changed Dr. Mitro's orders for salt poor albumin for Mrs. K. This was absolutely true and incontrovertible as it is written in the patient's chart. In addition, I have never made any false statements concerning Dr. C or any other member of the pulmonary group.

I believe that the peer review process was never meant to substitute for the open and free discourse in private between and amongst physicians. Such discourse, especially when critical, is absolutely necessary for the care of our patients. The reason for the First Amendment to the Constitution is to protect individuals from recriminations from powerful interests when criticism is mounted. This applies to the tyranny of the government as well as tyranny of powerful local interests such as school boards, as indicated in these cases. Certainly my expression of criticism of the pulmonary group because of the deaths of Mrs. K and Mr. W is protected from any restraint. While the peer review process is essential to the functioning of the hospital, the peer review law protects the hospital and the medical staff leadership from lawsuits based upon institutional actions taken against physicians. It does not apply to conversations between individual physicians not related to official functioning of the hospital. As you know, I have an intimate understanding of the peer review processes because I served as Chief of Medicine at Jefferson Hospital in 1993 and 1994. One of the main problems I had with the peer review system at that time was the fact that there was no effective peer review for the pulmonary group. Because they had an effective monopoly and were the only pulmonary group, there was no method for obtaining an independent peer review for their cases. It was deemed to be overly expensive to send these cases to outside physicians on a routine basis. Furthermore, I believe that your initial decision to have a collegial conference amongst the pulmonologists, cardiologists, and nephrologists, which you expressed at the meeting in early December was entirely appropriate. As you know, Dr. Laman agreed to this in front of everyone at the meeting. The fact that he subsequently reneged on this agreement and refused to have such a meeting is another indication of the arrogance of the pulmonary group. Had such a meeting occurred, the fact that Dr. Deliere and I totally agreed on the appropriate use of salt poor albumin in certain patients with congestive heart failure would have been disseminated to everyone. The subsequent disagreement between myself and Dr. C in the care of Mr. W would probably not have occurred. As Mr. W died several weeks later, there is a distinct possibility that had Dr. Laman not reneged on his agreement Mr. W would be alive today.

I think that the community that we serve would find it reprehensible if they found out that the physicians who care for them were in some way prohibited from criticizing their peers in private when the care of any patient was found to be inadequate by their own personal physician. I think that any attempt by the medical staff to prohibit such free and open discourse is not only not in the best interest of our patients, but is also illegal. In addition, any such policy would have to apply to all physicians equally and be incorporated through the appropriate bylaws amendment process requiring the votes of the majority of the medical staff. Any attempt to characterize free speech as being disruptive is completely farfetched and inappropriate. Any attempt to single me out because I have bipolar disease would not only be a violation of my Constitutional rights but also a violation of my statutory protections under the Americans with Disabilities Act.

6. Our Agreement

Concerning the conversation that you and Dr. Borrero had with Dr. Scott on March 8, 2001, I would like to refer to the letter which I sent to Dr. Scott and Dr. Borrero on December 21, 2000 (see enclosure). As you know, this letter was written by the hospital and I was asked to sign it. I did so with a few minor changes. That letter indicates that I gave permission for Dr. Borrero to provide Dr. Scott with "mutually agreed information." At the end of the letter it says "I release from all liability, grant absolute immunity to, and agree not to sue Dr. Paul Scott or South Hills Health System and its representatives (including specifically Dr. Borrero) for sharing the above information in an honest and accurate manner."

The letter which Dr. Borrero wrote to Dr. Scott on February 15, 2001 (see enclosure) and the subsequent conversation that you and Dr. Borrero had with Dr. Scott consisted mainly of information which had never been "mutually agreed" upon. In fact, despite my request, you and Dr. Borrero resolutely declined to discuss any of this with me. This clearly resulted in giving Dr. Scott false and misleading information, which was not "honest and accurate." In addition to the events which I have already discussed, Dr. Borrero told Dr. Scott that I threatened to sue him. This is absolutely untrue. What had, in fact, occurred was that I attempted to talk to Dr. Borrero about the meeting of December 21, 2000. Dr. Borrero said he did not have to talk with me. I agreed with him but told him that that would not prevent me from writing a letter or having my attorney write him a letter. However, I told him I much preferred to handle these matters in a collegial manner. He then saw fit to talk to me. Dr. Scott also told me that either you or Dr. Borrero had told him that I had said that my psychiatrist had told me that I could say anything to anyone. This is completely untrue. Not only has Dr. Scott never said that to me, I have never said that to anyone.

I think that you and Dr. Borrero have violated the agreement which we had based upon my letter of December 21, 2000. The information which you provided Dr. Scott was not mutually agreed upon and was not given in an honest and accurate manner. I want you to know that I am not a litigious person and I have no intention or desire to sue the hospital or anyone else. Dr. Scott and I welcome your input into my therapy and will continue to do so in the future. I know that by inundating you with numerous letters the pulmonary group made it virtually impossible for you to allocate enough time to discuss all of the issues with me directly. By doing this, I believe that they have caused you to violate our agreement. Providing false information to Dr. Scott serves no useful purpose and in fact is a total waste of time for everyone involved. In addition, by violating our written agreement, you place yourself and the South Hills Health System in jeopardy for legal action. I intend no such action; however, I must insist that in the future you abide by our agreement and that all information provided to Dr. Scott be "mutually agreed" upon and conveyed in an "honest and accurate manner."

7. Conclusions

I want you to know that I have no personal animosity towards the pulmonary group. My concerns were solely about Dr. C's care. Dr. Laman and I have been friends since 1984, but I have not allowed that friendship to cloud my best medical judgement. In fact, prior to Dr. C's arrival, the number of disagreements that I was having with the pulmonary group had been decreasing steadily over the years. In fact, I had a conversation with Dr. Deliere last December in which we fully agreed on the appropriate use of salt poor albumin in patients with cardiogenic pulmonary edema. Unfortunately, the pulmonary group's blind and unconditional support of Dr. C was probably influenced by their personal animosity towards me in addition to their desire to suppress legitimate criticism so that their virtual monopoly would not be jeopardized. My desire concerning the cases of Mrs. K and Mr. W has only been to educate and enlighten, not to harm anyone. I have been beset with boundless recriminations and attempts at character assassination aimed at silencing my legitimate concerns.

I have followed yours and Dr. Collins' directions completely. I have every intention of doing so in the future. I have not been disruptive in any way, and I have not violated the rules and regulations of the medical staff in any way. On the contrary, the behavior of the pulmonary group has been extremely disruptive. In addition, by participating in the orchestration of the letter writing campaign, as well as writing a letter himself, which contained false information, Dr. Sims has shown a dishonesty, lack of ethics, and lack of moral integrity that should not be tolerated in our institution. Certainly this lack of moral integrity has no place in the medical staff leadership. For this reason, I believe he should be asked to resign his position as Vice-President of the Medical Staff.

More importantly, I hope the medical staff leadership and hospital administration will work towards bringing fair competition from other pulmonary groups by allowing them to participate and compete on a level playing field at Jefferson Hospital. It is only then that the "magic of the marketplace" will overcome the arrogance and hubris that led to the deaths of Mrs. K. and Mr. W. Then perhaps they will not have died in vain. We owe it to them, to our future patients, and to ourselves.

Once again, I wish to thank you for your time and attention to this matter. I regret that you have had to devote so much time to this, but I believe that this was the fault of the pulmonary group and not myself. Please do not hesitate to contact me if you would like to discuss any of these or other issues further.

Very truly yours,

/s/ RICHARD R. SCHNEIDER

Richard R. Schneider, M.D., FACP, FACC

RRS/sgs

cc: Charles Cline, MD
Paul Scott, MD
Mr. Gary Perecko
Mr. Bruce Payton
Mr. Paul Verati

APPENDIX B

RICHARD R. SCHNEIDER, MD, FACP, FACC
Cardiovascular Specialist

September 16, 2001

Jan Jennings
President and C.E.O.
South Hills Health System
Coal Valley Road
P.O. Box 18119
Pittsburgh, PA 15236

Dear Mr. Jennings:

I am in receipt of a copy of a letter from Jean Mikula to my psychiatrist, Dr. Paul Scott (enclosure). This letter contains false and defamatory allegations. I am writing to seek your assistance.

I am accused of inappropriate behavior since 1997. I maintain that members of the hospital administration and medical staff leadership have engaged in outrageous behavior starting since March 17, 1997.

At that time, I performed a cardiac catheterization under excessive medication prescribed for my bipolar disorder by my psychiatrist, Dr. Alexandra Kreps. The patient suffered no injury and care was given over by me to Dr. Stuart Tauberg and Dr. V. Madhavan as I left for vacation. Upon my return from vacation, Dr. Arnold Fingeret, president of the medical staff, told me I was to take a "voluntary" medical leave of absence. I asked if there had been any other problems in my file, and he said "Some." He would not provide particulars.

Unknown to me at the time but later discovered by me, Ms. Terry Kostrub, vice-president for medical staff affairs, and Dr. Lawrence Adler were conspiring to allow Dr. Adler to steal my practice. Dr. Fingeret, Dr. Adler, and/or Ms. Kostrub gave false information to Dr. Thomas Hobbs, the director of the Physicians' Health Program. This information consisted of false allegations of drug and/or alcohol abuse and false allegations of sexual harassment. Dr. Hobbs, Director of the Physicians' Health Program, confirmed this to me in 1999 or 2000 in a telephone conversation and again on July 17, 2001 in his office in Harrisburg. In early 1999, while having lunch together in the hospital cafeteria, Dr. Fingeret told me that the single allegation of sexual harassment was "Bullshit." The falseness of this allegation can be confirmed by Kim Wagner and Sandra Harrod, both nurses in the ICU. Because of these false allegations I was kept out of work for six months. Members of Dr. Adler's group have told me that during that time he assured them I would never return to practice at Jefferson and they would be able to make money by taking over my practice. I can prove all of this.

In 1998, I quietly criticized the negligent care of one of my patients by a nurse in the I.C.U. He refused to listen, and I inadvertently raised my voice. I walked away to find the nurse in charge. He subsequently ran after me and made terroristic threats. There was no physical contact. I immediately called hospital security and subsequently filed a police report to this effect with the Jefferson Hills police. It remains on file. Mr. Fred Boehm, the hospital attorney at that time, told me in reference to my behavior: "That was nothing." The response of the medical staff leadership was to criticize me for raising my voice in the I.C.U. I documented this event with a letter at that time.

In early 2000, I asked Dr. Fingeret what was in my file that caused him to send me into the PHP in 1997. He refused to tell me and referred me to Dr. Collins, who was then president. Dr. Collins also refused to tell me. I persisted and was criticized for asking. At Dr. Collins' request, I put my request in writing. On January 21, 2000, Dr. Collins finally told me there had been nothing else in my file. Because of this, I met with the Physician Health subcommittee on March 10, 2000. Present were Mr. William Jennings, Dr. Collins, Dr. Mannheimer, Dr. Paternac, and Danielle Kruczak. I spent 45 minutes explaining the outrageous behavior of Ms. Kostrub and Dr. Adler. Dr. Collins described my presentation as "eloquent as usual." Nothing was done. You may confirm this with Bill Jennings.

More recently, Dr. William Sims, vice-president of the medical staff, has engaged in a campaign of character assassination against me because I privately criticized his group's care of two of my patients. This is documented in my lengthy letter to Dr. Wetschler dated April 12, 2001. After Dr. Wetschler received this letter, I asked him if there were any problems with it. He replied, "None." This indicated to me that all of it was true.

I have now been accused of having a physical altercation with a technician in the Cardiology Department on July 13, 2001. This is untrue. The physical contact did occur but was purely accidental. The technician involved, Juanita, misunderstood and misrepresented what occurred. I have never had a physical altercation with anyone in my more than 17 years at Jefferson Hospital. Because of this accusation, Dr. Wetschler, on July 16, insisted that I take another medical leave of absence. Of importance is the fact that on 7-20-01, Carol, a technician in the Cardiology Department, came to my office. She told me everyone in the department supported me. She said they thought what was done to me was wrong. She and Susan Dunn, an R.N. in the department, returned to my office the first week of August to voice the same opinion. I immediately put Carol on the phone directly with Dr. Wetschler. At that time, Susan Dunn said, "Anyone who knows you, Dr. Schneider, knows it was an accident."

Furthermore, the staff in the Cardiology Department has been complaining to me for some time concerning poor staffing, lack of break time, lack of lunch time, and unreasonable delays caused by the failure of cardiologists to show up for their tests. On July 13, two of my inpatients were forced to lie on stretchers in the department for over two hours, and another patient for three hours because of these delays. I was forced to leave patients waiting in the office. After completing the first test, the technician in question began arguing with me in front of the patient when I told her a patient in the office had to be seen before the second test. I felt badgered, and I am sure she felt abused by missing lunch and her concern for the abused patients. I called Terry Riffer and left a message on his voice mail that something had to be done about scheduling problems. I have brought this problem to Mr. Riffer's and Tony Masari's attention on prior occasions, the most recent on July 10. I also brought this to Dr. Lemis's attention on July 10. They had refused to correct the situation, saying there was nothing they could do. I believe this high stress, hostile work environment was the root cause of the interaction between the technician and me.

Dr. Wetschler told Dr. Hobbs on the speakerphone in my presence on July 17 that the principle reason he wanted me on medical leave of absence was that I was a perfectionist and expected other doctors to live up to my perfectionistic standards. I was trained to be a perfectionist during my ten years at The Mount Sinai Hospital in New York as a resident, fellow, and faculty member. I truly believe that it is only by striving for perfection that one can achieve excellence. Besides, who would want a cardiologist who is not a perfectionist? If we truly want Jefferson Hospital to be the "best community hospital in the United States," then we must always strive for perfection even if we know it can never be fully achieved. I believe I should be admired and emulated in my quest for excellence rather than attacked and castigated. Recent estimates that up to 100,000 people die each year in hospitals as a result of mistakes is probably a vast underestimation.

I lost the majority of my practice during my first LOA in 1997. I will probably lose the rest during the current one. I have been accused in writing by Dr. Wetschler of threatening to sue. This is untrue. I explicitly stated in my letter to Dr. Wetschler on 4-12-01 that I had no intention to pursue legal action. I wish no harm to Jefferson Hospital. I have always done my best to improve the quality of care provided to our patients. I have done this by my patient care and my service as Chief of Medicine in 1993-94 and Executive Committee 1993-96 in addition to other committees. I also applied for medical staff leadership in 2000, and I have taught part of the nurses' critical care course for many years. I know I may have ruffled a few feathers over the years, but it has always been in the best interests of the hospital and our patients. And, very importantly, I have never acted with malicious intent.

While I have not threatened to sue, I do believe the hospital should act in a lawful manner. When I told Dr. Wetschler in May or June that the hospital and medical staff leadership had to abide by the laws of the United States and the State of Pennsylvania, he disagreed with me. He responded by saying he thought they could do what they wanted, but he would check it out. I believe it is this fundamental difference in outlook that underscores my disputes with the medical staff leadership. I have outlined by positions in my letter to Dr. Collins dated 12-28-99 and my memo to Dr. Wetschler dated 7-10-98. Any organization that sees itself as above the law is certainly predisposed to abusing its power to the detriment of its constituents.

Since 1997, I have been victim to dishonest, self-serving, unethical behavior by some members of the medical staff leadership and hospital administration. This has been possible since 1997 because of my disability and my powerless position as a part-time solo practitioner. In addition, during the past several months, I gave permission to provide my psychiatrist, Dr. Paul Scott, correct and accurate information. Subsequent to this, members of the medical staff and hospital administration have provided Dr. Scott with what I believe to be false and defamatory information on at least three separate occasions. This is a continuation of the pattern begun in 1997. I have been implicitly warned by Dr. Wetschler that if I ask for due process in the hospital, I will surely be expelled from the staff. He said this would be a serious black mark on my record and should be assiduously avoided.

Most importantly, I want you to understand that my actions of the past few years have been motivated by trying to reform the medical staff procedures to prevent these kinds of abuses from harming other doctors unjustly in the future. I am desperate for some justice and have nowhere else to turn but to you. I ask for your understanding and intervention to put a stop to this highly discriminatory behavior. I would like to meet with you privately at any time to discuss further details of any of the above. I have written detailed documentation for most of it. I have provided you with this. I am fully cognizant of the sensitive nature of this, especially considering that you are new at the institution. I suggest you confer privately with Bill Jennings and Maryann Farmerie for their opinions of me. Thank you for your consideration.

Sincerely yours,

/s/ RICHARD R. SCHNEIDER, M.D.
Richard R. Schneider, M.D.

APPENDIX C

Speaker phone conversation with
Stanley Wetschler MD, Bruce Payton, and Richard Schneider, MD

October 17, 2001
9:30 a.m.

Sharon: "Clinical support services, this is Sharon."

Schneider: "This is Dr. Schneider. Mr. Payton and Dr. Wetschler are expecting my call."

Sharon: "Hold on one moment please."

Bruce: "Hey Dr. Schneider."

Schneider: "Hi Bruce, how are you?"

Bruce: "Good. I'm going to put you on speaker phone, one sec."

Bruce: "Dr. Schneider, Dr. Wetschler is here with me."

Wetschler: "Hi, Rich."

Schneider: "Hi Stan, how are you."

Wetschler: "Good, fine. Yourself?"

S: "Good."

W: "Good. Ah, I knew you called several weeks ago. I didn't call you back because I hadn't had any other communication with Dr. Frazier. What happened is, ah, that she had sent a letter and it's probably somewhere in file here or back in my office because typically if my name's on the cover even though it says, um, you know 'Medical Staff Office' sometimes we have found it in, you know, it goes back to Brentwood Medical Group and I haven't received it. But I did get a copy by fax yesterday. So I have all the information you have. Ahmm, how can I help you?"

S: "Well, I, ah, spoke with Dr. Hobbs and Dr. Frazier."

W: "Ahh."

S: "and they both seemed to think it was okay for me to, ahh, to go back off my leave of absence and I just wanted to know if there's anything else you need me to do."

W: "Well, first thing you need to do is send a letter. I think the process is once you've taken a leave of absence to either the MEC or the Executive Committee stating number one the reason and number two, what you've been doing during the leave of absence and, uh, and then, you know, I think we'll simply want to get some communication with Dr. Hobbs. You know, these are things we need to look at, and I think we need to get some communication with Dr. Scott, and then discuss where we go from here. Look, what, what did you, what have you been thinking about, or what have you been thinking about, or what have you been doing the last several weeks in terms of your planning? I know you had a lot of frank discussions with Dr. Frazier. During this period I think one of the first things we talked about is this being, ah, I kind of related this to my own situation, more of a period of opportunity for thinking about things in terms of your vision and where you want to be. Do you want to share any of those thoughts?"

S: "Sure. First of all I spoke to Dr. Hobbs yesterday. They had some trouble reaching you. I gave him your home phone number. Did he call you at home?"

W: "Yesterday I was out. Janie just had to go for her budget checkup."

S: "Do you have Dr. Hobb's phone number? You could give him a call."

W: "I'll be glad to give him a call. I think we need to communicate with him anyway."

S: "They were trying to reach you yesterday."

W: "Okay."

S: "His phone number is: 1-800…"

W: "Just one second."

S: "1-800-228-7823, and just ask for the Physician's Health Program."

W: "Right."

S: "My thoughts, as I told Jeannie, that I, er, I guess it was umm…"

W: "Several weeks ago."

S: "Yeah, at least several weeks ago and then I told her again."

W: "Uh huh."

S: "When I got back from Alabama that, um, my intention at the present time would be to go back on staff at Jefferson and to look for another position and when I find a position I'll resign from Jefferson or go on Courtesy Staff or something like that. Umm, but I have been looking and I haven't found anything. There are virtually no part time jobs available, and I have extensively been looking. And I can't work more than part time is the problem. So, umm, I may have nowhere else to go is the problem. And the only alternative may be to leave medicine completely, which I don't think is really the morally right thing to do."

W: "You said you've been looking and thinking about these things. What kind of things in medicine would you, would you consider? 'Cause Dr. Frazier and I, you know, she had mentioned that, ah, one of the things that she thought you would be very good with is some form of education."

S: "No, I've been looking all over. I've been looking for part time practice and I've been looking for part time, umm, at the, ah, you know, at UPMC, at the VA, umm, at West Penn. I talked to O'Toole's group at Shadyside, umm, I've been on the internet, I've put ads in the, umm, Allegheny County Medical Society Bulletin, in the Post-Gazette. I have really been looking hard. I've been, you know, really…and there's no, ah, right now there are no teaching, part time, teaching positions or part time practice positions available in cardiology, that I could find."

W: "Are you looking specifically in Pittsburgh?"

S: "Well, I have no choice because, you know, ah, the kids live in Pittsburgh and umm, I'm not going to leave the kids."

W: "Yeah, umm."

S: "I can't leave my kids. I would leave medicine before I'd leave my kids. I would have to. There's no question which comes first."

W: "And even in terms of insurance work or working for one of the HMO's, you know sort of administrative position."

S: "I don't have…."

W: "Here in Pittsburgh, we are, I have to agree with you it is a rather limited market."

S: "Right, but there are no, I do not have the educational background to, umm, to handle an administrative position, umm. I have thought about the possibility of teaching high school, umm, but that's out of medicine. And, umm, any position with an insurance company is going to be a full time position. Umm, I, you know, I've worked with Highmark as a, as a case reviewer, they have very few cases to review. And, ah, their people who work in the administration are not, uh, you know, except for the Medical Director they don't have any MD's working in their, uh, administrative aspects."

W: "Er, with your background, engineering, physiology, even when you, even when you look at high schools there are superb opportunities. For instance, they even teach anatomy and even some physiology."

S: "No, Stanley…."

W: "And they do have incredible possibilities at some of these, these institutions where…."

S: "But that would be leaving medicine. But no, I'm qualified to teach high school physics. I've already been down to the University of Pittsburgh and in touch with the state educational, ah, licensing bureau concerning what would be required to get a teaching certificate. And I met with the head of the School of Education at the University of Pittsburgh. I meant on the phone, and then I; she was out of town; I met with her assistant. I went through all that and I have all of my applications and every thing I would need. But I wouldn't be able to do that, um, until, umm… In other words, in order for me to do that, at a minimum I would have to take a two week course in the summer, and they only offer it in the summer. Or do a full year, but that's only offered as a cohort, meaning it has to start in September. So, I wouldn't be able to teach high school until, uh, September of 2002."

W: "Ah, well what I need to do is, you know, get… We need, we need to get some more information and basically, uh, I guess it goes through ah…."

S: "Well let me say this, Stanley, you know, I, I, um, I, you know, I've taken what you've told me very seriously about, ah, not getting into any kind of due process, ah, proceedings at Jefferson or investigations. So, I want to make it perfectly clear that I do not want to engage in those, and before I write a letter I want to make sure that the outcome is going to be positive. And if you want to talk with Dr. Hobbs and Dr. Scott first then once you reassure me that the outcome is going to be positive, then I'll write the letter. You can reassure me now. Because my understanding is that as President of the Medical Staff you can act, uh, alone."

W: "Ah, I, I guess I can, but I, I feel that, ah, you know, this has involved a long standing history of multiple, multiple people, multiple, multiple interventions. Ah, I feel, ah, ah, extremely, ah, I can I put it, uncomfortable. I do not want to speak, you know the word excathedral, ah, I do not want to see, ah, you know, ah, where you talked about the fact that you felt that sometimes, ah, I and others have, you know, pre judged…and I, I'm really concerned about any, ahm, perception that no matter what I say even after speaking to people will be an act of, of, pre, pre judgment. And this kind of history is, has happened not only with me but with others who have had… but I don't want to get into that situation. So, what ever I do, Richard, I would want to present, you know, you write the letter and, uh, present it to, ah, the Credentials Committee or the Executive Committee. It would be a, a decision by committee."

S: "Well Stanley, if you know…."

W: "I feel very, very strongly about that."

S: "I understand and, and you, you've warned me so strenuously against doing anything like that. Umm, that, umm, I'm reluctant to do it. Ah, and uh, as you know, I asked you at the beginning of August if there were any further requirements and you said you were going to put together a sub committee. And Bruce told me on Thursday that you never did that. So…."

W: "We did have a, a sub committee together, but quite frankly with you having taken this leave of absence and had a, had a chance to go out through this course reflect, there is no urgency to act at that time. Because, give an example, right now you've got some thinking, and quite frankly, this is an opportunity and you've done some rather popular things in terms of looking towards your future. You know, it seems, recreating the wheel, if you are, you know, create your own destiny. It took a lot of, a lot of time, a lot of energy, a lot of, umm…."

S: "Yeah, I may not be able to do anything until next September, ahm…."

W: "And, you know, it, it may take, quite frankly, you know, as President of the Medical Staff, I can't tell you that even having spoken with Dr. Hobbs and Dr. Jacobs, ah, that…."

S: "Who's Dr. Jacobs?"

W: "will be. Pardon?"

S: "Who's Dr. Jacobs?"

W: "Dr. Jacobs…that…."

S: "No, who's Dr. Jacobs?"

W: "That will be enough. I have to let you know, Jacobs, whatever."

S: "You mean Scott?"

W: "Dr. Scott. I'm sorry."

S: "Oh, okay."

W: "Yeah, Dr. Scott. Ah, you know that, that is necessarily… I just want to tell you, right off the bat, satisfied…."

S: "Let me ask you a question."

W: "that you would be…."

S: "Stanley, let me ask you a question."

W: "Back on."

S: "Let me ask you a question."

W: "Just be straight, straight and tell you that."

S: "Stanley, let me ask you a question."

W: "Okay."

S: "Okay. Ah, um, the implication when I took this leave of absence was that after I did the things that you required was, would be that I would be allowed back on staff. It seems to me that you're now changing the rules after the fact."

W: "Ah, I did not say that. And that's one of the, that's one of the reasons that, ah, I, I've got to be very careful in terms of what I say because you misconstrued... That's one of the first steps."

S: "Yeah. Let me ask you this Stanley. If you had made this clear, um, you know, then perhaps I wouldn't have even had to, um, go to Alabama."

W: "What, what was one of the things that I did make clear to you. What is one of the things that we presented to you? Just remember what the conversation was about. The conversation was about, ahh, you know, suspension. And then a whole process whereby, you know, you basically after listening to our conversation assessed the risk."

S: "You basically told me that the risk was that if I would either be suspended or take a voluntary medical leave of absence. There was nothing in between. And there was...."

W: "In fact, there is nothing in between that I know of."

S: "Right. Well, that to my way of thinking that, that is a significant problem. Because you, you confront somebody with a choice that there's not really a choice. It's more like, like a...I won't use the word extortion but I can't find the right word for it. It's, it's coercion."

W: "It's really not coercion because if you really think about it. We think, and I'm going to use the word 'we' not 'I', that this is all going, quite frankly, in your, in your best, best interest."

S: "Yeah, well my best interest would be to just have you put me back on staff now. And, uh, if you're really concerned about my best interest that, that would be the right thing to do. I think I've been pretty clear that I want to play ball with you, but I don't want to put myself at risk of being suspended or thrown off the staff. And you, you've already told me that if it goes to Executive Committee there's a good chance they're just going to throw me off the staff. Well, whether or not that's called pre judging or not, I don't know. And Bruce told me on Thursday that he was fairly convinced that if we did go to some kind of a hearing nobody would have the patience to listen to all the details going back to 1997."

W: "Well, people would have to listen, listen to that. But the point is you've been… You've been, this has been investigated and yes we go, we have to go through a whole…."

S: "There's never been an investigation."

W: "Quite frankly you've been given different codes of conduct that you've signed…."

S: "I've never signed a code of conduct."

W: "You didn't want to take the risk, Richard."

S: "Okay, that's exactly what I'm saying. I wouldn't want to take the risk."

W: "Therefore, this is, if you really sit down and maybe Dr. Frazier's talked to you about it, and Dr. Scott. What you're telling me after all these years I'm really concerned about your interactions with Dr. Scott because he should say 'Richard, this is the reality. What a, what a great thing Jefferson has done for you by suggesting this 'Leave of Absence' so that we can go on with your life. Get yourself reorganized to the point where Jefferson Staff feels it's okay for you to come back, that there's been some significant, significant changes in behavior. Some evidence…."

S: "Did you read Sandra Frazier's letter?"

W: "Oh I read it very carefully and I've spoken to Dr. Frazier."

S: "Right. And, uh, she, um, and as you know there's nothing in that letter that indicates that she thought I was disruptive in any way. She's just…."

W: "That's not, that's not entirely true. We'll let, we'll let our Medical Executive Committee, ah, you know, or Credentials Committee, ah, you know, read, read the letter."

S: "Okay, let me ask you another question, Stanley. You said that there's…."

W: "Clinical competence was fine. We're not arguing that at all."

S: "I know. I'm asking you about, you said that there's been investigations. To my knowledge there's never been an investigation."

W: "Investigation for what? In the past?"

S: "At any time. About me concerning any of these…."

W: "Investigations."

S: "There was only one investing…."

W: "Ah."

S: "There was only one investigation and that was the incident with Nurse M. in 1998. But there have been no investigations concerning, ahm, any of the things since 1998."

W: "Well, in terms of a lot of your behavioral issues that have come up wi, wi with the appropriate people have been spoken to. Let, without using that formal term 'investigation', let me just say that everything that's been alleged has been, ah, has been discussed with the appropriate parties and with yourself."

S: "Let me say this: there's never been a single episode, ah, of due process, ah, at any time, ah for me."

W: "Yes there has been. There's been collegial interventions on multiple…."

S: "Collegial interventions and due process are two different things."

W: "Collegial intervention is the first step."

S: "Well it's never gone, I have never…."

W: "Into prevention. The whole, ah…."

S: "Stanley, okay, look…."

W: "…the whole due process. But you know what, you have, you have an attorney and I'm not going to discuss law with you because we're really getting off the point. The point is you know what you need to do. I know what I need to do and we'll go from there."

S: "Well let me say this, Stanley, I went to the course in Alabama and I presented the details and I gave Sandy Frazier all the letters that I have sent or most of them."

W: "Yah."

S: "And I talked about all this stuff for five days."

W: "That's correct."

S: "And the only thing that they criticized me in any of my behavior was that I talked too much and don't listen enough. And, um, you know, it's hard for me to say to you that I've been guilty of all of these other things when after spending five days exploring everything in detail I haven't come away with anything else that they've said I've done wrong. So, what do you want to admit to?"

W: "You don't have to admit to anything, Richard. Because I don't think you're...we don't...nobody wants you to admit to anything. It's just a whole, a, it's the whole behavior pattern that I think, ah, we need to investigate to be sure that that has absolutely changed."

S: "Okay, let, let me ask you a question. Did you read the letter I sent to Jan Jennings?"

W: "Yes I did."

S: "Okay. I think, you know, you accused me of behavior since 1997. And that behavior was predicated on the abuse that the Medical Staff and the hospital administration heaped on me in '97. And since that time, ah, or since at least the beginning of 2000 or '99 I've been trying to, ah, point out the fact that, ah, the absence of due process concerning what happened in '97, ah, caused me to be punished for something I wasn't guilty of. And I've been trying to reform the Medical Staff procedures, and you've taken, ah, umbrage at that and I can understand it from your perspective. But you have to understand that, um, I believe that, ah, all of my behavior has been predicated about that. The incident with Wannitta, she lied and I'm going to prove it and, um, you know that was a complete accident. So, you may question my therapy with Dr. Scott, um, but you're not in a position to do that because you've never even talked to him and he doesn't talk to you. So it's not...."

W: "Richard, I have tried to talk to him."

S: "Right."

W: "But you're right, he doesn't talk to me. You're absolutely correct and therein lies, lies a big... But, you know what...."

S: "But he, does respond...."

W: "Oh Richard, that's...."

S: "He does respond to your letters, Stanley."

W: "But I'm just telling you straight out, let's just get this clear. With Dr. Hobbs he's not been able to have a meaningful, ah, dialogue with him and with even Dr. Frazier. So, it's not just Stanley. It's anybody who would be in this particular position."

S: "He doesn't talk to anybody. It has nothing to do with you."

W: "I think the fact is, Richard, we, we, you know, still when the perception is when we get all this information together, not the fact that you've gone through this course for five days, it's where, where is Richard Schneider now. I can go to a course. You can treat people in jail for ten years regarding certain aspects of criminality for instance. Ah, that doesn't mean because they went to a course they necessarily on that path. And I think that has to be clear. This is just, perhaps, perhaps and again I don't want to rush to prejudgment. Ah, a first step. And doctor mentioned, Dr. Frazier mentioned other things that she suggested you, you might want to consider. And I think she sent you that same letter where she suggested some other programs and ongoing, ongoing, ah, help."

S: "Well, I'll tell you the one thing I did...."

W: "I got the same letter you did, I suppose."

S: "Yes, one thing I did learn was that, you know, is to learn is to learn a little bit more about boundaries. Let other people talk and listen more, which I really think I've been able to incorporate rather well and I did incorporate down there as well. She didn't make any other recommendations. Ah, you know, she wants me in a group so I can learn how to listen and, and, ah, ah, and not hoard the conversation. I think that's legitimate."

W: "She also said, ah, she said it's basically, and again, you have the letter in front of you, it's basically up to the medical staff leadership to, to assess everything that we're going have, we're going to have available to us."

S: "Okay, well, that, that's correct and I can't dispute that."

W: "And, and that's what our job will be."

S: "Okay, well, all I want...."

W: "What information...."

S: "Right."

W: "And then we have to make, make that final assessment."

S: "Well let me, let me make a request of you then. Ah, why don't you just, you know, take our conversation as a verbal indication that I'm interested in coming back and find out, ah, find out from the appropriate people whether their going to allow it. And let me know. And if they're not going to allow me to come back then I'll, you know, then I'll obviously have to resign. But I can't, ah, allow myself to be put in a position where I'm voted against."

W: "I think before I do that, Richard, although I understand what you say and I would say to you: 'What a great idea', but in terms of...."

S: "Well that's exactly what you…."

W: "Put that in a letter form."

S: "That's exactly what you told me to do. You told me that, to avoid any, um, hearings or due process because it would be unlikely that it would turn out positive for me. So, you're giving me two conflicting bits of advice."

W: "No, I'm not really giving you two different, two conflicting bits of advice. Put it in a letter and then it can go to the appropriate review, you know, ah, Executive Committee, MEC, and then…."

S: "Well, you know what I can do, Stanley, I'll write the letter and I'll say: 'Are there any further requirements that you have for me before coming back from leave of absence.' "

W: "Okay, put that in the letter, but also put down in the letter the reason for the leave of absence and what you do, what you've been doing in the meantime."

S: "Um."

W: "That would be, that would be helpful, 'cause…."

S: "Okay, but I'm not going to ask to come back until you say it's going to go through."

W: "I can't, you know, I can't, I can't say."

S: "Well then you'll have…. That's the best I can do right now. And, um, I'll just have to do that, because you've warned me very clearly not to get into any due process. And anything that would, you know, would be a commitment on my part would expose me to that risk. I don't believe I'd get a fair hearing."

W: "Well."

S: "And I don't…and I think that Bruce reinforced that."

W: "The perception of a 'fair'…you would get a hearing from, from those who have not been involved in any of, you know…."

S: "Yeah, but I still don't think it would be fair."

W: "Quite frankly, we, we'd have to search for people who would, who would, ah, who would not have any previous, ah, you know, I'd say involvement to our _____."

S: "Right."

W: "Clearly, Bill Sims would not be one of those people who would be involved in a fair hearing committee. You understand that and I understand that."

S: "Right."

W: "And, ah…."

S: But on the other hand I don't think that, that Chuck Cline or you, um, or, or Borrero, or any of those people would give me a fair hearing."

W: "We might have to go to a different county; you know how they do here for the murder trials."

S: "Right."

W: "You know _____ everybody, everybody, I'm not trying to be funny. But you know a lot of people, a lot of people on the staff _____ for all the many years, if you count up the number of people who have been involved in different committees in front of which this kind of information has come; there are a lot of people who have already been involved."

S: "Well, you know I've never had a complaint from any other member of the medical staff before this episode with Mrs. C. and Mr. W. And that was sixteen years with no complaints. So, I think that that's important for you to understand too."

W: "Oh, I understand that. But the…. You're absolutely correct, but over the last number of years…."

S: "It's only been since 19…."

W: "It seems to be that, I'm sure Dr. Scott has talked to you about that pattern of, of escalation and I would hope he's spoken to you about it."

S: "Well, umm...."

W: "Then, of course, that's privileged communication between you and Dr. Scott but I just have to, have to let you know what our collective thinking is. We're, we're, you know, we're concerned about you, Richard. I have to make this clear and when we had this discussion after this last event, we just discussed our view and we tried to present to you the different routes that one can go. And the one that would be least onerous, the one that would be the least traumatic is to simply, and again you have the choice, to just step away for awhile, get whatever you need to do. Reassess this opportunity and go on."

S: "Well it's been three months now, Stanley, and I've told you where I stand."

W: "Okay, but I think, I think, that, ah, we need to look at all this information and, uh, you know, go from there. So, I think what we need to do is, uh, you send a letter and I'll get a hold of Dr. Hobbs and basically document for the record our conversation and, um, present this information to the appropriate committee."

Payton: "I do think you could. I think you're right. I think there are physicians who have been totally removed from you in, in activities have no idea what's gone on in the past. I do think those physicians are here on staff."

S: "Well, I can tell you...."

P: "I would think you really have to, you really have to weigh those risks."

S: "Well, ah, let me tell you...."

P: "We can't do this for you. You have to weigh those risks."

S: "Well, Bruce, that, that's not the tone of what you said on Thursday. But be that as it may, Stanley's made it perfectly clear to me. And I think, um, that it would be an enormous risk to take and, um, and I think that, that it's unfortunate, um, that there's no middle ground here. Um...."

P: "Well, I'm sorry that you got the impression that I was saying you wouldn't get a fair hearing. I was just trying to reiterate the long history. I think the time involved in it. I think the complexity of the issues. That's what I was really talking about and really trying to get you to look at your position relative to the process."

S: "Well, I have been very intensely."

P: "I know. I've made that real clear to Dr. Wetschler. I think that you're really, you know, that you're really weighing out the positives and negatives of moving forward."

S: "Yeah, I mean, what I'm looking at a situation where I may have nowhere to go. Um, I don't think it would be good for anybody if I left medicine, frankly."

P: "I also told Dr. Wetschler, and I'm also going to say it in front of you, that we did discuss... I told him this morning that your practice base is dwindling, and I think that, you know...."

S: "Right."

P: "We want to, you know, we need to rethink about the prospects for you going forward. And, again, I want to just reiterate what Dr. Wetschler says. If there's anything we can do to help you outside of the normal Medical Staff structure let us.... You know what I'm saying, let us know. I want to make that point very clear to you."

S: "Can you give me...."

P: "If there is something that we can do, um, and I don't know what that might be. Let us know."

S: "Can you, will you...See, I don't either. Do you have any ideas what you might be able to do?"

P: “I, I kind of thought, and I just heard you say that, that you were limiting your search to Pittsburgh. I guess I kind of envisioned you at NYU. Knowing of your caliber and your ability to teach, I kind of saw you at NYU or Columbia University. Ah, but now I hear you saying that you are limiting your search to Pittsburgh. I think that we could have gone, you know, have helped you with that search, a broader search. We have search firms that we work with all the time for physician recruitment. So, keeping that in the back of your mind, then if there’s something you want to talk about further, give me a ring and we’ll talk about it.”

S: “But you do understand I can’t leave my kids.”

P: “I hear you now. I was kind of seeing you at Columbia to be real honest.”

S: “I’ll tell you the truth, if I could be at Columbia or NYU I would be.”

P: “I could see you being there.”

S: “Right. Well thank you, that’s a compliment.”

P: “Ha, ha. Yeah.”

W: “And quite frankly. That can go with Dr. Frazier says. She can see you in teaching. She thinks that with your didactic abilities, and abilities to teach medical students, ah, that would be probably, from her perspective where you need to be, and I think she’s spoken to you about that. And, you know, one of the things she talked to me about was the fact that one of the perceptions of a lot of the people on the Medical Staff is they feel like they’re being lectured to, and I know she’s spoken to you about that.”

S: “Well, the way I perceive it is that, you know, I probably should be talking to people who want to learn, and that….”

W: “The point is, you know, that’s still your perception and maybe one of the reasons you’re not as far, you’re kind of getting there, but not still though quite get it.”

S: “No, what, well Stanley, I think….”

W: “And that’s something you need to work out with Dr. Scott.”

S: “Well Stanley, I think that you….”

W: “Helping you with that or not is really our concern. We’re concerned about the level of any kind of therapy you’ve been getting, not because Dr. Scott isn’t doing a good job. It’s because we’re looking at the results.”

S: “No, no I tell you Stanley….”

W: “The therapy is you.”

S: “The first thing, the first thing I had to…. Yes I talked to Dr. Frazier, okay….”

W: “Yeah.”

S: “is given who I am….”

W: “Right.”

S: “am I able to sit here and watch Mrs. C. die and watch Mr. W. die and not do anything about it. And watch the patients in the, in the treadmill lab being abused day after day, and not feeling like it’s an injustice.”

W: “And this is….”

S: “Well….”

W: “What you just said, Richard, is part of…. This is extremely important, this is…. I understand where you’re coming from, but from where we’re coming from that’s a sense of a philosophy and a way of behaving and interacting that’s still not in concert with moving forward.”

S: “Well, you know, I understand what….”

W: “That’s exactly what we’re talking about. So even though you’ve been off for three months.... From the writings and the other things, Richard, and Dr. Frazier's told me this. And she's told me, quite frankly, I know what she put in writing, you know she, she was concerned about being 'politically correct' and she told me that. But we discussed things frankly. She said: you may have had an iota, an iota of a glimpse in terms of some of these behavioral issues and, uh, those types of issues...."

S: "Basically what you...."

W: "...are involved in."

S: "You know it's the...."

W: "We're really not sure you've really moved on."

S: "That's what I hear you saying...."

W: "We have to make that judgment."

S: "Yeah, what I hear you saying...."

W: "Say it straight out...."

S: "I might have been...."

S: "Right, Stanley, let.... I hear you what you're saying...."

W: "All I'm saying is...."

S: "Let me paraphrase it. I'm glad you said it. You're basically saying that the fact that I complain about inadequacies of patient care in the way in which I do is not really acceptable at Jefferson Hospital and I understand that. Okay, ah, totally. Um, you know, and um, when you wrote me the letter saying I should do it in writing from now on, I did do it in writing after that. But the real issue here is that, um, I complained about the quality of care at the hospital and people didn't like that and I can understand why they didn't like it."

W: "It's the way, Richard, it's the manner."

S: "Well...."

W: "I mean, Bruce Payton has a problem with utilization or something like that he doesn't behave in a certain way that absolutely alienates, alienates people that's not disruptive. It's very organized and, and when these issues have come up over the last several years, ah, it's not the fact that you didn't have a good idea. It's the way that whole, all these issues have been communicated. And again, listen, you spent, you spent five or six days in Alabama talking about all this stuff and I'm not going to rehash it. But I think you need to just be, how could I put it, redirected."

S: "Well, let me tell you this, Stanley, I think the fact that I complained, ah, about things and as it's well documented I believe I went through all the appropriate, um, hospital procedures. Ah, and I did it through the proper channels. I think that's well documented, and basically what you're saying is that you're going to kick me off the staff because you don't like my personality. Well, I don't think that's, that's really an excellent reason."

W: "Yeah, you know, it's not personality. It's definition of what disruption, disruption is. And that's what people are going to look at and there's a whole bunch of definitions for that. It really has nothing to do with personality. Personality is sort of a broad, broad, ah, term. But it's the way that there have been recurrent patterns of ways that you've expressed or…."

S: "Well, you told Dr. Hobbs that the reason you wanted me to go to Alabama was because: 'I was a perfectionist who expected other doctor's to live up to my expectations.' I mean, I heard…."

W: "One reason, Richard."

S: "Yeah, well that was one reason. And then, you know…."

W: "There's about umpteen more. And, you know, ah, as I say, it's the whole, the whole definition of what we call, call disruption. Ah, you know…."

S: "Well, you know, I, I told Bruce this, I told…."

W: "It's the operation of the hospital."

S: "Right, I told Bruce, you know, on Thursday, um, that I considered this whole thing, you know, an issue of First Amendment rights and free speech."

W: "That's perfectly okay and that may be delusional to some extent."

S: "Right, I understand that."

W: "The ability of others to do their jobs. Ah, you know, creating in some sense a hostile work environment. Ah. Again, you can exercise your ability, your First Amendment ability, but if it creates, for instance, a hostile work environment, that's not conducive."

S: "Well, the conversations that I had with people were in private and I don't know that having a private conversation with people...."

W: "I think we talked about that and, you know, we're still off on the same thing. And we're not, we're not hear to discuss the specifics. I think we just have to talk about the broad generalities in terms of what you've gone through, where you're going or where you're not going. And, uh...."

S: "I can tell you this, Stanley, you've never gone into specifics with me on anything."

W: "Okay, Richard, and that's part of the delusional nature, perhaps that you feel no specifics have been gone into. I can't help you with that. Dr. Frazier did have, I think she told me that you had given her that letter you had sent me."

S: "Right."

W: "And uh, you know, she took a few deep breaths and, uh, you know, ah, you know, read that. And, uh, you know, she certainly is aware, and other people are aware that there are specifics. But we don't want to, I don't have to sit here and defend the fact that we have or have not...."

S: "Well, let me ask you one; let me ask you one quick question,

Stanley. You know, after the spring, and I wrote you that letter, everything quieted down. And it wasn't until, you know, Wannitta complained about me that you took the action you took. So, I assume that that was the precipitating factor, correct?"

W: "Let me ask you something, Richard."

S: "I'm sorry, did you say 'right?' "

W: "That you took the action you took?"

S: "No, no, in other words, the fact that Wannitta complained about me was the reason why you took the action that you took."

W: "Ya, if you were.... Let me say this, if you were a member of..., if you worked for the hospital. If you look at the hospital's policies, okay, the hospital's policy, if you're a worker in that lab, not a doctor, and you did the same thing. What do you think would happen?"

S: "Well, I'm not saying...."

W: "You know what would happen."

S: "I'm not saying that what you did was not appropriate given what she told you, okay."

W: "And what we, what we basically.... Correct."

R: "So, so I mean, so you were basically acting on, based upon what she told you, right?"

W: "I, I would say basically that and uh, uh I'm not going to give you the specifics, but that's one of the things that we based this on. Correct."

S: "Right. That was the precipitating event, right?"

W: "Precipitating event was that action, correct."

S: "Right, and if that hadn't happened, you would not have had a cause for action at that time."

W: "At that point in time?"

S: "Right."

W: "Ah, at that point in time that's, that's, that's probably true."

S: "Okay."

W: "That's true. Okay."

S: "All right, well then, then that's all I need to know."

W: "All right, listen, I've got to get to the office and I will try to craft a letter and I will send it to you. And, and I'd like you to call Dr. Hobbs, um, and, you know, he, he, uh, he'll give you his opinion. His opinion, what he told me yesterday was that he didn't think it would be a problem for me to get back on staff."

W: "Remember. I want to make it clear to you also that we're going to get all this information and then it's not going to be me who will make up this decision as to where we go. It's going to be, ah, by committee."

S: "Which committee?"

W: "I think it goes through Credentials Committee and then to the MEC."

S: "Okay."

W: "Okay."

S: "So, you're basically you're saying that this has got to, you know, ahm, go through, ah, a lot of different people. But, I know I've been on leave of absence before and, ah, you know, there was, ah, no question at that time that I would be allowed back on staff."

W: "I want to tell you something, Richard. If you address the hospital policy, if you address the hospital policy, ah, not for people on the work force, ahm, you will see that what you've gone through is extremely collegial, although you may not think so at this time, because in a word, there's a very good chance you or anybody else, uh, would have been gone. Bang, right then and there. Okay. And

Bruce, there is documentation, not in our bylaws per se but, but the hospital, the hospital bylaws."

S: "Referring to what?"

W: "If you are referring to your activities with, ah, Wannitta."

S: "I see, okay."

W: "Just, I want you to understand that. I want you to understand this. That if you were a worker in that same work place and did this, okay…."

S: "Ahumm."

W: "You would be probably summarily dismissed."

S: "The only, the only problem with that is, is that she's lying."

W: "Well, you know, I, I…."

S: "Cause that not's what happened…."

W: "Involved, involved in, in, you know, that at this point in time."

S: "Well I, did you take that into consideration that maybe she was lying?"

W: "I always take that into consideration."

S: "Do you think she…."

W: "And by the way, it's…."

S: "Do you think she might…. Do you think she had a motive for lying?"

W: "You know, again, I, I'm not going to get into this discussion at this point in time. It's, it's completely inappropriate."

S: "Well, it was the factor that caused you to make me go on leave of absence."

W: "But I'm not going to get into the specifics, Richard. We, we felt that we did an adequate job of, ah, I use the word 'looking into to this matter' at that time investigating it and, ah…."

S: "Okay."

W: "Going from there. All right."

S: "All right."

W: "All right."

S: "Take care."

W: "Thank you. Bye, bye."

APPENDIX D

IN THE COURT OF COMMON PLEAS OF ALLEGHENY COUNTY, PENNSYLVANIA

RICHARD R. SCHNEIDER, M.D., Plaintiff, v. WANITTA ANDERSON, an individual; STANLEY S. WETSCHLER, M.D. an individual; DAVID LAMAN, M.D., an individual; WILLIAM R. SIMS, M.D., an individual; SOUTH HILLS HEALTH SYSTEM, D/B/A JEFFERSON REGIONAL MEDICAL CENTER ARNOLD E. FINGERET, M.D., an individual THERESE KOSTRUB, an individual TERRY RIFFER, an individual Defendants	No.: GD-02023114 COMPLAINT IN CIVIL ACTION

Filed on Behalf of Plaintiff:
RICHARD R. SCHNEIDER, M.D.

Attorney of Record for this Party:
MICHAEL A. CASSIDY, ESQUIRE
Pa. ID: 26351

TUCKER ARENSBERG, P.C.
1500 One PPG Place
Pittsburgh, PA 15222
412.566.1212

A JURY TRIAL IS DEMANDED

IN THE COURT OF COMMON PLEAS OF ALLEGHENY COUNTY, PENNSYLVANIA

RICHARD R. SCHNEIDER, M.D., No.: GD-02023114
Plaintiff,
v.
WANITTA ANDERSON, an individual
STANLEY S.WETSCHLER, M.D. an individual;
DAVID LAMAN, M.D., an individual;
WILLIAM R. SIMS, M.D. an individual;
SOUTH HILLS HEALTH SYSTEM, D/B/A
JEFFERSON REGIONAL MEDICAL CENTER
ARNOLD E. FINGERET, M.D., an individual
THERESE KOSTRUB, an individual
TERRY RIFFER, an individual
Defendants

COMPLAINT IN CIVIL ACTION

AND NOW comes the Plaintiff, Dr. Richard R. Schneider, M.D., by and through his attorneys Tucker Arensberg P.C. and specifically Michael A. Cassidy, Esquire, and files the following Complaint and in support thereof avers the following:

1. Plaintiff Richard R. Schneider, M.D. (hereinafter referred to as Dr. Schneider) is a Physician licensed to practice medicine in the Commonwealth of Pennsylvania residing at 722 Shady Avenue, Pittsburgh, PA 15232.

2. Defendant South Hills Health System, formerly D/B/A Jefferson Regional Hospital, and now D/B/A Jefferson Regional Medical Center (hereinafter referred to as Jefferson Hospital) is a Non-Profit Corporation licensed by the Commonwealth of Pennsylvania to operate a hospital at 575 Coal Valley Road, Jefferson Borough, PA 15025.

3. Defendants Stanley S. Wetschler M.D., David Laman, M.D., Willliam R. Sims, M.D. and Arnold E. Fingeret, are physicians licensed to

practice medicine in the Commonwealth of Pennsylvania who reside in the Commonwealth of Pennsylvania, and were, at all times relevant hereto, members of the Medical Staff of Jefferson Hospital. Defendants Wanitta Anderson, Therese Kostrub and Terry Riffer and individuals residing in Allegheny County, Pennsylvania and were at all times relevant hereto employees and agents of Jefferson Hospital.

4. At all times relevant and material hereto, the Defendant South Hills Health System owned and operated Jefferson Hospital and had under their control and supervision the employees, agents, representatives and servants thereof.

5. At all times relevant hereto, the Defendants Stanley S. Wetschler, William R. Sims, and David Laman were acting within their authority as active members of the Medical Staff, authorized representatives, agents, servants, and/or employees of Jefferson Hospital and was operating within their authority as same at the time of the incident(s) described herein.

6. At all times relevant and material hereto, the Defendant Stanley S. Wetschler was operating as President of the Medical Staff (or Chief Medical Officer) whose duties, obligations, and authority are defined and delineated in the Bylaws of the Medical Staff of the Hospital which are attached hereto as exhibit "A."

7. At all times relevant and material hereto, Defendant William R. Sims, Defendant David Laman, Defendant Wanitta Anderson, any and all members of the Medical Staff, and any and all employees of South Hills Health System D/B/A Jefferson Hospital were acting as authorized representatives, agents, servants, or employees of South Hills Health System D/B/A Jefferson Hospital and were operating within their authority as same at the time of the incident(s) and actions described herein.

8. At all times relevant and material hereto, the conduct and actions of the parties were governed by the Pennsylvania Human Relations Act, (43 Pa. C .S. A. §955, et seq. as said statute relates to the acts and incidents described herein.

9. At all times relevant and material hereto, said Bylaws of the Medical Staff were and are a binding contract by and through which the

Board of Directors of Jefferson Hospital delegates to the departments and committees of the Medical Staff, and specifically to certain officers of the staff, chiefs of those departments and members of those committees, duties and responsibilities for monitoring the quality of medical care in the hospital and reporting thereon to the Board and the authority and responsibility to make recommendations to the Board concerning an applicant's appointment, reinstatement and/or reappointment to the Medical Staff of the hospital and the clinical privileges such applicant shall enjoy at the hospital. The Bylaws of the Medical Staff further compels each Physician appointed to the Staff to act in accordance with the Bylaws of the Medical Staff.

10. At all times relevant and material hereto, the Bylaws, as amended from time to time, constitute a Contract between Jefferson Hospital and the individual members of the Medical Staff.

11. At all times relevant and material hereto, the Bylaws delineate the rights and duties of the parties hereto in connection with the incidents and actions described herein.

12. At all times relevant and material hereto, the conduct of the parties described herein is governed by the Pennsylvania Peer Review Protection Act 63 P. S. C. A. §425.1-4.

13. The Plaintiff's application for appointment to the Medical Staff, and the clinical privileges extended thereto, was approved by the Board of Directors at Jefferson Hospital ("the Board") and the Plaintiff began practicing medicine as a full-time member of the Active Medical Staff in the areas of Internal Medicine and Cardiology at Jefferson Hospital on or about April 30, 1984.

14. Pursuant to the contractual requirements as outlined in the Bylaws of the Medical Staff, the Plaintiff has at all times material hereto acted in accordance with said Bylaws, and has consistently upheld each obligation and standard outlined therein

15. At all times relevant hereto, the Plaintiff had a diagnosed disability and/or impairment, specifically bipolar disorder.

16. At all times relevant and material hereto, and throughout his dis-

tinguished career as a Physician, the Plaintiff has vigorously upheld his professional and ethical duty as a Physician to be an advocate for the highest possible standards of patient care and professional responsibility.

17. Pursuant to said duty, the Plaintiff has, at all times material hereto and throughout his distinguished career as a Physician, occasionally drawn into question the acts and/or omissions of other Physicians where said acts and/or omissions may not have been optimal or suitable to effectuate the highest standard of patient care, and in order to protect his patients from foreseeable and preventable harm.

18. As the result of the Plaintiff's laudable adherence to the highest medical and professional standards and to his sworn duty as a Physician, the Plaintiff has drawn into question the acts and omissions of Physicians on the Medical Staff of Jefferson Hospital.

19. On or about June of nineteen ninety-eight (1998) in response to the Plaintiff's laudable exercise of professional responsibility described above, the Defendant South Hills Regional Health Systems D/B/A Jefferson Hospital, William R. Sims, David Laman, and Stanley Wetschler, in their respective capacities and through their agents, employees, authorized representatives, servants, or other authorized parties, initiated and undertook and/or willingly participated in a campaign designed to discredit, discourage, undermine, stifle, and otherwise prevent the Plaintiff's lawful and ethical expressions of professional concern for the care of patients at Jefferson Hospital. Specifically, the Plaintiff drew into question the acts and/or omissions of the Defendants and/or their agents and employees on at least five (5) separate and distinct occasions. As the result of, and in retaliation for, each separate and distinct occasion, the Defendants continued their contrived and duplicitous scheme and campaign against the Plaintiff, which was designed to:

a. Avoid any potential liability as the result of their acts;
b. To discourage the Plaintiff from continuing his advocacy on behalf of his patients;
c. To cause pain, injury, and damage to the Plaintiff,
d. To create the false impression that the Plaintiff was habitually inappropriate and/or incompetent in his dealings with members of the Medical Staff;

e. To create a hostile work environment;
f. To undermine the Plaintiff's efforts to have his clinical privileges reinstated after medical leave;
g. To cause the Plaintiff to resign from the Medical Staff, and;
h. To cause the Board to revoke the Plaintiff's appointment to the Medical Staff of Jefferson Hospital and/or reduce or terminate Plaintiff's clinical privileges.

20. Said campaign was effectuated through a contrived and duplicitous scheme involving:

a. False accusations negligently leveled against the Plaintiff;
b. False accusations recklessly leveled against the Plaintiff;
c. False accusations against the Plaintiff which were negligently and/or recklessly repeated and/or published;
d. The deliberate interference with the Plaintiff's relationships with his patients;
e. The deliberate solicitation of employees to slander and defame the Plaintiff;
f. Violations of the Plaintiff's rights as defined in the Bylaws, in that said slanderous allegations were never investigated;
g. The violation of the Plaintiff's rights as outlined and defined by the Pennsylvania Human Relations Act;
h. Reckless and outrageous conduct directed at the Plaintiff;
i. Reckless and outrageous conduct directed at the Plaintiff in retaliation for his efforts to provide the highest standard of medical care;
j. The willful and intentional failure to notify the Plaintiff that defamatory allegation were being circulated among the medical staff;
k. The willful abuse of the immunity afforded good faith peer review issues; and
l. Fraudulent misrepresentations involving unsubstantiated claims and accusations.

21. As the direct and proximate result of said campaign and the contrived and duplicitous scheme employed to effectuate it, the Defendants South Hills Regional Health Systems D/B/A Jefferson Hospital Stanley S.

Wetschler, William R. Sims, and David Laman, in their respective capacities and through their agents, employees, authorized representatives, servants, or other authorized parties, established an abnormal and hostile work environment, with a pattern and/or practice of unlawful conduct undertaken with the intent to harm the Plaintiff and/or his patients, which forced the Plaintiff to, first, take a leave of absence then, after the Defendants' acts prevented his return to Medical Staff, to then finally resign under duress from the Medical Staff.

22. Plaintiff has been effectively denied access to any income from the Practice of Medicine by the acts of the Defendants, ultimately creating severe financial distress and duress for the Plaintiff.

23. The Plaintiff's resignation was coerced by the Defendants, as the Plaintiff was advised by Defendant Stanley Wetschler, after the Plaintiff had taken a voluntary medical leave in reliance upon Defendant Stanley Wetschler's assurance and representation that he would be reinstated and reappointed to the Medical Staff with fully restored clinical privileges, that his request for reinstatement of his clinical privileges and/or his reappointment to the Medical Staff, pursuant to the By-Laws, would in fact not be approved and that, as the result thereof, said refusal would be reported to the National Practitioners Data Bank as an adverse peer review action. This report would effectively prevent him from practicing medicine at any time in the future at any other health care facility.

24. Said duress and coercion was directly and proximately caused by the aforementioned campaign and the contrived and duplicitous scheme employed to effectuate it which was perpetrated by the Defendants South Hills Regional Health Systems D/B/A Jefferson Hospital and Stanley Wetschler, William R. Sims, and David Laman in their respective capacities and through their agents, employees, including but not limited to the Defendant Wanitta Anderson, authorized representatives, servants, or other authorized parties.

25. The Plaintiff's decision to resign was caused by the fraudulent and malicious misrepresentations made by and/or on behalf of the Defendants South Hills Regional Health Systems D/B/A Jefferson Hospital, Stanley S. Wetschler, William R. Sims, and David Laman, in their

respective capacities and through their agents, employees, authorized representatives, servants, or other authorized parties.

26. As the result of the aforesaid campaign and the contrived and duplicitous scheme employed to effectuate it which was perpetrated by the Defendants South Hills Regional Health Systems D/B/A Jefferson Hospital, Stanley Wetschler, William R. Sims, and David Laman, in their respective capacities and through their agents, employees, authorized representatives, servants, or other authorized parties, the Plaintiff has suffered serious financial detriment and serious personal injuries, some of which are permanent.

COUNT I
DEFAMATION
RICHARD R. SCHNEIDER, M.D.
V.
WANNITTA ANDERSON

27. The averments contained in paragraphs 1-26 are incorporated by reference as if set forth fully herein.

28. On or about July 13, 2001, the Defendant Wanitta Anderson, by word and deed, communicated and/or caused to be communicated and published a defamatory allegation of assault & battery, an indictable and/or socially notorious offense, in connection with an incident involving the Plaintiff and Defendant Wanitta Anderson, against the Plaintiff to the members of the Medical Staff of Jefferson Hospital, the employees of said hospital, and the general public.

29. The Defendant Wanitta Anderson, by word and deed, communicated and published or caused to be communicated and published said defamatory allegation of assault & battery despite the falsity of said allegation.

30. The Defendant Wanitta Anderson, by word and deed, communicated and published or caused to be communicated and published said defamatory allegation of assault & battery despite the fact that she knew or should have known of the falsity of said defamatory allegation.

31. Those individuals who heard and/or read the defamatory accusations understood said defamatory accusations, and said defamatory accusations of Defendant Wanitta Anderson.

32. The Defendant Wanitta Anderson's said defamatory allegations ultimately resulted in the Plaintiff being forced to take a medical leave of absence, and ultimately caused the Plaintiff to resign under duress from his position as a Physician on the Active Medical Staff at Jefferson Hospital.

33. The Defendant Wanitta Anderson, acted with reckless disregard for the truth of her accusations in the following regards:

a. By making oral and/or written accusations of assault & battery with no basis in fact;
b. By making oral and/or written accusations of assault & battery with reckless disregard for the rights of the Plaintiff; and,
c. By making oral and/or written accusations of assault & battery in the face of verifiable denials by the Plaintiff.

34. As a result of the Defamation of the Plaintiff as a direct and indirect result of the actions of Defendant Wanitta Anderson, the Plaintiff has suffered the following injuries, some of which may be permanent in nature:

a. He has suffered from the loss of professional esteem
b. He has suffered from severe shame and embarrassment;
c. He has suffered from situational depression;
d. He has suffered from alienation from friends and professional colleagues;
e. He has suffered from the inability to practice medicine;

35. Plaintiff has sustained the following damages as a result of his injuries:

a. He has endured great pain, suffering, inconvenience, embarrassment, mental anguish, and emotional and psychological trauma;
b. His general health, strength, and vitality have been impaired;
c. He has been unable to enjoy various pleasures of life that he has previously enjoyed;
d. He has incurred medical expenses;

e. He will incur medical expenses in the future;
f. He has lost income; and,
g. He has lost future earning capacity.

WHEREFORE, Plaintiff seeks a judgment against Defendant Wanitta Anderson for compensatory damages in excess of the jurisdictional amount for compulsory arbitration.

COUNT II
PUNITIVE DAMAGES
RICHARD R. SCHNEIDER, M.D.
V.
WANNITTA ANDERSON

36. The averments in paragraphs 1-35 are incorporated by reference as if fully set forth herein.

37. The conduct of the Defendant Wanitta Anderson, more fully set forth above with respect to the communication of defamatory allegations which she knew or should have known were baseless and false constitutes willful, wanton, and reckless misconduct amounting to a blatant disregard for the rights and privileges of the Plaintiff.

38. As the result of said conduct, Defendant is liable to Plaintiff for punitive damages.

WHEREFORE, Plaintiff seeks a judgment against Defendants Wanitta Anderson for punitive damages in excess of the jurisdictional amount for compulsory arbitration.

COUNT III
DEFAMATION
RICHARD R. SCHNEIDER, M.D.
V.
SOUTH HILLS HEALTH SYSYTEM D/B/A JEFFERSON REGIONAL MEDICAL CENTER
And STANLEY S. WETSCHLER, M.D.

39. The averments contained in paragraphs 1-38 are incorporated by reference as if set forth fully herein.

40. On or about July 16, 2001, the Defendants South Hills Regional Health Systems D/B/A Jefferson Hospital, and Stanley Wetschler, in their respective capacities and through their agents, employees, authorized representatives, servants, or other authorized parties, by word and deed, communicated and/or caused to be communicated and published a defamatory allegation, specifically by repeating false allegations of assault & battery made by defendant Wanitta Anderson, an indictable and/or socially notorious offense, against the Plaintiff to the members of the Medical Staff of Jefferson Hospital, the employees of said hospital, and the general public.

41. The Defendants South Hills Regional Health Systems D/B/A Jefferson Hospital and Stanley Wetschler, in their respective capacities and through their agents, employees, authorized representatives, servants, or other authorized parties by word and deed, communicated and published or caused to be communicated and published said defamatory allegation of assault & battery despite the falsity of said allegation.

42. The Defendants South Hills Regional Health Systems D/B/A Jefferson Hospital and Stanley Wetschler in their respective capacities and through their agents, employees, authorized representatives, servants, or other authorized parties, by word and deed, communicated and published or caused to be communicated and published said defamatory allegation of assault & battery despite the fact that they knew or should have known of the falsity of said defamatory allegation.

43. Those individuals who heard and/or read the defamatory accusations understood the defamatory accusations, and the defamatory accu-

sations of Defendant South Hills Regional Health Systems D/B/A Jefferson Hospital and Stanley Wetschler, in their respective capacities and through their agents, employees, authorized representatives, servants, or other authorized parties, ultimately resulted in the Plaintiff taking a forced leave of absence in order to avoid a suspension based on the false and improperly investigated defamatory allegations.

44. The Defamatory allegations ultimately forced the Plaintiff to resign under duress from his position as a Physician on the Active Medical Staff at Jefferson Hospital.

45. The Defendant South Hills Regional Health Systems D/B/A Jefferson Hospital and Stanley S. Wetschler, in their respective capacities and through their agents, the Medical Staff, employees, authorized representatives, servants, or other authorized parties acted with reckless disregard for the truth of their accusations in the following regards:

a. By making oral and/or written accusations of assault & battery with no basis in fact;
b. By making oral and/or written accusations of assault & battery without an investigation warranted by the seriousness of the charge;
c. By making oral and/or written accusations of assault & battery with reckless disregard for the rights of the Plaintiff;
d. By misrepresenting the facts surrounding the incident, including but not limited to the falsification and fabrication of statements and evidence about said incident; and,
e. By making oral and/or written accusations of assault & battery in the face of verifiable denials by the Plaintiff.

46. As a result of the Defamation of the Plaintiff as a direct and indirect result of the actions of Defendant South Hills Regional Health Systems D/B/A Jefferson Hospital and Stanley S. Wetschler, in their respective capacities and through their agents, the Medical Staff, employees, authorized representatives, servants, or other authorized parties, the Plaintiff has suffered the following injuries, some of which may be permanent in nature:

a. He has suffered from the loss of professional esteem
b. He has suffered from severe shame and embarrassment;
c. He has suffered from situational depression;

d. He has suffered from alienation from friends and professional colleagues;
e. He has suffered from the inability to practice medicine.

47. Plaintiff has sustained the following damages as a result of his injuries:

a. He has endured great pain, suffering, inconvenience, embarrassment, mental anguish, and emotional and psychological trauma;
b. His general health, strength, and vitality have been impaired;
c. He has been unable to enjoy various pleasures of life that he has previously enjoyed;
d. He has incurred medical expenses;
e. He will incur medical expenses in the future;
f. He has lost income; and,
g. He has lost future earning capacity.

WHEREFORE, Plaintiff seeks a judgment against Defendant South Hills Regional Health Systems D/B/A Jefferson Hospital and Stanley S. Wetschler, M.D. for compensatory damages in excess of the jurisdictional amount for compulsory arbitration.

COUNT IV
PUNITIVE DAMAGES
RICHARD R. SCHNEIDER, M.D.
V.
SOUTH HILLS HEALTH SYSYTEM D/B/A JEFFERSON REGIONAL MEDICAL CENTER
And STANLEY S. WETSCHLER, M.D.

48. The averments in paragraphs 1-47 are incorporated by reference as if fully set forth herein.

49. The conduct of the Defendant South Hills Regional Health Systems D/B/A Jefferson Hospital and Stanley S. Wetschler, M.D. in their respective capacities and through their agents, the Medical Staff, employees, authorized representatives, servants, or other authorized parties,

more fully set forth above with respect to the communication of defamatory allegations which they knew or should have known were baseless and false, constitutes willful, wanton, and reckless misconduct amounting to a blatant disregard for the rights and privileges of the Plaintiff.

50. As the result of said conduct, Defendants are liable to Plaintiff for punitive damages.

WHEREFORE, Plaintiff seeks a judgment against Defendant South Hills Regional Health Systems D/B/A Jefferson Hospital and Stanley S. Wetschler, M.D. for punitive damages in excess of the jurisdictional amount for compulsory arbitration.

COUNT V
BREACH OF CONTRACT
RICHARD R. SCHNEIDER, M.D.
V.
SOUTH HILLS HEALTH SYSYTEM D/B/A JEFFERSON REGIONAL MEDICAL CENTER,
STANLEY S. WETSCHLER, M.D.,
WILLIAM R. SIMS, M.D., AND DAVID LAMAN, M.D.

51. The averments contained in paragraphs 1-50 are incorporated by reference as if fully set forth herein.

52. At all times relevant hereto, the Defendant South Hills Regional Health Systems D/B/A Jefferson Hospital and Stanley S. Wetschler, M.D., William R. Sims, M.D., and David Laman, M.D. in their respective capacities and through their agents, the Medical Staff, employees, authorized representatives, servants, or other authorized parties, were contractually obligated to act in Good Faith and to follow the procedures and processes outlined specifically under the heading "DUE PROCESS PROCEDURES" of the Medical Staff Bylaws as they related to actions affecting the Plaintiff in his capacity as a Medical Staff Appointee as defined within said Bylaws.

53. At all times relevant and material hereto, the Plaintiff was denied

the protection afforded by the Bylaws due to the willful, intentional, and wanton breach by the Defendants. Specifically, the Defendants routinely breached the provisions contained in Article VII, which establishes specific rights pertaining to initiation of investigative procedures against Medical Staff members such as the Plaintiff, as well as the notice requirements contained therein in connection with any such investigation.

54. At all times relevant hereto, said Defendants were under a contractual duty to act on the basis of information and belief or, alternatively, an investigation, in connection with any complaints made against the Plaintiff.

55. In direct and willful breach of the provision of the Bylaws as it relates to Information and Belief, the Defendants conveyed to the Plaintiff their intent to recommend that the Credentials Committee and/or Executive Committee should investigate the July 13, 2001 allegations despite the lack of a good faith information and belief or, alternatively, without conducting an appropriate investigation.

56. The Defendants thus conveyed to the Plaintiff their intention and willingness to subsequently represent to the Credentials Committee and/or Executive Committee that the recommendation for investigation was prompted by Information and Belief or, alternatively, was the result of an investigation on behalf of the Defendants.

57. As the result of said communications, the Plaintiff was coerced into taking a Medical Leave in order to avoid suspension and/or dismissal from the Medical Staff based on a threatened investigation and hearing of the Credentials Committee and/or Executive Committee when said investigation and/or hearing would be based on false allegations, and, ultimately, the Plaintiff was forced by the Defendants' acts, both individually and collectively, to resign his position on the Medical Staff.

WHEREFORE, the Plaintiff respectfully requests judgment against the Defendants for:

a. Damages in the amount representing the amount of income the Plaintiff has lost as the result of the forced resignation from the Medical Staff.
b. Interest thereto; and,
c. The cost of this suit.

COUNT VI
PUNITIVE DAMAGES
RICHARD R. SCHNEIDER, M.D.
V.
SOUTH HILLS HEALTH SYSYTEM D/B/A JEFFERSON REGIONAL MEDICAL CENTER
STANLEY S. WETSCHLER, M.D.
WILLIAM R. SIMS, M.D., AND DAVID LAMAN, M.D.

58. The conduct of the Defendant South Hills Regional Health Systems D/B/A Jefferson Hospital, William R. Sims, M.D., David Laman, M.D., and Stanley S. Wetschler, M.D., in their respective capacities and through their agents, the Medical Staff, employees, authorized representatives, servants, or other authorized parties, more fully set forth above, constitutes willful, wanton, and reckless misconduct amounting to a blatant disregard for the rights and privileges of the Plaintiff.

59. As the result of said conduct, said Defendants are liable to Plaintiff for punitive damages.

WHEREFORE, Plaintiff seeks a judgment against Defendant South Hills Regional Health Systems D/B/A Jefferson Hospital, David Laman, M.D., William R. Sims, M.D., and Stanley S. Wetschler, M.D. for punitive damages in excess of the jurisdictional amount for compulsory arbitration.

COUNT VII
BREACH OF CONTRACT
PROMISORY ESTOPPEL
RICHARD R. SCHNEIDER, M.D.
V.
SOUTH HILLS HEALTH SYSYTEM D/B/A JEFFERSON REGIONAL MEDICAL CENTER
STANLEY S. WETSCHLER, M.D.
WILLIAM R. SIMS, M.D., AND DAVID LAMAN, M.D.

60. The averments contained in paragraphs 1-59 are incorporated by reference as if set forth fully herein.

61. Following an alleged incident involving an employee of the Hospital, specifically a technician in the stress lab on or about July 13, 2001, involving baseless and fabricated allegations, the Defendant Stanley S. Wetschler, M.D. met with the Plaintiff on or about July 16, 2001, and communicated to him his recommendation that the Plaintiff should take a voluntary medical leave, during which he should undergo a "comprehensive, independent assessment and evaluation by a Physician mutually acceptable" after which, he should apply for reinstatement of his clinical privileges and/or reappointment to the Medical Staff, and to present his case to the Committee which would then be convened. Defendant Stanley S. Wetschler, M.D. then, through words and acts, led the Plaintiff to reasonably believe that, if he complied with said instructions, his clinical privileges would be reinstated and/or that he would be reappointed to the Medical Staff.

62. In good faith, reasonable reliance upon the Defendant Stanley S. Wetschler, M.D.'s promise that he would be reappointed upon his return, the Plaintiff took the aforementioned Medical Leave, during which time he sought and obtained said assessment and evaluation.

63. In the absence of the aforementioned communication with the Defendant Stanley S. Wetschler, M.D. the Plaintiff would not have reasonably taken said leave and would have remained on the Medical Staff.

64. Upon his return from said leave, the Plaintiff informed the Defend-

ants of his plans to request a reinstatement of his clinical privileges pursuant to the instructions of the Defendants and in compliance with the relevant provisions of the Bylaws of the Medical Staff, and, pursuant thereto, initiated communications as to the best way to effectuate said plan to have his clinical privileges reinstated.

65. The Defendants informed the Plaintiff that they would not approve a reinstatement of the Plaintiff's clinical privileges upon his completion of his medical leave. Instead, Defendant S. Wetschler, M.D. at this time broke his promise, and represented to the Plaintiff that any request for reinstatement of the Plaintiff's clinical privileges upon his completion of his medical leave, as well as any future attempt to seek redress pursuant to his Due Process rights under the Bylaws of the Medical Staff, would certainly have a negative result because, as the Defendant Stanley S. Wetschler, M.D. represented, the evidence against the Plaintiff in connection with the July 13th incident was irrefutable and the would certainly result in the Plaintiff's dismissal from the Medical Staff, and that said dismissal would result in a negative report to the National Physician's Data Bank, effectively ending the Plaintiff's medical career.

66. The Plaintiff, in taking said medical leave in reasonable reliance upon the Defendant Stanley S. Wetschler M.D.'s promise of reinstatement of the Plaintiff's clinical privileges upon completion of said leave, voluntarily forfeited property that he would have otherwise retained had he not taken said leave, including his Due Process Rights under the Bylaws, the right to a full and open hearing where witnesses could be called and accusers could be cross-examined by an attorney, and substantial monetary compensation including past and future income.

67. Further Injustice can be avoided only by enforcing the Promise and Agreement, made by the Defendants, that, if the Plaintiff took a voluntary leave instead of pursuing his Due Process rights as stipulated in the Bylaws, the Plaintiff would be reappointed after taking said Medical Leave.

WHEREFORE, the Plaintiff respectfully requests judgment against the Defendants for:

a. Damages in the amount representing the amount of income

the Plaintiff has lost as the result of the Voluntary Medical Leave;

b. Damages in the amount representing the amount of income the Plaintiff has lost as the result of the forced resignation from the Medical Staff.
c. Interest thereto; and,
d. The cost of this suit.

COUNT VIII
FRAUDULENT MISREPRESENTATION
RICHARD R. SCHNEIDER, M.D.
V.
SOUTH HILLS HEALTH SYSYTEM D/B/A JEFFERSON REGIONAL MEDICAL CENTER,
STANLEY S. WETSCHLER, M.D.,
WILLIAM R.SIMS, M.D., AND DAVID LAMAN,M.D.

68. The averment contained in paragraphs 1-67 are incorporated by reference as if set forth fully herein.

69. On or about July 16, 2001, Defendant Stanley S. Wetschler represented to the Plaintiff that he (Stanley Wetschler) possessed evidence substantiating an alleged complaint by an employee, specifically a technician in the stress laboratory, who claimed that the Plaintiff engaged in disruptive, inappropriate, and physically violent behavior in said stress lab, including allegations of assault on said technician. Defendant Stanley S. Wetschler, M.D. informed the Plaintiff that there had been an investigation of the allegations made by said stress lab technician, and that there was evidence, specifically a patient's statement, that substantiated and confirmed the allegations made by said stress lab technician.

70. As the result of the Plaintiff's alleged conduct, the Defendant Stanley S. Wetschler essentially presented the Plaintiff with an ultimatum, wherein the Plaintiff was essentially forced to choose between either: (a) facing a full investigation and hearing by the Executive Committee based on the investigated and corroborated allegation contained in the technician's complaint, which would, as Defendant Wetschler represented,

unquestionably result in a suspension and/or dismissal from the Medical Staff and a correlative career ending adverse peer review report to the National Practitioners Data Bank, or; (b) taking an immediate medical leave, where the Plaintiff would be subjected to humiliating and embarrassing psychiatric evaluations. The Defendant Stanley S. Wetschler represented and recommended to the Plaintiff that he choose the latter, as said medical leave would allow the Plaintiff to apply for reinstatement of the Plaintiff's clinical privileges upon his completion of his embarrassing and humiliating psychiatric evaluation. The Defendant Stanley S. Wetschler represented that he would support the Plaintiff in his request for reinstatement of the Plaintiff's clinical privileges upon his completion of his medical leave.

71. The Plaintiff reasonably relied on Dr. Wetschler's representation and he took said leave, where he endured the humiliating and embarrassing psychiatric evaluation. Upon completion of his treatment, Plaintiff initiated dialogue with the Defendants, based on his reasonable understanding of his prior conversation with the Defendant Stanley Wetschler, in order to ascertain the most efficacious manner in which to proceed towards the reinstatement of the Plaintiff's clinical privileges.

72. The Defendants, including Defendant Stanley S. Wetschler then represented to the Plaintiff that any future attempt to seek redress pursuant to his Due Process rights under the Bylaws of the Medical Staff would certainly fail because, as the Defendant Stanley S. Wetschler represented, the evidence against the Plaintiff in connection with the July 13th, 2001 incident was irrefutable, and, therefore, that any attempt on the Plaintiff's behalf to either dispute the Hospital's findings or, in the alternative, to request reinstatement of the Plaintiff's clinical privileges would inevitably fail, resulting in the Plaintiff's dismissal from the Medical Staff. The Plaintiff and the Defendants knew any dismissal from the Medical Staff, or any negative result from an application for reappointment and/or reinstatement of the Plaintiff's clinical privileges, would result in an adverse peer review report to the National Practitioners Data Bank, and that such a report would effectively bar the Plaintiff from practicing medicine with any health care organization. Therefore, the Plaintiff was forced to submit his resignation from the Medical Staff of Jefferson Hospital in

order to: (a) preserve his ability to practice medicine in the future, and; (b) to avoid further financial distress.

73. Defendant Stanley S. Wetschler, as President of the Medical Staff, and the Defendant Hospital, were under a contractual duty to conduct a thorough investigation of the allegations, including taking statements from all involved parties and witnesses, and, thereafter, to present the known facts of the Hospital's internal investigation to the Plaintiff, thus allowing the Plaintiff to make an informed and reasonable decision on his best course of action in connection with this serious matter. The Defendant Stanley S. Wetschler represented to the Plaintiff that he and the Defendant Hospital had fulfilled this duty, and that his representations concerning the facts surrounding the July 13th incident, and the Plaintiff's rights and options in connection thereto, were good faith representations.

74. The Defendants emphatically did not fulfill this duty, and instead intentionally failed to properly inform the Plaintiff of statements made by witnesses to the alleged incident, which, if properly conveyed, would have effectively exonerated the Plaintiff of the egregious allegation contained within the said technician's complaint. Instead of informing the Plaintiff that exculpatory evidence existed, the Defendants explicitly denied the existence of said evidence. Specifically, the Defendants, collectively and through the acts of Stanley S. Wetschler, M.D. informed the Plaintiff that a patient had provided corroborating eye-witness testimony to the incident as described by said technician when, in fact, no hospital representative actually spoke to said patient; when approached, said patient recounted the incident in a way that effectively exonerated the Plaintiff of any serious wrongdoing in connection with said incident. The Defendants deliberately deceived the Plaintiff as to the existence and contents of said patient's statements in order to give the Plaintiff an inaccurate and misleading impression of the facts of his case, and, therefore, of his rights in connection thereto.

75. The above listed misrepresentations made by the Defendants, including Stanley S. Wetschler, were material to the Plaintiff's decision to first take a medical leave and then, ultimately, to resign his position as a Member of the Medical Staff. Specifically, said representations negatively affected the Plaintiff's rights and options in connection with complaints

arising from the incident of July 13, 2001. To wit: (i) had the Plaintiff known of the existence of exculpatory evidence, he could have effectively challenged the allegations of improper behavior in a subsequent Executive Committee hearing, where witnesses would have provided said exculpatory testimony in connection with the July 13th incident, thus preserving his position as a Member of the Medical Staff of Jefferson Hospital, and; (ii) had the Plaintiff known that the Defendants had no intention of favorably receiving a request for reinstatement of the Plaintiff's clinical privileges and/or any subsequent reappointment application, he would not have subjected himself to the humiliation of a medical leave and an embarrassing psychiatric evaluation in reliance upon their representation that they would support said reappointment and/or reinstatement of the Plaintiff's clinical privileges.

76. The Defendants, including Stanley S. Wetschler, made said representations concerning the facts surrounding the alleged incident and the options available to the Plaintiff falsely, with knowledge of their falsity and/or with reckless disregard as to the truth or falsity of said representations.

77. Said misrepresentations were made with the calculated intent of misleading and inducing the Plaintiff into relying, to his detriment, on said representations and their truthfulness.

78. The Plaintiff's reliance on the truthfulness of the Defendant Stanley S. Wetschler's representations was reasonable, as (i) the Defendant Stanley S. Wetschler, was a longstanding and respected colleague of the Plaintiff, and; (ii) the Defendant Stanley S. Wetschler was the President of the Medical Staff, and was thus under a contractual obligation to inform the Plaintiff of his options with objectivity and fairness.

79. As the proximate result of the malicious, calculated, and fraudulent misrepresentations of the Defendant Stanley S. Wetschler, the Plaintiff has been forced to resign from his position as a member of the Medical Staff and, thus, has sustained the following injuries:

a. He has suffered from the loss of professional esteem
b. He has suffered from severe shame and embarrassment;
c. He has suffered from situational depression;

d. He has suffered from alienation from friends and professional colleagues; and,
e. He has suffered from the inability to practice medicine as a Cardiologist.

80. Plaintiff has sustained the following damages as a result of his injuries:

a. He has endured great pain, suffering, inconvenience, embarrassment, mental anguish, and emotional and psychological trauma;
b. His general health, strength, and vitality have been impaired;
c. He has been unable to enjoy various pleasures of life that he has previously enjoyed;
d. He has incurred medical expenses;
e. He will incur medical expenses in the future;
f. He has lost income; and,
g. He has lost future earning capacity.

WHEREFORE, Plaintiff seeks a judgment against Defendants South Hills Regional Health Systems D/B/A Jefferson Hospital, William R. Sims, David Laman and Stanley S. Wetschler for compensatory damages in excess of the jurisdictional amount for compulsory arbitration.

COUNT IX
TORTIOUS INTERFERENCE WITH CONTRACT
DR. RICHARD R. SCHNEIDER
V.
STANLEY S. WETSCHLER,
WILLIAM R. SIMS, M.D., AND DAVID LAMAN, M.D.

81. The averments contained in paragraphs 1-80 are incorporated by reference as if set forth fully herein.

82. At all times relevant and material hereto, the Defendants herein named were members of the Medical Staff at Jefferson Hospital.

83. On or about June 1998, the Defendants undertook a campaign in

the form of a contrived and duplicitous scheme, effectuated through false accusations, defamation, slander, and libel, which was designed and intended to discredit and defame the Plaintiff's character and to compromise his ability to perform his duties as a physician and to convince the Board to dismiss or discipline the Plaintiff and/or to force the Plaintiff to resign by creating an unreasonably hostile work environment.

84. To that end, the Defendants knowingly and maliciously made false statements and/or accusations, or maliciously and actively solicited others to make statements and/or accusations that they knew or should have known to be false, in a malicious and intentional effort to inaccurately portray the Plaintiff to the Hospital's Board of Directors, and to the other members of the Medical Staff, as an individual who consistently engaged in unacceptable behavior and/or professional conduct.

85. To that end, the Defendants intentionally and maliciously sought to create a hostile work environment in which the Plaintiff could not effectively practice medicine.

86. At all times relevant hereto, the Defendants improperly and maliciously, and in violation of the ByLaws of the Medical Staff, conspired to withhold and did in fact withhold from the Plaintiff the information contained in their complaints about the Plaintiff.

87. At all times, the Defendants knew that the Plaintiff's conduct was governed by the Bylaws of the Medical Staff, and that the behavior and/or professional conduct they inaccurately and irresponsibly attributed to the Plaintiff was proscribed by said Bylaws.

88. The Defendants knew or should have known that their contrived and duplicitous scheme would eventually undermine the Plaintiff's position on the Medical Staff and would eventually cause the Plaintiff to lose his contractual status as a Medical Staff Member.

89. As the direct and proximate result of the their contrived and duplicitous scheme, employing the use of false accusation, misinformation, and defamatory information communicated to others with reckless disregard for the truth, directly created a hostile work environment that was designed to compromise his professional and personal reputation within the Hospital

and was designed to discredit and humiliate the Plaintiff, and which ultimately resulted in the Plaintiff becoming the target of disciplinary procedures which endangered his position as a member of the Medical Staff.

90. As the proximate result of the malicious, calculated, and fraudulent misrepresentations made by the Defendants with the intent of interfering with the Plaintiff's contractual relationship with the Hospital as a member of its Medical Staff as outlined in the contract created by the Bylaws, and the slanderous, libelous, and defamatory communications made by the Defendants with the intent of interfering with the Plaintiff's said contractual relationship with the Hospital as a member of its Medical Staff, the Plaintiff has been forced to resign from his position as a member of the Medical Staff and, thus, has sustained the following injuries, some of which may be permanent in nature:

a. He has suffered from the loss of professional esteem;
b. He has suffered from severe shame and embarrassment;
c. He has suffered from situational depression;
d. He has suffered from alienation from friends and professional colleagues; and,
e. He has suffered from the inability to practice medicine as a Cardiologist.

91. Plaintiff has sustained the following damages as a result of his injuries:

a. He has endured great pain, suffering, inconvenience, embarrassment, mental anguish, and emotional and psychological trauma;
b. His general health, strength, and vitality have been impaired;
c. He has been unable to enjoy various pleasures of life that he has previously enjoyed;
d. He has incurred medical expenses;
e. He will incur medical expenses in the future;
f. He has lost income; and,
g. He has lost future earning capacity.

WHEREFORE, Plaintiff seeks a judgment against Stanley S. Wetschler, William R. Sims and David Laman for compensatory damages in excess of the jurisdictional amount for compulsory arbitration.

COUNT X
INTENTIONAL INFLICTION OF EMOTIONAL DISTRESS
RICHARD R. SCHNEIDER, M.D.
V.
SOUTH HILLS HEALTH SYSTEM D/B/A JEFFERSON REGIONAL HOSPITAL
STANLEY S. WETSCHLER, M.D.
WILLIAM R. SIMS, M.D., AND DAVID LAMAN, M.D.

92. The averments contained in paragraphs 1-91 are incorporated by reference as if set forth fully herein.

93. At all times relevant and material hereto, and throughout his distinguished career as a Physician, the Plaintiff has vigorously upheld his professional and ethical duty as a Physician to be an advocate for the highest possible standards of patient care and professional responsibility.

94. Pursuant to said duty, the Plaintiff has, at all times material hereto and throughout his distinguished career as a Physician, occasionally drawn into question the acts and/or omissions of other Physicians where said acts and/or omissions were not optimal or suitable to effectuate the highest standard of patient care and Professional Responsibility. As the result of, and in retaliation for, the Plaintiff's laudable adherence to the highest standards of patient care and Professional Responsibility, the Defendants, collectively and individually, and in continuation of a contrived and duplicitous scheme that was effectuated through outrageous conduct, engaged in a malicious, reckless and irresponsible campaign involving slanderous, libelous, and defamatory communications to the Hospital and to other members of the Medical Staff. The following is an illustrative, though not exhaustive, list of patient care incidents in which the Defendants intentionally subjected the Plaintiff to outrageous behavior in retaliation for his interventions and desire to secure the best medical care for his patients:

I. In or about August 2000, the Plaintiff initiated a "salt poor albumin treatment" for one of his patients. An agent of the Defendants, specifically a Pulmonary Physician, discontinued said treatment without consulting the Plaintiff. The Plaintiff ultimately was forced to assert his authority in order to continue the albumin treatment and to thereby save the patient's life. Unfortunately, in direct violation of the By-Laws and in violation of the accepted Peer Review process incorporated therein, and in malicious retaliation against the Plaintiff, the Defendants, including William R. Sims and David Laman, acting individually and through their agent, a Pulmonary Physician, caused slanderous, defamatory, and outrageous allegations to be written and/or orally communicated to the Board and/or to other Staff Members, including members of the Credentials Committee and the Peer Review Committee, in connection with this incident.

II. In or about December 2000, the Plaintiff once again initiated a salt poor albumin treatment for a patient of his who was suffering from congestive heart failure. Once again, the Defendants, acting through their agent, a Pulmonary Physician, in direct contravention of the Plaintiff's explicit instructions, initiated a treatment based on her misdiagnosis of ARDS. Unfortunately, as the result of the inadequate care provided by the responsible physician, the patient died. Subsequently, in direct violation of the By-Laws and in violation of the accepted Peer Review process incorporated therein, and in malicious retaliation against the Plaintiff, the Defendants, including William R. Sims and David Laman, acting individually and through their agent, a Pulmonary Physician, caused slanderous, defamatory, and outrageous allegations and complaints to be written and/or otherwise communicated to member Board and/or to other members of the Medical Staff Members, including members of the Credentials Committee and the Executive Committee, in connection with this incident.

III. In or about January 2001, the Plaintiff objected to the excessive increase in I.V. fluids for a patient that was listed for palliative care. Needless to say, filling a patient's lungs with fluid is not consistent with keeping him comfortable, and the Plaintiff ordered the I.V. solution reduced. Unfortunately, in direct violation of the By-Laws and in violation of the accepted

Peer Review process incorporated therein, and in malicious retaliation against the Plaintiff, the Defendant William R. Sims, acting individually and through his agents and associates, caused slanderous, defamatory, and outrageous allegations to be written and/or orally communicated to the Board and to other Staff Members in connection with this incident.

IV. On or about November, 2000, another patient died as the result of acts of the Defendants and/or their agents, employees, or servants. The Defendants agent, specifically a Pulmonary Physician, initiated a treatment of excessive intravenous fluid to a patient of Dr. Schneider's. As the result of the introduction of excessive fluids, the patient died. In addition, said Pulmonary Physician discontinued albumin treatment in this patient in direct contravention of the consulting nephrologist's orders. Unfortunately, in direct violation of the By-Laws and in violation of the accepted Peer Review process incorporated therein, and in malicious retaliation against the Plaintiff, the Defendants, specifically William R. Sims and David Laman, acting individually and through their agent, a pulmonary physician, caused slanderous, defamatory, and outrageous allegations to be written and communicated to the Board and to other Staff Members, including members of the Credentials Committee and the Peer Review Committee in connection with this incident.

V. In June of 1998, an elderly female patient of the Plaintiff's in the I.C.U. unit of Jefferson Hospital suffered a heart attack with recurrent heart pain. The Defendants failed to notify the Plaintiff of his patient's condition for approximately twelve (12) hours, and instead gave the patient a glass of ginger ale as treatment for said heart attack. When the Plaintiff brought these reckless and negligent acts to the attention of the Defendant, the Defendant, through their agent (here a large male nurse) responded indignantly, threatening the Plaintiff with grievous bodily harm. The Defendant investigated the incident and, despite the outrageous and assaultive acts of said male nurse, the Defendants once again caused slanderous, defamatory, and outrageous allegations of misconduct by the Plaintiff to be written and/or communicated to the Board and to other Staff Members in connection with this incident. Said allegations ultimately resulted in a reprimand of the Plaintiff based on said slanderous, defamatory, and outrageous allegations.

95. The Defendants, and specifically Stanley S. Wetschler, violated the By-Laws of the Medical Staff through their above-listed acts, specifically Articles V and VII, in that they noted the above listed incidents in the Plaintiff's file without (i) notifying the Plaintiff of their presence or (ii) investigating the incidents with the vigor that their obvious gravity warranted.

96. As a direct result of the desire of the Defendants to eliminate the Plaintiff and his valid criticism of the negligent medical care provided to patients at Jefferson Hospital, the Defendants engaged in said contrived and duplicitous campaign, employing the use of false accusation, misinformation, and defamatory information communicated to others with reckless disregard for the truth, which was designed to:

a. Discourage the Plaintiff from upholding his professional and ethical responsibilities;
b. To discredit and defame the Plaintiff to his colleagues, the other Staff Members;
c. To discredit the Plaintiff before the Board of Directors;
d. To avoid potential liability for negligent patient care, and;
e. To prevent the disclosure of numerous incidents of negligent patient care.

97. The cumulative effect of said contrived and duplicitous scheme directly and/or indirectly created a hostile work environment for the Plaintiff, which was designed by the Defendants and their agents to compromise the Plaintiff's professional and personal reputation within the Hospital, to invite unwarranted disciplinary action against the Plaintiff, and to discredit and humiliate the Plaintiff.

98. Said contrived and duplicitous scheme, undertaken by the Defendants with the intent of causing the Plaintiff severe mental and emotional distress, was so outrageous in character and so extreme in degree

as to go beyond all possible bounds of decency, and to be regarded as atrocious and utterly intolerable in a professional hospital setting and in a civilized community.

99. As the result of Defendants' outrageous conduct the Plaintiff has suffered the following injuries, some of which may be permanent:

a. He has suffered from the loss of professional esteem;
b. He has suffered from severe shame and embarrassment;
c. He has suffered from depression;
d. He has suffered from alienation from friends and professional colleagues;
e. He has suffered from the inability to practice medicine as a Cardiologist;
f. He has suffered from a loss of sense of well-being; and,
g. He has suffered from shame and humiliation.

100. As the result of the Defendants' conduct, the Plaintiff has suffered and will continue to suffer the following damages as the result of his injuries:

a. He has incurred medical expenses;
b. He will incur medical expenses in the future;
c. He has lost income; and,
e. He has lost future earning capacity.

WHEREFORE, Plaintiff seeks a judgment against Defendant South Hills Regional Health Systems D/B/A Jefferson Hospital, David Laman, William R. Sims and Stanley S. Wetschler, for compensatory damages in excess of the jurisdictional amount for compulsory arbitration.

COUNT XI
BREACH OF CONTRACT
RICHARD R. SCHNEIDER, M.D.
V.
SOUTH HILLS HEALTH SYSTEM D/B/A JEFFERSON REGIONAL MEDICAL CENTER
STANLEY S. WETSCHLER, M.D.,
WILLIAM R. SIMS, M.D., AND DAVID LAMAN,M.D.

101. The averments in paragraphs 1-100 are incorporated as if set forth fully herein.

102. At all times material and relevant hereto, the conduct of the named parties was governed by the Medical Staff Bylaws and, more specifically, Article V of said Bylaws as they relate to conduct in connection with Peer Review of the members of the Medical Staff.

103. Said provision of the Bylaws organizes a "Peer Review" Committee organized under the Pennsylvania Peer Review Protection Act.

104. The Defendants, through their acts in connection with the contrived, duplicitous, slanderous, and defamatory campaign described herein, have violated the Peer Review Protection Act, and have thus breached the Contract, by: (i) violating the confidentiality requirements in connection with the proceedings and records of said committee; (ii) providing said committee information they knew or had reason to believe to be false; and (iii) shielding from the Plaintiff information not properly intended for protection under the Peer Review Act.

105. Said violations of the Peer Review Act are a breach of the aforementioned contractual clause of the By-Laws, which incorporates by reference said Peer Review Act.

106. Said Breach created a contaminated review process, wherein the Plaintiff was denied the Due Process rights guaranteed by the Bylaws of the Medical Staff. As the direct result of the denial of said rights, and as the direct result of the inaccurate and prejudicial information said breach allowed to enter any prospective Peer Review process, the Plaintiff was

coerced into taking a leave, and ultimately forced to resign under duress his position on the Medical Staff.

WHEREFORE, the Plaintiff respectfully requests judgment against the Defendants for:

a. Damages in the amount representing the amount of income the Plaintiff has lost as the result of the coerced Medical Leave;
b. Damages in the amount representing the amount of income the Plaintiff has lost as the result of the forced resignation from the Medical Staff.
c. Interest thereto; and,
d. The cost of this suit.

COUNT XII
BREACH OF CONTRACT
RICHARD R. SCHNEIDER, M.D.
V.
SOUTH HILLS HEALTH SYSTEM D/B/A JEFFERSON REGIONAL MEDICAL CENTER
STANLEY S. WETSCHLER, M.D.,
WILLIAM R. SIMS, M.D., AND DAVID LAMAN, M.D.

107. The averments in paragraphs 1-106 are incorporated as if set forth fully herein.

108. At all times material and relevant hereto, the conduct of the named parties was governed by the Medical Staff Bylaws and, more specifically, Article V of said Bylaws as they relate to conduct in connection with Impaired or Disabled members of the Medical Staff.

109. Said Article delineates the procedure to be followed in the event that a complaint is filed against an impaired member of the Medical Staff. Specifically, the Impaired Medical Staff Committee is delegated to investigate any complaints allegedly related to any physically or mentally impaired Staff Member, and contact the involved medical Staff member to establish a voluntary treatment program.

110. The Bylaws then stipulate that, upon the successful completion of a treatment program by the involved Medical Staff Member, the Impairment Committee is directed to prepare and implement a program of reinstatement for the Medical Staff Member without "humiliation or rejection by the other Staff Members."

111. In connection with the July 13, 2001 incident, the Plaintiff was contacted by Defendant Stanley S. Wetschler, who, acting as the President of the Medical Staff, suggested that the Plaintiff complete a voluntary treatment program pursuant to the By-Laws; the Plaintiff performed his duty by successfully completing a voluntary treatment program.

112. Despite the Plaintiff's successful completion of the treatment program, the Defendants deliberately and intentionally failed to prepare and implement a program of reinstatement for the Plaintiff that would avoid humiliation or rejection, as stipulated by the By-Laws.

113. As the direct result of the Defendants' said Breach of their contractual duties under the Bylaws of the Medical Staff, the Plaintiff was effectively denied reinstatement of his clinical privileges upon his completion of his medical leave, and, further, the Plaintiff was informed that his reappointment to the Medical Staff would not be approved, and the Plaintiff was forced to resign his position on the Medical Staff.

WHEREFORE, the Plaintiff respectfully requests judgment against the Defendants for:

a. Damages in the amount representing the amount of income the Plaintiff has lost as the result of the Voluntary Medical Leave;
b. Damages in the amount representing the amount of income the Plaintiff has lost as the result of his forced resignation from the Medical Staff.
c. Interest thereto; and,
d. The cost of this suit.

COUNT XIII
UNLAWFUL DISCRIMINATION
43 P.S.§955
RICHARD R. SCHNEIDER, M.D.
V.
SOUTH HILLS HEALTH SYSTEM D/B/A JEFFERSON REGIONAL MEDICAL CENTER
STANLEY S. WETSCHLER, M.D.,
WILLIAM R. SIMS, M.D., AND DAVID LAMAN, M.D.

114. The averments in paragraphs 1-113 are incorporated as if set forth fully herein.

115. At all times material and relevant hereto, the conduct of the named parties was governed by the Pennsylvania Human Relations Act, hereinafter referred to as "the act."

116. At all times relevant and material hereto, the Plaintiff had a diagnosed mental impairment; specifically, the Plaintiff was diagnosed in 1995 as having bipolar disorder.

117. The Plaintiff has been under a Physician's care since said diagnosis, and has at all times followed the directives and recommendations of said Physician as they related to the treatment of said disorder.

118. At all times relevant and material hereto, said mental impairment did not substantially restrict the Plaintiff's ability to perform major life activities. Specifically, the Plaintiff was able to work effectively without further accommodations.

119. In July of 2001, the Defendants, through their individual acts and through the acts of their agents, forced the Plaintiff to take a medical leave of absence as the result of unfounded allegations of improper behavior made by a Hospital Employee, specifically, Wannita Anderson.

120. The Defendants referral of this matter to the Impairment Committee indicates that said Defendants regarded said Employee's unfounded, unverified, and unexamined allegation of misconduct as a manifestation of the Plaintiff's known and treated diagnosed mental

impairment despite; (i) the lack of credible corroborating evidence that the incident occurred in the manner described by Wanitta Anderson, and; (ii) the lack of any evidence that the Plaintiff was, at the time of the alleged incident, in any way substantially limited in performing a major life activity as the result of said impairment

121. To the extent that the Plaintiff was, at any time relevant and material hereto, substantially limited in any major life activity, specifically the major life activity of working, said substantial limitation was only as the result of the attitude of the Defendants towards his impairment.

122. As the result of the Defendants' violation of the Plaintiff's rights as a protected individual under 43 P.S.§955, the Plaintiff has suffered the following injuries, some of which may be permanent:

a. Severe mental anguish;
b. Severe embarrassment; and,
c. Severe Shame and Humiliation.

123. As the result of the Defendants' violation of the Plaintiff's rights as a protected individual under 43 P.S.§955, the Plaintiff has suffered the following damages as the result of his injuries:

a. He has incurred medical expenses;
b. He will incur medical expenses in the future;
c. He has lost income; and,
e. He has lost future earning capacity.

WHEREFORE, Plaintiff seeks a judgment against Defendant South Hills Regional Health Systems D/B/A Jefferson Hospital, David Laman, M.D., William R. Sims, M.D., and Stanley S. Wetschler, M.D., for compensatory damages in excess of the jurisdictional amount for compulsory arbitration.

COUNT XIV
UNLAWFUL DISCRIMINATION
43 P.S.§955
RICHARD R. SCHNEIDER, M.D.
V.
SOUTH HILLS HEALTH SYSTEM D/B/A JEFFERSON REGIONAL MEDICAL CENTER
STANLEY S. WETSCHLER, M.D.,
WILLIAM R. SIMS, M.D., AND DAVID LAMAN, M.D.

124. The averments in paragraphs 1-123 are incorporated as if set forth fully herein.

125. At all times material and relevant hereto, the conduct of the named parties was governed by the Pennsylvania Human Relations Act, hereinafter referred to as "the act" as it relates to the treatment of Independent Contractors.

126. At all times relevant and material hereto, the Plaintiff, the Plaintiff had a diagnosed non-job related mental impairment; specifically, the Plaintiff was diagnosed in 1995 as having bipolar disorder.

127. Said impairment substantially limited one or more major life activity. Specifically, said impairment substantially limited the Plaintiff's ability to work full time.

128. On or about July 16, 2001 the Plaintiff sought a reasonable accommodation from the Defendant. Specifically, the Plaintiff asked the Defendant to perform his stress tests prior to noon.

129. The Defendant violated the Plaintiff's rights as a protected individual under 43 P.S.§955, in that the Defendants failed to initiate an interactive process to determine whether the Plaintiff may have been able to perform the essential functions of his job with said reasonable accommodation.

130. As the result of the Defendants' violation of 43 P.S.§955, the Plaintiff has suffered the following injuries, some of which may be permanent:

a. Severe mental anguish;
b. Severe embarrassment; and,
c. Severe Shame and Humiliation.

131. The Plaintiff has suffered the following damages as the result of his injuries:

a. He has incurred medical expenses;
b. He will incur medical expenses in the future;
c. He has lost income; and,
d. He has lost future earning capacity.

WHEREFORE, Plaintiff seeks a judgment against Defendant South Hills Regional Health Systems D/B/A Jefferson Hospital, David Laman, M.D., William R. Sims, M.D., and Stanley S. Wetschler, M.D., for compensatory damages in excess of the jurisdictional amount for compulsory arbitration.

COUNT XV
BREACH OF CONTRACT
RICHARD R. SCHNEIDER, M.D.
V.
SOUTH HILLS HEALTH SYSTEM D/B/A JEFFERSON REGIONAL MEDICAL CENTER
STANLEY S.WETSCHLER, M.D.,
WILLIAM R.SIMS, M.D., AND DAVID LAMAN, M.D.

132. The averments contained in paragraphs 1-131 are incorporated by reference herein as if set forth fully.

133. On or about December 1999, the Defendants circumvented the procedural safeguards and processes outlined in Article V of the By-Laws as they related to, among other subjects, the Plaintiff's Clinical Privileges to perform Catheterization Procedures on his patients. Specifically, the Defendants began a contrived and duplicitous letter writing scheme designed to falsely characterize the Plaintiff's case volume as "low," and to raise unfounded questions of competence related to the Plaintiff's case selection for Catheterization.

134. Said acts were a direct violation and breach of the By-Laws as they relate to both: (i) initiating a Peer Review of the Plaintiff's acts in connection with Catheterization of patients, and; (ii) the Plaintiff's reappointment and/or reinstatement to the Medical Staff upon completion of his medical leave, in that the allegations contained in said letters were: (a) not properly investigated; (b) improperly circulated among the Members of the Medical Staff, and; (c) the Plaintiff was not notified of the existence of said allegations by the Defendants in the proper manner.

135. Said breach(s) created a contaminated peer review process, wherein the Plaintiff was denied the Due Process rights guaranteed by the Bylaws of the Medical Staff.

136. Said breach(s) created a contaminated environment in which the process of reinstatement of the Plaintiff's clinical privileges upon return from medical leave, as well as any subsequent reappointment application process, would be clouded by allegations of which the Plaintiff did not receive proper notice, and which, as personal attacks which were improperly circulated among members of the Medical Staff, were not properly shielded from the Plaintiff under Peer Review as it is incorporated into the Bylaws.

137. As the direct and indirect result of the contamination of the Peer Review Process through an open letter writing campaign designed to discredit and humiliate the Plaintiff, the Plaintiff's peer review file was inundated with accusatory letters containing false allegations of improper behavior which, but for the fraudulently constructed shield of peer review, could have been rebutted by the Plaintiff.

138. As the direct and indirect result of the Defendant's breach(s) as described herein, the Plaintiff was ultimately forced to first take a medical leave and then, ultimately, to resign from his position as a member of the Medical Staff.

WHEREFORE, the Plaintiff respectfully requests judgment against the Defendants for:

a. Damages in the amount representing the amount of income the Plaintiff has lost as the result of the coerced Medical Leave;
b. Damages in the amount representing the amount of income

the Plaintiff has lost as the result of the forced resignation from the Medical Staff.

c. Interest thereto; and,
d. The cost of this suit.

COUNT XVI
CIVIL CONSPIRACY
RICHARD R. SCHNEIDER, M.D.
V.
SOUTH HILLS HEALTH SYSTEM D/B/A JEFFERSON REGIONAL MEDICAL CENTER,
STANLEY S. WETSCHLER, M.D., WILLIAM R. SIMS, M.D.,
DAVID LAMAN, M.D., ARNOLD E. FINGERET, M.D.;
THERESE KOSTRUB; AND TERRY RIFFER

139. The averments contained in paragraphs 1-138 herein are incorporated by reference.

140. Defendant Arnold E. Fingeret, M.D. is a resident of and a physician licensed to practice in the Commonwealth of Pennsylvania, and at all relevant time was an officer of the medical staff of Jefferson Hospital.

141. Defendant Therese Kostrub is a resident of the Commonwealth of Pennsylvania and at all relevant times was an employee of Jefferson Hospital including but not being limited to serving as the Vice President of Medical Staff Services.

142. Defendant Terry Riffer is a resident of the Commonwealth of Pennsylvania and at all times relevant hereto was an employee of Jefferson Hospital, including but not being limited to serving as the Administrator of the Cardiac catheterization laboratory at Jefferson Hospital.

143. It is believed and averred that all Defendants agreed, conspired and acted in concert to professionally discredit Plaintiff and cause the ultimate relinquishment of his medical staff membership and clinical privileges.

144. As the direct and indirect result of the Defendant's breach(s) as

described herein, the Plaintiff was ultimately forced to first take a medical leave and then, ultimately, to resign from his position as a member of the Medical Staff.

WHEREFORE, the Plaintiff respectfully requests judgment against the Defendants for:

a. Damages in the amount representing the amount of income the Plaintiff has lost as the result of the coerced Medical Leave;
b. Damages in the amount representing the amount of income the Plaintiff has lost as the result of the forced resignation from the Medical Staff.
c. Interest thereto; and,
d. The cost of this suit.

APPENDIX E

Mediation Statement
on behalf of
Richard R. Schneider
June 4, 2004

Michael A. Cassidy, Esq.
Tucker Arensberg, P.C.
1500 One PPG Place
Pittsburgh, PA 15222
(412) 594-5515
mcassidy@tuckerlaw.com.

Introduction

Dr. Schneider has pursued this complaint against Jefferson Regional Medical Center (Hospital) because the Hospital, through various individuals, principally Stanley S. Wetschler, M.D., who have been medical staff officers or members or employees, have engaged in conduct which has illegally deprived Dr. Schneider of his medical practice and livelihood as a physician.

The primary injustice has been perpetrated through the perversion of the medical staff peer review process. The Hospital has adopted Medical Staff Bylaws (Exhibit A), which under Pennsylvania law constitute a contract between the Hospital and the individual members of the Medical Staff, and which assure the members, i.e., Dr. Schneider and other physicians, of certain rights, chief among them for purposes hereof are a collection of rights classified as due process rights. These due process rights are meant to insure that physicians may not be deprived of their Medical Staff rights (i.e., medical staff membership and clinical privileges) without the due process protections provided in the Bylaws.

The facts will show that Dr. Schneider was deprived of these protections, that Dr. Schneider's efforts to ensure quality patient care at the Hospital were seen as too aggressive and public for the Hospital's liking, that his disability, which has been recognized by the Hospital, was not accommodated as required by law and the Bylaws, and that this process was used by the Hospital and its agents to ruin Dr. Schneider's practice and disparage his reputation.

Dr. Schneider has averred a variety of causes of action in a Complaint (Exhibit B) to be filed against the Hospital and certain individuals, i.e., breach of contract, defamation, tortuous interference with contractual relationships, discrimination, and civil conspiracy. They are all components of an intentional course of conduct, the existence of which is not only inferred from the facts but confirmed by the Hospital's own internal documents, by which the Hospital has sought to terminate Dr. Schneider's relationship with the Hospital and remove him from its medical practice community.

It is important to realize at the outset that this is not a quality of care issue. Dr. Schneider was first appointed to the Medical staff of the Hospital in 1984. He has practiced there continuously (except for a medical leave of absence in 1997) without reservation until his most recent reappointment. Dr. Schneider was reappointed to the Medical staff on January 7, 2000 for the 2000—2001 biennial term without reservation.

Dr. Schneider has a recognized medical disability which does not compromise his ability to practice medicine. This condition prompted his first medical leave of absence in 1997, and initiated Dr. Schneider's participation in Pennsylvania's Physicians Health Program (PHP) and the Hospital's Physician Health Committee (Health Committee) process. Even as far back as 1997, the Hospital was attempting to manipulate this process by including unfounded and disparaging allegations regarding Dr. Schneider's personal life, which allegations were subsequently proven unfounded by the Menninger Clinic.

Dr. Schneider has a long history of patient care disagreements with the Hospital, and in particular with the Hospital's largest pulmonary care group, regarding the standards for the appropriate care of patients. A partial list of some of these incidents is contained in Count X of Complaint. It is not coincidence that included in Dr. Schneider's primary accusers are these physicians with whom he has argued regarding these patient care issues.

Hospital's Health Committee Obligations

Dr. Schneider's participation in PHP and the Health Committee began in 1997. The Health Committee is created and its rule and obligations defined by Article V—Part L of the Medical Staff Bylaws. It is intended as a program to assist physicians with a variety of impairment and is specifically defined as constituting a peer review program "entirely separate from any disciplinary or enforcement activities established or authorized by these Bylaws."

The Health Committee function includes several key responsibilities on behalf of impaired physicians, i.e.,

1. evaluation [V-L(2)(b)(1)];

2. establishment of a voluntary treatment program where necessary [V-L(2)(b)(3)];
3. upon successful completion of a treatment program, "the preparation and implementation of a program to reinstate the medical staff member without humiliation or rejection" [V-L(2)(b)(5)].

The gravamen of this case is that the Hospital used this process as a means to induce Dr. Schneider to take a medical leave of absence in July 2001 following an incident with a technician that was clearly related to a patient care issue and which was grossly exaggerated by the Hospital and used by the Hospital to force Dr. Schneider to take another medical leave of absence. The Hospital made no attempt to accommodate Dr. Schneider even though it categorized this as an impairment issue. Once Dr. Schneider had voluntarily agreed to cooperate with the Health Committee, the Hospital ignored its obligations and denied Dr. Schneider his due process rights and intentionally disregarded the recommendations of the Health Committee adopted by the memo entitled "Confidential & Privileged," dated July 26, 2001 (Exhibit C).

It is clear from the record, as far back as 1997, that the Hospital recognized Dr. Schneider's disability. The meeting minutes prepared by Dr. Fingeret on April 10, 1997 for the Health Committee (Exhibit D) establish this as a Health Committee issue, but also clearly indicate that Dr. Schneider was not advised of other personal issues which the Hospital was investigating, particularly his alleged sexual harassment, which was not mentioned in the minutes of the meeting with Dr. Schneider of April 11, 1997 (Exhibit E). The Hospital has explicitly promised Dr. Schneider that it would establish a Code of Conduct, if necessary.

- Dr. Wetschler's letters to Dr. Schneider, dated 3/8/01 and 4/27/01, and attached as Exhibits F and G, commit the Hospital to establishing a Code of Conduct;
- Following the incident with Ms. Anderson, Dr. Wetschler met with Dr. Schneider, Dr. Santiestaban, Terry Riffer and Jean Mikula on July 16, 2001 and Dr. Schneider was advised that independent evaluation and treatment would be required, as indicated in Dr. Wetschler's letter dated July 18, 2001 (Exhibit H).

Hospital Intent

Dr. Schneider immediately requested a leave of absence and agreed to and completed the independent evaluation and treatment recommended by PHP. As soon as Dr. Schneider requested his leave of absence, the Hospital ostracized him and denied him the protections that were not only contractually provided by the Medical Staff Bylaws but which had also been individually promised to him on several occasions.

- At a meeting on July 18, 2001, the minutes of which are attached as Exhibit I, after hearing a review of Dr. Schneider's situation, Jan Jennings, the CEO of the Hospital, determined before the independent evaluation and treatment had even started, in fact on the same day that Dr. Schneider was advised of the requirements for his leave of absence, that the Hospital "consider that this physician ends his relationship with our institution."
- On November 15, 2001, Dr. Wetschler corresponded with Dr. Frazier at UAB, indicating that Dr. Schneider's "behavior in the hospital environment is a mute (moot) point," clearly indicating that the Hospital had no intention of preparing or establishing a program for reinstatement as required by the Bylaws. (Exhibit J) As a matter of fact, following the leave of absence, the Hospital permitted no further involvement by the Health Committee.
- The Hospital took these unilateral actions in direct contravention of the conclusions of the Physician Health Committee, confirmed by the memo entitled "Confidential & Privileged," dated July 26, 2001 and attached as Exhibit C, that the Hospital should work with PHP to develop "Step #1 Inpatient Program" and "Step #2 Development of Behavioral Contract."

Hospital Positions Unsupported

The Hospital has placed significant emphasis on Dr. Schneider's historically contentious relationship with the Hospital, his failure on refusal to accept his responsibility for his impairment issues, and the seriousness of the incident involving Ms. Anderson. These explanations are both inaccurate and self serving.

- PHP's letter states that Dr. Schneider was "in compliance with all aspects of the agreement for participation and continues in stable recovery from impairment."
- The report from the University of Alabama at Birmingham's Center for Psychiatric Medicine (UAB), dated September 28, 2001 (Exhibit K), where Dr. Schneider completed his evaluation, describes Dr. Schneider as "a dedicated, intelligent and compassionate physician" and states that Dr. Schneider "did seem to gain some insight," "admitted that generally he did not listen well," "seems connected and invested in his therapy," "was able to practice and receive feedback from his peers" and "seems genuinely interested in self-improvement."
- Mr. Porter, the patient who witnessed the Wannitta Anderson incident, who was not even contacted by the Hospital, as confirmed by Dr. Wetschler's letter to Dr. Schneider of November 21, 2001 (Exhibit L) described the incident as "no big deal." A copy of Mr. Porter's statement, obtained by Joel Dresbold, Esq., is attached hereto as Exhibit M.

Although the Hospital has cloaked its actions with regard to Dr. Schneider as a sincere effort by various medical staff members to engage in "collegial intervention," their conduct in fact flouts the very protections the Hospital established via the Health Committee and the due process rights in the Medical Staff Bylaws in favor of a process intended to protect the individual interests of select members of the medical staff, which was the same process utilized in 1997 and in 2001. The process described by the Hospital as "collegial intervention," allegedly utilized with regard to Dr. Schneider, did not even exist until June 18, 2001, four years after his first leave of absence.

Compliance with LOA Conditions

Dr. Wetschler's letter to Dr. Schneider, dated July 18, 2001, clearly stated that Dr. Schneider could be required to undergo comprehensive independent evaluation and assessment and, following that "we will discuss whatever next step would be appropriate." Dr. Schneider performed his required responsibilities:

a. He completed his program at UAB and obtained a report to PHP, dated September 28, 2001, (Exhibit M) a copy of which was provided to the Hospital, stating that Dr. Schneider should continue individual therapy, that there were no quality of care issues or patient care restrictions, that Dr. Schneider's psychological ability to practice should be deferred to his psychiatrist, that Dr. Schneider should continue with PHP, and that Dr. Schneider's reinstatement should be based on standard operating protocol.

b. PHP issued a letter on October 15, 2001 (Exhibit N), indicating that Dr. Schneider was in full compliance with its program.

c. Dr. Schneider's private psychiatrist, C. Paul Scott. M.D., provided as opinion, dated September 13, 2001 (Exhibit O) stating that Dr. Schneider was compliant with his treatment and that his prognosis was good.

Reinstatement Denied

Dr. Schneider repeatedly asked the Hospital what else he should do to secure his reinstatement, but the Hospital had already decided to freeze Dr. Schneider out of the Hospital. Although the Hospital may allege that Dr. Schneider never formally requested reinstatement, the Hospital's conduct made that impossible.

- The Health Committee did not fulfill any of its contractual responsibilities following Dr. Schneider's leave of absence and his attempts to be reinstated—in fact, it was permitted to do ***absolutely nothing.***
- Dr. Wetschler's letter to Dr. Schneider dated November 21, 2001, stated that the Hospital had already decided, without any Health Committee input and without any due process protections, that "it would not be appropriate for any Medical Staff review process to begin regarding the possible reinstatement" and that Dr. Schneider's rights should "simply expire."
- Dr. Wetschler specifically warned Dr. Schneider that he would not receive a fair hearing at the Hospital.

However, neither Dr. Wetschler nor the Hospital have the right to decide what due process procedures should or should not be provided to Dr. Schneider.

Conclusion

Dr. Schneider has communicated his concerns to the Hospital on numerous occasions, including but not limited to a long letter to Jan Jennings, CEO of the Hospital, dated September 16, 2001 (Exhibit P). It is clear that Dr. Schneider suspected illegal, inappropriate and discriminatory treatment as far back as 1997. It is clear from Exhibit Q, the Hospital list of events involving Dr. Schneider, which contains 112 entries, that the Hospital was duplicitously investigating and compiling a dossier regarding Dr. Schneider. Article VII—Part C—Section 3 of the Medical Staff Bylaws requires a decision by the Executive Committee to conduct an investigation and notice to the physician under these circumstances, which is another due process safeguard completely disregarded by the Hospital.

The cumulative affect of this illegal action has been to completely and totally deprive Dr. Schneider of his ability to practice medicine, ruin his reputation as a physician, and sever his existing relationships with his patients and referring physicians in the medical community.

In 1996, the last full year in which Dr. Schneider was able to practice medicine without restrictions and impediments manufactured and imposed by the Hospital, his income from his practice was $350,000, excluding health insurance, fringe benefits, etc. Assuming he was permitted to practice through *normal* retirement age of 65 on even a part-time basis (i.e., 50% or less), Dr. Schneider has suffered or will suffer loss of income alone in excess of $2,625,000, excluding damages for defamation and emotional distress. We believe that the Hospital's actions have damaged Dr. Schneider's reputation and caused significant emotional suffering and distress. Therefore, we believe the appropriate remedy should be damages of _____, letters to all of the treating facilities or physicians (i.e., Drs. Frazier, Hobbs and Scott) and an agreed response to any peer review inquiries exonerating Dr. Schneider, and a commitment by the Hospital to adhere to the existing process for assuring the protection of the due process procedures for all other physicians.

List of Exhibits

A. Medical Staff Bylaws
B. Complaint
C. Confidential & Privileged Memo, July 26, 2001
D. Minutes: Impaired Substance Committee, April 10, 1997
E. Minutes: Schneider Meeting of April 11, 1997
F. Stanley S. Wetschler, M.D. letter to Richard R. Schneider, M.D., March 8, 2001
G. Stanley S. Wetschler, M.D. letter to Richard R. Schneider, M.D., April 27, 2001
H. Stanley S. Wetschler, M.D. letter to Richard R. Schneider, M.D., July 18, 2001
I. Confidential & Privileged Memo, July 18, 2001
J. Stanley S. Wetschler, M.D. letter to Sandra L. Frazier, M.D., November 15, 2001
K. UAB/Sandra L. Frazier, M.D., letter to Thomas Hobbs, M.D.
L. Stanley S. Wetschler, M.D. letter to Richard R. Schneider, M.D., November 21, 2001
M. Porter Statement/Joel M. Dresbold letter to Richard R. Schneider, M.D., October 30, 2001
N. PHP/Thomas R. Hobbs, M.D., letter to Stanley S. Wetschler, M.D., October 15, 2001
O. C. Paul Scott, M.D., letter to Jean Mikula, September 13, 2001
P. Richard R. Schneider letter to Jan Jennings, September 16, 2001
Q. Hospital Confidential Dossier

BUS_EST: 195835-2 019955-106022

INDEX